Researches in

BINOCULAR VISION

Researches in
BINOCULAR VISION

By

Neil

KENNETH N. OGLE, Ph.D., M.D. (h.c.), D.Sc. (h.c.)

Head, Section of Biophysics, and Consultant in Visual
Physiology, Section of Ophthalmology, Mayo Clinic;
Professor of Physiological Optics, University of
Minnesota Graduate School of Mayo Foundation
Rochester, Minnesota

152. 1
Og 5r

ILLUSTRATED

HAFNER PUBLISHING COMPANY
New York   London

1964

Original published 1950
Reprint 1964

Printed and Published by:
HAFNER PUBLISHING COMPANY
31 EAST 10th STREET
NEW YORK, NEW YORK, 10003

Library of Congress Card Catalogue No. 64-8322

© Copyright 1950, Mayo Foundation

Lithographed in the U.S.A.
by NOBLE OFFSET PRINTERS, INC.
New York, N. Y. 10003

Foreword to Second Printing

I am sure nearly every author of an out-of-print book, on learning that a new printing is to be made, wishes he could rewrite the entire book because now he knows there is so much more to report than when the original manuscript was written. Certainly this is true in my case. With increased costs of publishing, however, I am grateful that the original volume is being reprinted, and I am indeed indebted to Hafner Publishing Company for doing this. Minor corrections in the text are being made. A bibliography of the pertinent literature from 1949 to 1963 is appended, which should make the book more useful for reference. Again, the clinical aspects of binocular vision and especially of aniseikonia will not be stressed, the emphasis remaining on the basic research originating at the Dartmouth Eye Institute.

I wish to express my gratitude to the Mayo Clinic and especially the Section of Publications for their assistance in making this book possible.

Kenneth N. Ogle

May 1, 1964

Foreword

THIS BOOK is an outstanding example of how an author should present his researches in a difficult subject.

In the first place all the work of other investigators is given due weight. A frequent fault in presenting a subject like binocular vision is to leave out—even ignore—the work of others in the field. An author who does this usually does it because he is ignorant of what others have done, he has not sought out the sources of our knowledge in the field he is investigating, or he may do it from a motive of self-glorification. His own investigations may be a repetition of what has already been done. The fact that what he finds is new to him makes him think it is new to everybody, that no one has thought of that before. Some of these investigators are more interested in proving that they are the first to discover some truth than they are in establishing the validity of their findings.

Dr. Ogle is a conspicuous example of the research worker who is more interested in proving the exact truth than in proving that he is the one to whom credit should be given. The casual reader will therefore miss some of Dr. Ogle's original discoveries which are so numerous all through the book, but he will gain a clearer conception of the whole because it is presented impersonally and in a self-effacing way.

The second outstanding feature is the constant impression the reader will get that Dr. Ogle is never satisfied with a partial proof. The searching keenness of his mind shows mathematical training. He knows when a thing is proved and is never satisfied with a dilution of a scientific proof.

Ames was most unusual as the originator of ideas in binocular vision. Dr. Ogle's role has been to subject these general ideas to scientific analysis, reject the false and place the true on unassailable foundations. Ogle has carried out this role not only through his original contributions to this field but also through the integrated account presented in this monograph.

This book will immediately take its place as the authoritative source of the dependable basic truths so far discovered in the ever enlarging field of binocular vision. It will serve as a model for future investigators to follow.

WALTER B. LANCASTER, M.D.

Preface

THE GREATER PART of the subject matter in this book is based upon the researches in binocular vision conducted at the Dartmouth Eye Institute at Hanover, New Hampshire. An attempt is made to summarize and integrate the significant parts of that work into our general body of knowledge of the visual processes.

The Institute terminated its activities July 1, 1947, after eighteen years of rather intensive research on problems in physiologic optics and the application of the results of that research to clinical ophthalmology and to visual science in general.[37] The researches were initiated by Adelbert Ames, Jr., with a small group in the physics building at Dartmouth College. Later the group became a department of the Dartmouth Medical School, and finally this was expanded into the Dartmouth Eye Institute by the late Alfred Bielschowsky, M.D. The clinical activities were instigated by Walter B. Lancaster, M.D., professor of ophthalmology, Harvard Medical School, and the early clinical work was supervised by E. H. Carleton, M.D., professor of ophthalmology of the Dartmouth Medical School at Hanover. During the entire period of the existence of the organization, however, Mr. Ames remained actually the head, and in those eighteen years it was he who provided the motivating spirit and the enthusiasm for the research.

The generous grants of Mr. John D. Rockefeller, Jr., and later those of the Rockefeller Foundation, provided the basic financial support. These grants together with the gifts of many interested friends, and in particular those of the American Optical Company (which also put at the disposal of the research group its optical manufacturing facilities), made possible the scope and continuity of the various activities.

In this volume I have attempted to present only nonclinical aspects of the researches in binocular vision, though frequently data obtained in the clinic are used for supporting evidence. I have drawn heavily upon the literature published by the various members of the group, but I am also including data heretofore unpublished. The particular approach to, and choice of, the subject matter and many of the conclusions in this book are my own and in many respects may not coincide with those that others of the group might have made. Again, it is not attempted to make this a comprehensive text on binocular vision, but rather to organize and integrate the particular researches, the greater part of which have been published in a number of different and somewhat unrelated journals. Many of the researches discussed here are not completely worked out, and in some instances the results reported must be considered only as preliminary. Additional research will be necessary to solve the problems adequately.

My personal indebtedness to Adelbert Ames, Jr., is very great. It was he who first interested me, as a student in physics, in the field of physiologic optics. In later years as a colleague, I was constantly influenced by his particular approach and uncanny insight into the problems of vision, though at times our separate conclusions were not in agreement. This book is a witness to the collaboration of many who followed the trail that he blazed.

Moreover, I cannot minimize the contributions of the various other members of the Institute, whose willing cooperation and patient application to the tasks at hand made possible many of the results included here. It is only fitting that the other men and women who were sometime members of the Department of Research in Physiological Optics and of the Dartmouth Eye Institute should be listed:

Rudolph Amann, LL.B.
Handford Auten, M.D.
Ethel J. Babbitt, B.S.
Robert E. Bannon, B.S.
S. Howard Bartley, Ph.D.
Robert J. Beitel, Ph.D.
Alfred Bielschowsky, M.D.
    (deceased)
Lorna Billinghurst
Carl Breisacher, M.D.
Hermann M. Burian, M.D.
Elmer H. Carleton, M.D.
Herbert F. Childs, M.A.
Eloise Chute, M.A.
Arthur F. Dittmer, Ph.D.
    (deceased)
Vincent J. Ellerbrock, Ph.D.
Milo Fritz, M.D.
Gordon H. Gliddon, Ph.D.
Paul Boeder, Ph. D.

Werner Herzau, M.D.
Ranald Hill
Camilla Hübscher
Henry A. Imus, Ph.D.
Walter B. Lancaster, M.D.
Arthur F. Linksz, M.D.
Leo F. Madigan, M.A.
Paul W. Miles, M.D.
J. Miles O'Brien, M.D.
Robert H. Peckham, Ph.D.
Kenneth L. Roper, M.D.
Otto Schniebs
Lawrence P. Sparks, M.A.
Leon Straw (deceased)
Rudolph T. Textor, B.S.
Milton Thorburn
Wendell Triller, B.S.
Rita Walsh, B.S.
E. Craig Wilson, B.S.
Julius Neumueller

To many of these I am personally indebted, but especially so to Gordon H. Gliddon, Hermann M. Burian and Walter B. Lancaster.

I am also indebted to the Mayo Clinic and the Mayo Foundation for the cooperation which has made this volume a reality. I am grateful to Dr. Charles Sheard, who read critically the entire manuscript, and to Dr. C. W. Rucker of the Section on Ophthalmology for his suggestions in the preparation of Chapter 1. I am indebted to Dr. John R. Miner who edited the material for this volume. Much credit also is due to Miss Lorette Hentges for her work with the manuscript.

Permission to reprint illustrations and excerpts from the texts of papers published in the following journals is herewith gratefully acknowledged: Archives of Ophthalmology, American Journal of Ophthalmology, Journal of the Optical Society of America, American Journal of Psychology.

KENNETH N. OGLE

Rochester, Minnesota
October, 1950

Contents

PART III

THE PROBLEMS IN BINOCULAR VISION WHEN CHANGES ARE MADE IN THE RELATIVE MAGNIFICATIONS OF THE IMAGES OF THE TWO EYES

PART IV

THE EXPERIMENTAL AND THEORETICAL BASES
FOR ANISEIKONIA

Introduction

BINOCULAR VISION is the coordinated behavior of the two eyes by which a single perception of external space is obtained and by which its greatest achievement, the specific sensation of stereoscopic depth perception, is made possible.*

We have two eyes and two retinal images, but normally we experience only a single perception of space, because, we are taught to say, those images are "fused." The eyes must be directed and their movements coordinated in order that this fusion may be maintained. On the other hand, the dissimilarities that occur between the retinal images of the two eyes by virtue of their observing space from two slightly different positions, provide the stimuli for the most accurate space localization; namely, stereoscopic vision. These attributes of binocular vision necessitate a delicate, precisely controlled and stable organization of both the sensory and motor systems of the two eyes. Visual spatial localization is the primary need of the individual if he is to live effectively in the world of objects about him. The means by which we perceive the forms, sizes and distances of objects in space and their relative orientation to each other provide a most complex problem of psychophysiology.

The dioptric images that are formed on the retinas of the two eyes are essentially flat (two-dimensional) and, while they contain the data from which a concept of space can be derived, they certainly lack in themselves the three-dimensional characteristics of the objects observed. In trying to understand the processes of binocular vision, we are concerned in the main with the physiologic and functional organization of the two eyes—how they work together and how they convey the information about external space to the higher brain centers.

For purposes of discussion we can often consider the general problem in two parts—the *sensorial* and the *motor* (muscular) relationships. The first deals with the problems of perception and particularly space perception, while the second deals with the means for coordinated eye movements so necessary for maintaining binocular single vision. These two aspects cannot be separated in descriptions of the actual use of the eyes. In much of this book, however, we are going to be concerned with the sensorial coordination of the two eyes.

* Leonard Troland wrote ". . . there must be a science of binocular sensations, which is concerned with the manner in which experience varies as a function of the relationship between the right and left afferent systems (of the two eyes)."

Such studies are essentially studies of function, and, in almost every instance, measurements depend on visual experience, and in particular on some phase of the space sense. We are concerned not only with the optics and physiology of the visual processes, but also with psychophysics as the link between the stimulation by the dioptric images of the retinas and the emergence of the visual experience.

Space and form perception must be considered a synthesis of: (1) the patterns of the dioptric images on the retinas, which are determined by the geometric optics and by the particular optical characteristics of the eyes as cameras; (2) the characteristics of the retina and the neurologic processes by which the retinal stimuli are transmitted to the brain; (3) the psychic modifications and amplifications of the neurologic "images" from past associations and experiences of the individual in relating the visual, auditory and cutaneous sensations with his surroundings, and (4) the modifying and masking effects of the attention and the motivations of the individual.

The plan of the book is to describe in order those researches which have dealt, first, with the specific sensorial organization of the two retinas; second, with those functional processes known as fusion; third, with the functional effect of altering the relative magnification of the images of the two eyes, especially upon the space sense; and last, with the anomalous condition of aniseikonia as a factor in efficient binocular vision and its bearing upon our concepts of the stability of the organization between the two retinas.

The anatomy and neurology of the visual processes provide a groundwork for understanding this organization. One important part of our insight into these processes must come, at present, by inference from the facts obtained in the functional and sensory responses of the eyes under controlled experimental conditions.

Part I

THE ORGANIZATION AND SENSORY
COOPERATION OF THE
TWO RETINAS

CHAPTER 1

The Structure of the Visual Pathways

INTRODUCTION

THE BASIC FACTS of the neuroanatomy and neurophysiology of the visual mechanisms are important in our understanding the visual sensory and motor responses of the individual. We shall very briefly review the structure of the visual pathways.

Because of the extreme complexity of the brain our knowledge of its structure and functional characteristics has come slowly. During the middle part of the nineteenth century it gradually became evident that the human brain was not an equipotential structure, that all activity within it was not diffuse and that any one part could not take over the functions of another part. Although it has been known for some time that the visual centers of the brain lie at the occipital lobes, it is only during the past few decades that research workers have established the fact that the retinas are projected spatially onto the cortex of the medial surfaces of these lobes.

The methods used to study the structure of the visual pathways are: (1) neurohistologic examination of sections of the brains of animals and of man, in which the atrophied cells are identified following destructive lesions or ablation of parts of the visual system or following the occlusion of certain arteries; (2) the tracing of neurons by means of special staining technic; (3) the charting of blind areas in the visual field of individuals whose brains could later be studied at necropsy; (4) the electrical method (a) of determining location of cortical activity following light stimuli directed to specific locations in the retinas of living specimens (Talbot and Marshall), and (b) of determining fields of potential differences between areas in the cortex following strychninization of specific points of the exposed cortex (Bonin, Garol and McCulloch).

The most evident characteristic of the projection of the retina to the cortex is the sharply defined division in that projection into right and left halves. The nerve fibers from the left halves of the retinas (concerned with the right half of the visual field) proceed to the left side of the brain, and the nerve fibers from the right halves of the retinas (concerned with the left half of the visual field) proceed to the right side of the brain. The fibers from the nasal parts of the retinas decussate or cross over at the chiasm to the opposite (contralateral) lobe, while those from temporal parts of the retinas pass to the lobe on the same (ipsilateral) side without crossing. This division is sharply made along vertical lines through the foveas of the two eyes. It is now believed that there is no bilateral representation of the foveas on the two occipital lobes.[207]

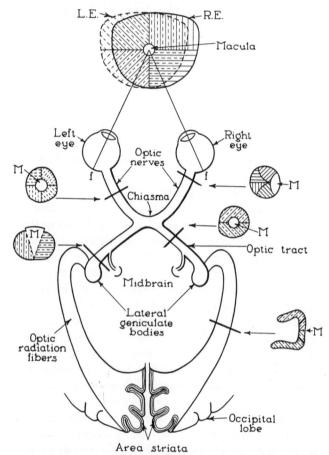

Fig. 1. Schematic representation of the probable course of the fibers of the optic visual pathway.

The course of the various main nerve fibers from the retinas is usually described in three parts (Fig. 1); the optic nerves, the optic tracts and the optic radiations.

THE OPTIC NERVE

The neurons from the various ganglion and bipolar cells leading from the photoreceptor elements in the retina head for the optic disk, where they make nearly a right-angle turn, and pass through the eyeball as a single bundle—the optic nerve. The fibers tend to maintain a topologic relationship corresponding to the positions on the retinas where they originated, although the particular arrangement changes slightly between the eyeball and the optic chiasm in that the fibers from the macula take a more central position in the nerve (Fig. 1). At the chiasm, the fibers which have arisen from the nasal side of the retina cross to join those from the temporal side of the retina of the other eye.

THE OPTIC TRACT

The optic tracts consist of extensions of the same nerve fibers which compose the optic nerves and chiasm. The fibers from corresponding areas of the two retinas are somewhat intermingled with each other, and the macular fibers occupy the central portion of the tract. A small group of fibers concerned with pupillary reflexes leaves the optic tract as it passes posteriorly and enters the pretectal region.

The fibers of the tracts terminate in the lateral geniculate bodies, where there are cells which act as relay stations for impulses arriving from the retina on their way to the cortex. As the fibers enter the lateral geniculate body, they become rearranged into a series (possibly six) (Clark) of well-defined laminations of alternately crossed and uncrossed fibers. Three of the layers correspond to the fibers from one eye, the other three to the fibers from the other eye. Fibers of corresponding points are thus juxtaposed with possibly some overlapping. In spite of this lamination, however, the fibers from corresponding areas in the two retinas are arranged topographically (Fig. 1). Fibers from the upper half of the retina terminate in the medial part of the lateral geniculate body, and those from the lower half terminate in the lateral part. Those from the macula occupy a large wedge-shaped area in the central and posterior parts of this body.

Because of this precise arrangement, it is possible to map out the point-to-point representation of the retina in the lateral geniculate body. In spite of the proximity of the crossed and uncrossed fibers from corresponding retinal areas, present evidence indicates that the terminal ends of the fibers maintain functional independence, and that no fusion of impulses takes place there. There are also reasons for believing that there is a multiplication of fibers leaving the terminal ganglion cells of the fibers from the optic tract, and that they are connected by extensive reciprocal overlapping of branched neurons.

THE OPTIC RADIATIONS

Fibers leaving the lateral geniculate body course to the visual cortex of the occipital lobe by way of the optic radiations. The visual cortex is located in the region of the calcarine fissure on the medial surface of the occipital lobe and extends to its posterior pole.

Throughout their course the fibers of the optic radiations run in a more or less parallel order, and those fibers pertaining to corresponding areas of the retinas are intermingled and maintain a faithful topologic order (Fig. 1). Moreover, the terminal areas of these fibers on the cortex are organized topologically, with an effective point-to-point projection of the lateral geniculate body on the cortex, and therefore of corresponding areas of the retinas to the cortex. The horizontal meridian of the retinas is projected at the depth of the calcarine fissure; the macular areas correspond to the tip of the occipital lobe; the upper and lower quadrants of the retina are projected onto the regions above and below the calcarine fissure, respectively.

THE OCCIPITAL CORTEX

The visual cortex is known as Brodmann's area *17*, and surrounding this concentrically are two other areas: *18*, the parastriate area, and *19*, the peristriate area, which are also concerned with visual functions.

In the cortex of the brain a series of laminae can be differentiated histologically, and these have been numbered from *I* to *V* from the surface inward. In layer *IV* of the visual cortex of the occipital lobe are two strata separated by a myelinated layer (*IV b*) which appears as a white band in the otherwise gray matter. This band is called the "striate area," and here are the ends of the optic radiation fibers that terminate chiefly in *IV c*. "Hence, if (as seems certain) the impulses from corresponding points in the two retinas remain distinct within the limits of the geniculate body, they must be brought into the most intimate relation as soon as they are projected on to the cortex, and it may be inferred that the cortical mechanism for the fusion of the two images necessary for stereoscopic vision is very localized spatially" (Clark).

Again in the visual cortex there is a marked magnification of the number of terminal neurons, as there is in the retina and also in the lateral geniculate body. Because of the multiple and reciprocal overlapping, impulses from a point on the retina could be transmitted to a much larger area at the striate cortex. A circle at the fovea of the retina corresponding to a visual angle of 1 minute of arc (about 0.005 mm.) is represented on the cortex by an area of 0.5 mm., which represents a magnification of 10,000 times in area.[224] However, Lorente de Nó argues that if ". . . the neuron is a summation apparatus, which reaches the threshold of excitation only when a certain number of its synapses are active, it is clear that, physiologically, the projection of the retina on the cerebral cortex may be point-like."

Many of the experimental facts of fusion, stereoscopic vision and such phenomena as the induced effect (Chapter 15) require an activity of the visual processes as a whole, and hence the existence of long association fibers between various parts of the brain cannot be denied. There is evidence, however, that no visual commissural association fibers from the area striata exist in the corpus callosum.[31] The parastriate area *18* and the peristriate area *19*, which surround the area striata, are believed to be concerned with visuomotor and visuopsychic, or visuosensory, functions, respectively. Certainly the area striata has short association fibers to area *18*, and area *18*, in turn, not only has associations with areas *17* and *19* but also affects area *18* of the corresponding contralateral cortex in the other lobe.[22] Stimulation of area *19*, however, appears to be localized, except that it seems to inhibit all other activity of the entire cortex associated with visual responses. Thus it is assumed that area *19* must project to some cortical region not connected to other parts of the occipital cortex. Certainly it is clear that there must be efferent nerves that connect the visual centers of the cortex directly with the motor centers of the brain and the spinal cord.

CHAPTER 2

The Theory of Corresponding
Retinal Points

OBJECTIVE AND SUBJECTIVE SPACES

THE EYES and the visual processes transform the objective world through light stimuli into the *subjective* world of form, spatial relationships and color.

Hering was the first to insist on a clear distinction between the objective (physical) and the subjective (experiential) worlds. This aspect of vision was emphasized by Hofmann, who wrote (in translation):

It is a familiar fact that we do not always see objects in our environment exactly in the shape and spatial arrangement that is "actually" theirs, according to the totality of our experience. Especially striking differences arise from the fact that all objects observed from a great distance appear much smaller than when observed close to. The apparent size relations of the separate parts of objects which have a considerable depth extension do not coincide with the actual ones. . . . Accordingly we must differentiate between real objects and the visual perceptions that are elicited by "subjective visual objects." The totality of all the simultaneous visible *subjective visual objects* forms the *subjective visual space*, or the *subjective visual field*. In objective space these correspond to the *objective visual field*, that is, that portion of actual space that is visible to us at one time in one given eye position.

But the difference between the spatial characteristics of the external object and its corresponding subjective visual object, between objective visual space and subjective visual space, is even more extensive than the above examples show, since they only illustrate the manifold contradictions between the two. When we apply a measuring rod to an object, and measure its extent, we do indeed obtain its *objective* extent, but we do not ascertain any information as to the *subjective* size of the measuring rod or the object that we have measured with it. Under certain conditions the two objects may appear to be of different size. Look with one eye, while the other is closed, at a window several meters away. Then hold one finger so close in front of the active eye that you have to accommodate on it with difficulty. As soon as this is done, the window shrinks and seems smaller than when one observes it without the effort of accommodation. Of course, a measuring rod behaves in precisely the same way if it is applied to the window at that time. Thus, the objective size of the window gives us no information as to the *subjective* size, either of the measuring rod or of the object—the window—that it measures. The spatial extent of objects does not give us any standard for the size of subjective, visual objects.

. . . We can only demonstrate *changes* in the standard of the subjective visual field. In ourselves we can determine those changes subjectively by comparison with former experiences, such as in the above experiment with the window. In the case of other individuals, we usually have to resort to such comparisons and the statements of the people concerned. In view of the above, it is impossible to compare the absolute size of subjective visual objects with the imagined real size of objects. We can only compare the size relationships of subjective visual objects and the mutual position of the corresponding external objects.

Thus, we assume that an object in objective space may be displaced without deformation and without changes between related points, and therefore that the geometric laws of Euclid hold. In visual space, this is not true. As an object recedes, not only does it appear to become smaller but its shape appears to change, this change being greater in the depth extent than in height or width. Many other discrepancies between the two spaces have been established. Thus, there must be a clear understanding of the fact that the objective world and the subjective world are incommensurate. It is only important that, whatever relationship exists between objective and visual space, it should be fairly stable if the individual is to act effectively in the physical world.

LOCALIZATION ACCORDING TO DIRECTION

The space sense is usually discussed under two categories—the *sense of direction* and the *sense of distance*. We shall be concerned with the first of these in what follows. Phylogenetically the sense of direction probably is the earlier.

It is an everyday experience that different objects in the field of view are perceived in different directions with respect to our bodies, and the differences in these directions certainly are related to the actual angular separation of those objects referred to the eye. This ability to discriminate differences in direction is attributed to the discrete character and arrangements of the receptor elements in the retina—which effectively comprise a mosaic of separated and insulated light-sensitive elements. We are forced to assume that to each of these elements there is attached a specific psychic "local sign" (Lotze).[118] When the element is stimulated, the individual experiences that specificity as a particular subjective direction, with his body as the origin.

Visual acuity or, more precisely, resolving power, is the keenest differentiation of this type that can be made. This, of course, depends not only on the dimensions and density of the receptor cells but also on the useful optical characteristics of the eye. The so-called "form" sense also has as its basis the discrimination of separated stimuli and the subsequent appreciation of extension.

When the eye is directed to a given fixation point, the image of that point falls on the fovea, and the subjective direction associated with the retinal elements of this fixation point is called the *principal visual direction* (Hering). Objects whose images fall away from that point are experienced as being in a direction to the right, left, above or below. This is essentially Tschermak's[230] concept of subjective direction according to breadth and height. Thus every point in the whole visual field has a psychic counterpoint mediated by the retinal mosaic, which gives rise to a subjective visual direction always relative to the principal visual direction corresponding to the point of fixation. It must be clear that the principal visual direction is not an absolute direction but it also is relative. The apparent absolute direction of objects in the visual field depends on many other factors and tends to remain the same irrespective of eye or body movements.

The foveas, then, when stimulated give rise to the principal visual direction. Stimulation of adjacent retinal points gives rise to specific subjective directions relative to the principal directions according to breadth and height, these directions being approximately proportional to the distance of a given element from the fovea. This discrimination of direction obviously becomes less exact toward the periphery of the retina, because there the discrete makeup of the retina becomes cruder.

The entire monocular visual field is thus elaborated. The subjective directions constitute primary sensory correlates to the retinal elements and, following the Hering school, are considered preformed and stable.

THE BINOCULAR VISUAL FIELD—CORRESPONDING POINTS

In the overlapping of the visual fields in binocular vision when both eyes are directed to the same object, there must be retinal elements of one eye which will give rise to the same subjective visual direction as would elements of the other eye when stimulated. By definition these elements, each of which gives rise to the same *primary* visual direction, would be said to be *corresponding*. As brought out in the preceding chapter, there are anatomic reasons for believing that the stimulation of corresponding retinal points affects the same region of the cortex, where corresponding visual pathways from both eyes terminate and are elaborated adjacently.

By means of mirrors, Fischer[73] has demonstrated the correspondence of those peripheral retinal elements that under ordinary conditions can never be used simultaneously because the nose of the individual occludes that part of the binocular field of vision.

The basic fact of *binocular* direction localization is expressed in the law of *identical visual directions,* a law first stated by Hering. The classic experiment can be described as follows. Suppose one stands about 2 feet (about 61 cm.) before a window through which he has a view out-of-doors. While holding his head steady, with the right eye closed, he directs his left eye to a distant object out-of-doors somewhat to the right. Suppose this object is an evergreen tree, and the more this is set off from surrounding objects the more vivid will be the experiment. While fixating the tree he makes a small crayon mark on the window pane in line with his eye and the tree. Now the left eye is closed and the right eye is opened and directed to the same mark on the pane, and out-of-doors in line with it a distant object is identified, for example, a chimney.

Both eyes are then opened and directed to the mark on the pane (Fig. 2). Immediately the images of this mark "fuse"; the mark is seen as *one* straightforward direction (the principal visual direction) relative to the body. Thus both of the foveas give rise to the *same* subjective direction.

While fixating the mark on the pane, one observes that the mark also appears in line with both the tree and the chimney. Both will be seen more or less at the same time, perhaps one more vivid for one instant and then the other, according to which eye is the more dominant in the rivalry. One sees, therefore, the mark, the tree and the chimney in the *same* straight-forward subjective direction, in spite of the widely separated difference in their actual directions relative to the observer. All other objects in the background that contains the tree and chimney are correspondingly dis-placed so that the tree and chimney occupy the central portion of the binocular visual field and are seen in the principal visual direction. This

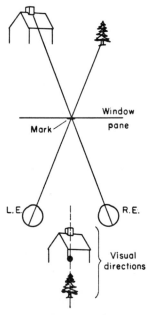

Fig. 2. The experiment which demonstrates Hering's law of the identical visual direction of the two foveas.

experiment shows that all objects which lie in the path of the chief rays to the foveas of the two eyes will appear to be in the same subjective direction, irrespective of their actual positions relative to the observer. Objects are seen in the direction in space according to the parts of the retinas on which their images fall and are not seen in their actual directions.

It can also be shown that if the eyes continue to fix the mark on the window pane, one may locate a second mark at the side of the first for which two other distant objects are also seen in an identical subjective direction. The particular retinal elements* of each eye which give rise to the same primary subjective direction are designated *corresponding*

---

* The term "retinal element," or "retinal point," will be used here in the sense defined by Sherrington as "the retinocerebral apparatus engaged in elaborating a sensation in response to excitation of a unit area of retinal surface."

retinal points (elements). The foveas corresponding to the fixation point are therefore the central pair of corresponding retinal points. From what has been said, retinal correspondence is interpreted as a preformed and stable arrangement.

It must be borne in mind in this discussion of the stimulation of single retinal points that because of the ever-present varying though small involuntary eye movements (physiologic nystagmus) (Adler and Fliegelman), no one element will continue to be stimulated for more than an instant. In speaking of the stimulation of a retinal element we must consider in every case the *statistical mean* position about which the eye movements will fluctuate.[87] These involuntary eye movements in no way vitiate the concepts of visual direction or of corresponding points. In fact, they may even account for a higher resolving power of the retina[129, 162] than could be expected from the size of the retinal elements and the size of the light diffusion disk on the retina.

The theory of the identity of corresponding points was first proposed by J. Müller in 1826; it was further developed by Panum[200] in 1858 and Nagel[173] in 1861, but finally was stated with greatest clarity by Hering in 1879. The development of so-called "anomalous retinal relationships" in squint does not contradict the theory of stable arrangements of corresponding retinal points. In fact, Hofmann, Bielschowsky and Tschermak,[231] the last a squinter, have regarded the phenomena as direct evidence that the normal correspondence is an innate preformed arrangement.

Hering wrote:

> The original idea stated by Müller, by which the correspondence of the retinas is an innate arrangement, is widely opposed. It has been declared further that the correspondence of spatial values on both retinas is gained during the life of the individual, although the partial crossing of the optic nerve fibers at the chiasma, and the frequently observed hemianopias of corresponding parts of the retinas, proves that correspondence is founded on an anatomical basis. Even though we may deny to visual perception any inborn spatial attribute, and prefer to regard the spatial values of retinal points solely as a result of individual experience, we must give consideration to the facts and admit that there exists between corresponding points an innate functional basis, through which spatial interpretation of the sensations derived from corresponding points, be it sensory or motor, or both, follow a definite path.

Granting that corresponding retinal elements are preformed, the problem is still present as to how stable is this organization, especially as regards the psychic correlates of those elements, and under what conditions can this organization be changed. Is the functional organization of the two eyes, including the binocular processes in the cortex, a fixed one? The mapping of the relative locations of the corresponding points in the two eyes would provide us with an accurate picture of how the two retinas of the binocular visual apparatus are organized.

THE HOROPTER

The study of the organization of the two eyes has been approached from a geometric and from a functional point of view; the older writers considered it mostly from the geometric. If the two retinas (they said) could be super-imposed with the foveas and the horizontal meridians accurately registered, then it was supposed that a needle put through the two retinas at any place would pierce points (called "cover" points) which would be corresponding retinal elements. Similar, and essentially the same, is the statement that when the eyes are observing the sky at night binocularly and fixating a given star, the visual axes of the two eyes being then parallel, the images of every other star would fall on the two retinas at cover (identical) or corresponding retinal points.

The functional approach to an understanding of the sensory organization of the two eyes is to determine experimentally, for a given fixation point of the eyes, those points in space the images of which will fall on corresponding elements. The sum total or the loci of all those points which satisfy this condition are said to lie on the *horopter*. In a general way the horopter would be a surface of some kind in space that passes ideally through the fixation point, and any other point of which has images in the two eyes which fall on corresponding retinal points, and which therefore will give rise to one and the same primary sense of direction. The orientation and shape of this surface describes in a quantitative way the relationships between the positions of corresponding points in the two eyes relative to the foveas.

Images from object points in space which do not fall on corresponding elements are said to be *disparate*, and in terms of monocular vision each of the images would give rise to *two* different subjective primary directions. The farther such points are from the horopter the greater the disparity. Because the two eyes are arranged in the head horizontally, the horizontal meridian forms a convenient basis to describe disparities as horizontal or vertical. Horizontal disparities are the basis for the stereoscopic perception of depth.

Early writers on the subject attempted to ascertain the shape and orientation of the horopter entirely from geometric considerations, beginning with certain assumptions about the topologic location of corresponding points on the two retinas. Helmholtz[107] particularly used this approach to study the problem of the horopter mathematically. This consideration is complicated by the particular assumption regarding the cyclotorsional positions of the eyes and by the asymmetries in the monocular topologic organization of the corresponding elements on each retina.

Following the concept that specific primary subjective directional values are associated with each retinal element according to a height and a breadth referred to the directional value of the fovea as an origin, it follows that on each retina a series of more or less vertically arranged elements could be found, all of which would have the same subjective breadth values relative to the fovea. Such a series of lines constitutes *longitudinal* sections of the retina, since each has the same subjective longitudinal value. Similarly, there would be vertical sections, rows of elements each of which gives rise to the same subjective height values, again above the fovea. Meridians of equal breadth value in the two eyes would be corresponding, as would also be meridians of equal height value.

Helmholtz,[107] Volkmann and others found that in their eyes the apparent horizontal meridians of the two eyes coincided well with the actual horizontal meridian but that the apparent vertical meridians for the primary position of the eyes deviated from the true vertical meridians, in the sense that the tops of those meridians were rotated temporally.[*] The deviation between the apparent vertical meridians of the two eyes (the declination angle) greatly influences the position (inclination) of the horopter surface. Helmholtz had to make assumptions about this deviation in his mathematical study. Certain conclusions about the horopter surface can be drawn from these assumptions about the topology of corresponding points, and to a large extent such was Helmholtz' approach.

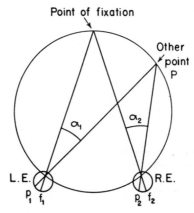

Fig. 3. The Vieth-Müller circle, the locus of points determined when the included angles α_1 and α_2 are equal.

Of more practical interest is the longitudinal horopter, which depends only on longitudinal sections of the retinas. If these sections are considered as being short enough, the longitudinal horopter approaches as a limit the intersection between the visual plane and the larger horopter surface. This is also the simplest approach to the study of the horopter, since it involves only plane geometry. On the basis of simple geometry and the concept of cover points, which means that retinal points in the two eyes which have the same horizontal distance from the fovea are corresponding, the longitudinal horopter is a circle that passes through the centers of curvature of the two eyeballs and the point of fixation (Fig. 3). First

[*] In view of the fact that cyclotorsional fusional movements occur so readily, depending upon the orientation of the objects in the visual field, the importance of these deviations as measured is questionable, and the experiments on which they were based have not ruled out the influence of these movements (see Chapter 10).

pointed out by Vieth in 1818 and later by Müller in 1826, this circle follows a very old geometric theorem that the included angles between lines drawn from any two points on the circumference of a circle to any other pair of points also on the circle are equal. This circle, now called the Vieth-Müller circle, remains the same as long as the point of fixation also lies on it.

CHAPTER 3

The Methods of Determining and
Analyzing the Empirical
Longitudinal Horopter

CRITERIA

WHEN THE EYES are directed to a fixed point in a suitable apparatus, and the fixation on that point is steadily maintained, other points can be arranged in space until they fulfill certain criteria that are said to specify the longitudinal horopter. Tschermak[231] has listed four criteria by which this can be determined; namely, (1) the position of each of the points (or vertical lines) is such that the primary subjective visual directions of the images as formed in the two eyes are identical; (2) the positions of all the points appear to lie in a frontoparallel plane that includes the point of fixation; (3) the positions of the points will lie in the "center" of the region of binocular single vision; (4) the positions of the points will be such that the stereoscopic sensitivity to changes in position will be a maximum. To these four, a fifth criterion could be added; namely, (5) the positions of the points are such that none provides a stimulus for a fusional movement of the eyes.

If we adhere strictly to our definition of corresponding retinal points, only the first of the foregoing criteria is the correct one; namely, that the points in space should be so placed that *each* has images in the two eyes that give rise to identical subjective *primary* visual directions; primary in the sense that *the visual directions are those associated with retinal elements were the images from the two eyes not fused.* This criterion is not an easy one to use experimentally or one that gives precise results (Chapter 4).

The second criterion—that of the apparent frontoparallel plane as originally postulated by Hering—is the simplest to use and gives most precise data, since it depends upon stereoscopic depth perception. Its validity is predicated upon the following argument. Stereoscopic perception of the difference in depth between the point of fixation and any other point in space depends on the disparity between the two retinal images of those points. In a schematic mechanistic sense, the sensation of depth appears to arise from a psychic appreciation of the number of subjective direction units corresponding to the number of retinal elements between the fovea

18

and the image in one eye compared to that in the other eye (Fig. 4). The binocular visual processes appreciate this difference, in an emergent sensation that the point P appears farther from, or nearer to, the observer than F. The farther from, or the nearer to, the observer P is as compared with F, the greater is the disparity and the greater is the sense of difference in distance. Thus, if P appears the *same* distance away as does F, corresponding to a zero depth difference, then the disparity between the images would also be zero, that is, the images of F and P in the two eyes would fall on corresponding retinal points. If the two images have zero disparity, then the primary subjective visual directions should be the same for each eye. Hering postulated that for a steady fixation of the eyes, a series of points lie on the horopter when so arranged in space that they are apparently the

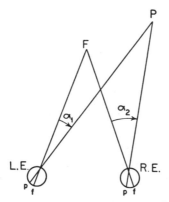

Fig. 4. The geometric disparity between the retinal images of two points is defined as the difference in the visual angles α_1 and α_2.

same distance away from the observer, so that they appear to lie in a plane parallel to the frontal plane* of the observer.† This is the criterion of the *apparent frontoparallel plane* and is the most used experimentally because it is the easiest and the most accurate.

Experiments have shown that the use of this criterion is not without its difficulties, as will be clear later. Even Tschermak insisted that it was reliable only under the conditions that (1) black plumb lines seen against a white background were used; (2) there was protracted observation, lasting at least longer than 0.8 second; (3) there was symmetrical convergence, and (4) any fundamentally potential outside influences on the interpreta-

* It should be recalled that the objective frontal plane is that plane which includes the interocular base line of the two eyes and is also perpendicular to the visual plane. The latter is that plane determined by the interocular base line and the point of fixation. The objective median plane is perpendicular to each of the foregoing planes and bisects the interocular base line.

† A fundamental ambiguity exists in this wording, for not all the points that lie in the frontoparallel plane will be equidistant from the subjective center of the individual. Only those near the point of fixation would correspond both to the plane and to the equidistance criterion. The logic for adhering to the apparent frontoparallel plane as Hering and others do is not entirely clear.

tion of the plane of the plumbs were avoided. However, subject to these reservations the criterion has proved useful.

The criterion of the "center" of the region of single binocular vision will be fully discussed in the next chapter. The criterion of the maximal stereoscopic sensitivity has been used, but it is a difficult one requiring prolonged and tedious experiments.

The fifth criterion is for the arrangement of points in space such that no *latent* stimuli exist for fusional movements of the eyes to any of the rods. The images of all are completely fused (Chapter 6). The subjective "feel-

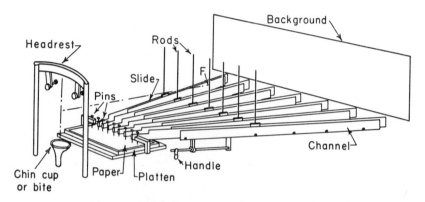

Fig. 5. A simplified sketch of the horopter apparatus.

ing" that a practiced observer often has when the rods of the apparatus are finally set for the apparent frontal plane may be in part due to this criterion. No easy experimental means exists for testing this criterion.

THE HOROPTER APPARATUS

The instrument used in our experiments was based on that of Tschermak,[235] but was improved so that data could be obtained easily at different visual distances and a permanent record of the data could be made. Actually, two instruments were used, the one for observation distances up to 1 meter and the second for an observation distance of 6 meters.

The first instrument (Fig. 5) consists of thirteen steel channels mounted so as to converge to a point directly below the midpoint of the interpupillary base line of the two eyes. The central channel lies in the median plane of the observer, and the others make angles of 1, 2, 4, 8, 12 and 16 degrees on each side of the central one. Sliding smoothly in these channels are narrow steel strips which support vertical small steel drill rods (to replace the threads of the Tschermak apparatus). Groups of these rods are mounted for use at visual distances of 20, 40 and 75 cm. from the interpupillary base line. The drill rods are mounted in special carriers that can be tilted back, thereby removing the rod from the field of view. The drill rods have diameters of 0.14, 0.32 and 0.6 mm. at the three visual distances. The movements of each of the slides, except the central one, are controlled by handles placed near the observer, these handles being staggered so that no cutaneous clues for the adjustment of the rods exist. At the front end of each of the sliding strips, a small punch is mounted which, when pushed, causes a pin prick in a sheet of cardboard supported on a platen beneath. By means of this arrangement a permanent record of the position of all the rods can be quickly and accurately made. Adjustment of the rods to the pins is accomplished by means of a telescope, a straight edge against the punches, and stationary punches on the apparatus.

The observer views the rods through a long horizontal slit aperture in a suitable screen* before the eyes and against a brightly and evenly illuminated white background. Care is taken that all objects in the room are excluded from the view, so that all empirical clues to depth perception are reduced to the minimum. A special headrest for supporting and holding the head before the apparatus is necessary. Often wax bites are fitted into this to fix a constant position of the head. To ensure symmetrical convergence and correct viewing distance, the headrest has features for adjusting the eyes to suitable aligning devices on the apparatus.

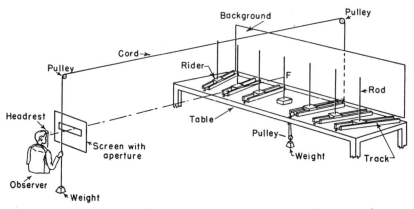

Fig. 6. Perspective sketch of the horopter apparatus used for an observation distance of 6 meters. Only seven lanes are indicated.

The observer himself adjusts all the rods, great care being taken that exact fixation on the central rod is maintained. The usual procedure, and one which tends to prevent "peeking" at the side rods being adjusted, is to set two rods on each side of the fixation point at the same time, first the two inner ones, then the next two, and so forth. Usually, after one round of setting all the rods, small subsequent changes in the positions of the rods had to be made. The final positions were thus found by a series of successive approximations. For the criterion according to the apparent frontoparallel plane, the observer set the rods so that he felt subjectively that they were in a plane and that the plane was parallel to his own subjective frontal plane. The subject usually experienced a specific sensation when the final adjustment had been made.

From five to seven groups of settings were made at one period of experimentation, these being recorded by the pin pricks in the paper on the platen. The series of settings were spaced about 1 cm. apart on the card. The

* This screen must be parallel to the interpupillary base line; otherwise it may introduce a small skewness in the final position of the rods.[146]

position of each point was then measured in millimeters from the objective frontoparallel plane through the fixation point by means of a transparent celluloid scale laid over the paper. For each lane (channel angle) the data were averaged and the mean variations were determined. These raw data were plotted directly to give the space-picture of the curve, as is shown, for example, in Fig. 11. Usually the ordinate distances are magnified ten times to facilitate the plotting and to illustrate better the deviations in the curve determined by the data.

At the observation distance of 6 meters the steel channels were replaced by wooden tracks, also converging to the midpoint of the interpupillary base line (Fig. 6). Capable of being moved on these were riders to which were attached long iron rods or wooden dowelings. These were adjustable by the observer by means of suitable cords over several pulleys. The positions of the rods in this case were read from a chart over the rods, and over which the pulley cords passed holding small indicator marks. This chart could not be seen by the observer.

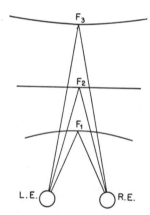

Fig. 7. Schematic illustration of the change in the shape of the apparent frontoparallel plane with change in observation distance generally believed to be typical.

Helmholtz had early simplified the horopter apparatus to consist of only three vertical cords, the center one of which could be displaced forward or backward out of the plane of the outer two. Thus one measurement sufficed to show the shape of the apparent frontoparallel plane.

THE HOROPTER DEVIATION

Both Hering and Helmholtz, and many subsequent workers, found that the curve of the apparent frontoparallel plane upon which the vertical cords had to be arranged, while the central cord was fixated in symmetrical convergence, did not lie on the Vieth-Müller circle as was expected, but actually between it and the objective frontoparallel plane. The degree to which this experimental curve deviated from the circle seemed to vary with the observation distance of the fixation point, the curve becoming more nearly flat as this point receded until, for some observers, it actually became flat and even curved slightly convexly for still greater distances (Fig. 7).

Furthermore, considerable differences have been found between individuals. Kröncke found, as did vom Hofe and Jaensch and Reich later, that for certain eidetic subjects, the apparent frontoparallel plane was convex at near vision and concave at a distance. Others were extremely variable at all observation distances. Kröncke found that for thirty-six subjects the observation distance at which the apparent frontoparallel plane (using six vertical threads) coincided with the objective frontoparallel plane averaged about 100 cm., with a range from 40 to 185 cm. Unfortunately, no data of the actual experiments were given, so that we cannot study them quantitatively. Nevertheless, the classic type is one in which the curve is concave at near, becomes flat at some observation distance (the "abathic" distance, Liebermann), and convex toward the observer for greater distances.

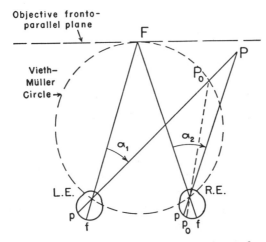

Fig. 8. The spatial asymmetry between the organization of retinal points corresponding to points on a horopter that lies outside the Vieth-Müller circle.

This change was taken as proof by some authors that corresponding retinal elements were not stable. However, Hillebrand[115] showed that the deviation of the curve from the Vieth-Müller circle could be explained by an asymmetry in the effective spatial positions of the corresponding elements in the two eyes or, what gives the same result, an optical distortion between the dioptric systems of the two eyes.

That an asymmetry between the two eyes accounts for the deviation of the curve from the Vieth-Müller circle can be seen from inspection of Fig. 8. The point P outside the Vieth-Müller circle lies on the horopter. Then its images fall on corresponding retinal elements. The geometry of the figure shows that the angular separation of the images of P from the images of the fixation point F is greater in the right eye than in the left. Only when the point falls on the Vieth-Müller circle, at P_0, will those angular separations be equal. Thus, for a horopter curve outside this circle, the angular separations of retinal elements of the right eye will be increasingly greater than those of the corresponding points of the left eye, for points on the right side of the fixation point. The reverse is true for points on the left side of the fixation point, where the angles of the right eye are increasingly smaller than those of the corresponding points of the left eye. Hillebrand showed furthermore that with this asymmetry, the shape of the horopter should change with observation distance in the manner described. Thus, this behavior of the curves with change in observation distance was actually evidence in favor of the stability of the corresponding retinal points. The departure of the experimental curve from the Vieth-Müller circle is now known as the Hering-Hillebrand horopter deviation. For the most part, the observations reported were qualitative, and it is not clear how Hillebrand

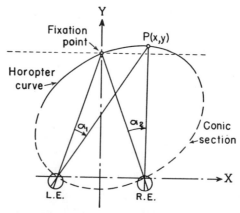

Fig. 9. How a portion of a conic section can be used to describe the shape and orientation of an empirical longitudinal horopter curve.

actually tested the validity of his theoretical equation by applying his data to it. Thus there is a need for a method by which the horopter data can be studied quantitatively.

ANALYSIS OF HOROPTER DATA

The following method has been developed[177, 179] by which horopter data can be studied quantitatively. We can assume that the horopter curve is a portion of a conic section (ellipse, circle, hyperbola and so forth), which passes through the point of fixation and the entrance pupils* of the two eyes, as does the Vieth-Müller circle. Two constants are necessary to describe this curve (Fig. 9). By suitable choice, the first of these, H, can describe

---

* Earlier writers have used the nodal points of the eyes instead of the entrance pupils. However, strictly speaking, the nodal point construction of chief light rays passing into the eye is correct only for sharp imagery, where the object and the retina upon which the image falls are conjugate. When both eyes are used this can be true only for the point of fixation itself in near vision. A light ray directed to the center of the entrance pupil, however, will always be that ray to the center of the blur circle on the retina. For practical purposes the error introduced by the use of either reference point is not significant.

the curvature of the horopter at the fixation point, and the second, R_0, can describe the degree to which the curve is skew with respect to the objective frontoparallel plane of the observer. Moreover, these constants are directly

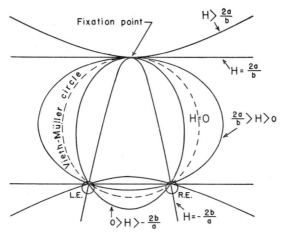

Fig. 10. A schematic representation of the family of conic sections determined by the magnitude of the parameter H in the equation.

related to the visual angles subtended at the two eyes by the fixation point and any other specified point on the curve by the equation

$$\cot \alpha_1 - R_0 \cot \alpha_2 = H \tag{1}$$

In this α_1 and α_2 are the longitudinal visual angles (Fig. 9) and H and R_0 are the two constants. This equation then explicitly describes the func-

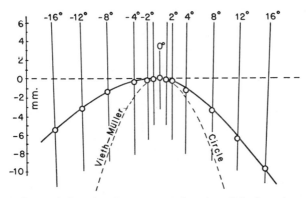

Fig. 11. A typical set of data for the apparent frontoparallel plane for an observation distance of 40 cm. The vertical dimensions have been increased tenfold.

tional relationship between corresponding retinal points in the horizontal meridian. If R_0 is unity, then the spatial difference between corresponding points of the two eyes depends only upon H.

Thus H is actually a measure of the asymmetry* between the spatial

* Tschermak called this asymmetry a "Ziehung," which means literally a "stretching."

dimensions associated with corresponding retinal points in the two eyes. If $R_0 = 1$, and if the longitudinal angles are small, we have approximately

$$\alpha_2 - \alpha_1 = H\alpha^2$$

where α is the average value of α_1 and α_2 (α's must be expressed in radians). The difference between longitudinal angles for corresponding points measured from the foveas is approximately proportional to the square of the peripheral angle, H being the constant of proportionality. When H is positive, angles of the right eye are progressively larger than the angles of the corresponding points of the left eye. If $H = 0$, $\alpha_2 = \alpha_1$, we have the Vieth-Müller condition of no asymmetry. For $H = 0.12$ (Figs. 11 and 12) at a peripheral angle of 10 degrees in the right field, the difference $\alpha_2 - \alpha_1$ is about 0.2 degree, or 2 per cent of the peripheral angle. On the left side

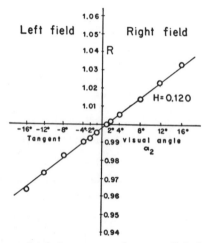

Fig. 12. The analytic graph of the apparent frontoparallel plane horopter data given in Table 1 and Fig. 11. The slope of the line which best fits the points determines H, and the intersection of this line on the ordinate determines R_0.

of the visual field, the angle of the right eye will be smaller by the same degree.

The other constant R_0 cannot differ greatly from unity, and actually is the ratio of the effective magnifications of the images of the two eyes (left to the right) in the horizontal meridian. Thus if $R_0 > 1$, the image in the left eye is the larger; if $R_0 < 1$, the image in the right eye is the larger. The per cent difference in magnification will be $100 \times (R_0 - 1)$.

The family of conic sections defined by these two constants is given by

$$Ax^2 - Bxy + Cy^2 - Dy - E = 0 \tag{2}$$

where

$$A = 1 - Hb/a(R_0 + 1)$$
$$B = (b^2 + a^2)\,(R_0 - 1)/ab(R_0 + 1)$$
$$C = 1 + Ha/b(R_0 + 1)$$
$$D = (b^2 - a^2)/b + 2Ha/(R_0 + 1)$$
$$E = a^2 - Hab/(R_0 + 1)$$

In this $2a$ is the interpupillary distance and b is the distance of the point of fixation from the interpupillary base line. When $R_0 = 1$, the sections are all symmetrical with respect to the median plane (both the coordinate axes). Figure 10 illustrates the family of curves obtained for symmetrical convergence of the eyes, ($R_0 = 1$) for different values of H. It should be clear that the constant H, therefore, can be used as a measure of the Hering-Hillebrand horopter deviation. For the condition $H = 0$, the curve coincides with the Vieth-Müller circle. As H increases positively, the curve

Table 1

TYPICAL SET OF DATA FOR THE APPARENT FRONTOPARALLEL PLANE AND THE CORRESPONDING ANALYTIC VALUES

LANE ANGLE	LEFT HALF VISUAL FIELD, DEGREES						
	-16	-12	-8	-4	-2	-1	0
Mean settings (mm.)*	-5.45	-3.20	-1.35	-0.19	-0.26	-0.11	
Mean deviation ($\pm$mm.)	1.45	0.82	0.48	0.23	0.14	0.12	
$R = \tan \alpha_2 / \tan \alpha_1$	0.9627	0.9725	0.9816	0.9898	0.9915	0.9940	
Mean deviation in R $\pm$	0.0020	0.0016	0.0014	0.0013	0.0016	0.0034	

LANE ANGLE	RIGHT HALF VISUAL FIELD, DEGREES						
	0	1	2	4	8	12	16
Mean settings (mm.)*		-0.14	-0.32	-1.16	-3.38	-6.56	-9.64
Mean deviation ($\pm$mm.)		0.11	0.21	0.31	0.59	0.89	1.62
$R = \tan \alpha_2 / \tan \alpha_1$		1.0000	1.0002	1.0047	1.0129	1.0215	1.0325
Mean deviation in R $\pm$		0.0031	0.0025	0.0018	0.0018	0.0017	0.0022

* These distances are measured perpendicularly from the objective frontoparallel plane, taken positive away from the observer and negative toward the observer. Data of K. N. O. Observation distance = 40 cm.

departs from the Vieth-Müller circle and its curvature becomes less. When $H = 2a/b$, the curve becomes a straight line at the fixation point and coincides with the objective frontoparallel plane. If H is greater than $2a/b$, the curve becomes convex to the subject. It is clear, therefore, that we can have an infinite number of *geometric* horopter curves, of which the Vieth-Müller circle is but one, depending on the constants H and R_0.

It is not difficult to find H and R_0 from any set of data such as those given in Table 1 and illustrated in Fig. 11. Rewrite equation (1) as

$$R = \tan \alpha_2 / \tan \alpha_1 = H \tan \alpha_2 + R_0$$

in which R is the ratio of the tangents of the longitudinal angles subtended at the left and right eyes by the fixation point and any given data point.

R must be computed for each point of the data.* These are then plotted on a graph, with tan α_2 as the abscissa and R as the corresponding ordinate. The data points should then fall approximately on a straight line. Such an analytic graph is shown in Fig. 12, for the same data given previously. The slope of this line is equal to H, and the intercept on the ordinate is R_0. From the graph we find $H = 0.120$, and $R_0 = 0.9966$, or the right image is equivalently larger than the left by 0.34 per cent. The fact that these data fall quite well on a straight line out to visual angles of 16 degrees shows that representing the data by a conic section is quite justified.

With this mathematical tool it is now possible to examine critically the actual data obtained for the longitudinal horopter according to the several criteria, and those data as influenced by changes in observation distance and changes in the relative magnifications of the images in the two eyes.

---

* Where many data are to be analyzed, it is convenient to prepare tables or graphs for each channel angle of the apparatus which give R for each position of the rod measured perpendicularly from the objective frontoparallel plane. One finds $R = (1 + Z)/(1 - Z)$ where $Z = [x^2 + (y - B)^2 - A]/2Axy$, in which $A = (b^2 + a^2)/2b$ and $B = (b^2 - a^2)/2b$, x and y being the coordinates of the point (Fig. 9). $2a$ is the interpupillary distance and b is the observation distance.

CHAPTER 4

Studies of the Empirical Longitudinal Horopter

THE CRITERION OF THE APPARENT FRONTOPARALLEL PLANE

THE SETTING of the rods of the horopter apparatus according to the criterion of the apparent frontoparallel plane depends only upon stereoscopic vision—the stereoscopic perception of depth. The precision of those settings will then depend upon stereoscopic acuity (Chapter 12). We shall be concerned here with the character of the data obtained by this criterion (1) when the image of one eye is magnified by a suitable lens,

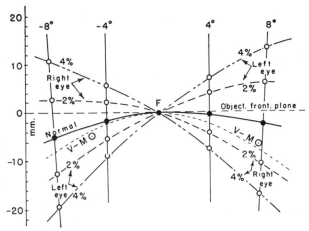

Fig. 13. Influence of magnifying lenses before one eye on the position of the apparent frontoparallel plane. Data of R.H.D. for 40 cm. observation distance. Vertical dimensions increased tenfold.

and (2) when the observation distance is changed. Later the implication of the results to the stability of corresponding points and the validity of the criteria will be discussed.

The Change in the Magnification of the Image of One Eye. If one places an afocal magnification lens (Chapter II) before one eye while making settings on the horopter apparatus, the apparent frontoparallel plane will become skew about the fixation point, being nearer on the side of the eye having the increased magnification.

Hillebrand[114] was the first to show that at near vision a thick sheet of glass before one eye causes a rotation of the apparent frontoparallel plane. Such a sheet of glass has an angular magnification (see p. 126). When Erggelet[66] placed a contact lens in one eye to produce a high farsightedness (artificial aphakia) and corrected this with a $+13$ D. ophthalmic lens, he found that the apparent frontoparallel plane was rotated about the fixation point through a large angle. He had, of course, introduced a large difference in the magnifications of the images of the two eyes.

Table 2 and Fig. 13 show the characteristic type[35, 113, 179] of change in the shape of the space curve itself when 2 per cent and 4 per cent magnification lenses are placed successively before the right and left eyes. To simplify

Table 2

TYPICAL SETS OF DATA FOR THE APPARENT FRONTOPARALLEL PLANE AS INFLUENCED BY THE MAGNIFICATION OF THE IMAGE OF ONE EYE*

LENS MAGNIFICATION	MEAN SETTING	LEFT FIELD, DEGREES			RIGHT FIELD, DEGREES		R_0	PER CENT R_0
		−8	−4	0	4	8		
4% R. E.	mm.	+10.43	+5.73		−7.70	−16.66	0.9655	R. 3.45
	R	0.9545	0.9612		0.9700	0.9758		
2% R. E.	mm.	+2.26	+2.06		−4.20	−10.43	0.9837	R. 1.63
	R	0.9732	0.9795		0.9885	0.9937		
Normal	mm.	−5.36	−1.86		−0.16	−2.10	1.0046	L. 0.46
	R	0.9934	1.0005		1.0096	1.0150		
2% L. E.	mm.	−12.70	−5.60		+4.26	+6.46	1.0258	L. 2.58
	R	1.0136	1.0196		1.0325	1.0374		
4% L. E.	mm.	−19.50	−9.00		+7.26	+13.70	1.0439	L. 4.39
	R	1.0332	1.0387		1.0478	1.0560		

* Data of R. H. D. Observation distance = 40 cm. P. D. = 58 mm.

the experiment only the 4 and 8 degree lanes on each side of the fixation point were used in the horopter apparatus. The greater the difference in magnification the greater is the rotation of the curve about the fixation point. Figure 14 shows the equivalent analytic curves for these data. Clearly the significant change is in the R_0 value, which is exactly to be expected. These values are shown in Table 2. Striking also is the fact that the H values for the Hering-Hillebrand deviation are essentially constant for the series.*

The degree to which the values of R_0 determined from the experiment agree with the magnifications introduced by the lenses is shown in Fig. 15, which gives the results of three subjects, including those of R.H.D. of Fig. 14. Clearly the data lie on straight lines at a 45 degree angle, indicating a 1:1 relationship. These data are important because they show that the

* For larger magnification differences and even equal magnifications of both images of the eyes, a change in H by a factor of R_0 would be evident.[179]

retinal organization at the one visual distance is stable and that the settings
of the apparent frontoparallel plane under these experimental conditions

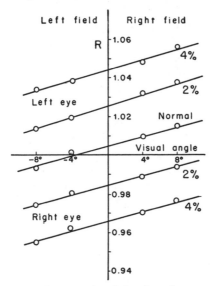

Fig. 14. The analytic graphs of the data shown in Fig. 13.

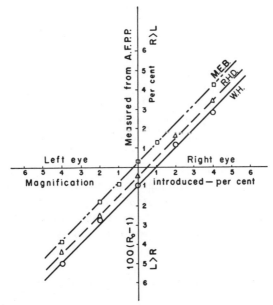

Fig. 15. The 1:1 relationship between the magnification introduced and the corresponding effect upon the apparent frontoparallel plane. Data of 3 observers include those
of R.H.D. of Figs. 13 and 14.

must be almost uninfluenced by monocular factors to spatial localization,
which if present would tend to dampen the pure stereoscopic perception.

The Change in Apparent Frontoparallel Plane With Observation Distance. Hillebrand pointed out that if a functional asymmetry exists between the spatial patterns of corresponding retinal points in the two eyes, and this asymmetry remains constant, then the shape of the horopter should change with observation distance.

In terms of our analysis, a fixed asymmetry would be indicated by a constant H in equation (1) of the previous chapter. Since the value of H corresponding to the objective frontoparallel plane is $2a/b$ (where, as before, $2a$ is the interpupillary distance and b is the observation distance), it is clear that $H_f = 2a/b$ decreases with observation distance. For a constant H_0 there would be some distance b_0 for which the horopter would coincide with the objective frontoparallel plane ($b_0 = 2a/H_0$). At a nearer observation distance than b_0, H_0 would be smaller than H_f and accordingly the curve would be concave to the observer; at a greater distance than b_0, H_0 would be larger than H_f and the curve would accordingly be convex to the observer.[121]

Data for the apparent frontoparallel plane have been obtained by three observers[11] for the observation distances of 20, 40 and 76 cm. and 6 meters on the instrumentation described in the previous chapter. The data of one of the observers are illustrated in the space and analytic graphs in Figs. 16 and 17, respectively. The data for the 40 cm. observation distance are shown in Figs. 11 and 12 of the previous chapter. From the analytic graphs by inspection or by the method of least squares, one can obtain the best fitting lines to the data, and hence find the corresponding value of H, which will be the slope, $\triangle R/\triangle (\tan \alpha_2)$.

The results[11, 113] for four observers are summarized in Table 3. These are also illustrated graphically in Fig. 18, in which is included also for comparison the line corresponding to the $H_f = 2a/b$ for the objective frontoparallel plane. These data are plotted according to the diopter value of the observation distances. The other data marked "nonius" are those obtained by the criterion of equating of primary subjective directions, and will be discussed in the next section.

Inspection of the data and the figures shows at once that for the apparent frontoparallel plane, H is *not* constant for all observation distances, but rather markedly increases the nearer is the fixation point. Were it constant, the data would fall on a line parallel to the abscissa, and intersect the H_f line at that distance for which the longitudinal horopter would coincide with the objective frontoparallel plane. On the basis of these data we cannot say even approximately that the H values are constant for all observation distances.

We may also find in the literature data which bear upon this problem. In almost every case cited, a test involving three vertical threads was used in which the outer two threads were placed in the objective frontoparallel plane of the observer, in symmetrical convergence, and the center thread was adjustable forward or back until the observer saw all three threads in

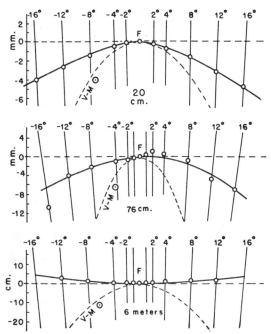

Fig. 16. The spatial representation of the data for the apparent frontoparallel plane for one observer for different observation distances. The data for the distance of 40 cm. are shown in Fig. 11. The vertical dimension has been magnified in each of these graphs.

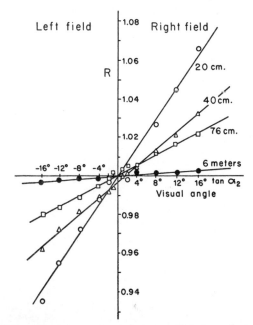

Fig. 17. The analytic graph of the apparent frontoparallel plane data of one observer for four observation distances, corresponding to the data shown in Figs. 11 and 16.

Table 3

RESULTS FOR FOUR OBSERVERS SHOWING THE QUANTITATIVE VALUES (H) FOR THE HERING-HILLEBRAND HOROPTER DEVIATION FOR THE APPARENT FRONTOPARALLEL PLANE AND THE NONIUS HOROPTER FOR SEVERAL OBSERVATION DISTANCES

OBSERVER		OBSERVATION DISTANCES			
	Cm.	20	40	76	600
	Diopters	5	2.5	1.3	0.16
K. N. O.	AFPP*	0.226	0.122	0.080	0.016
	Nonius†	0.132	0.113	0.076	‡
A. A.	AFPP	—	0.136	0.070	0.013
	Nonius	—	0.096	0.046	‡
F. D. C.	AFPP	0.186	0.110	0.056	0.007
	Nonius	0.136	0.097	0.050	‡
	Cm.	30	40	60	
	Diopters	3.3	2.5	1.6	
W.H.	AFPP	0.094	0.086	0.035	

* Criterion of apparent frontoparallel plane
† Criterion of equating primary subjective visual directions
‡ Not possible to obtain on apparatus used

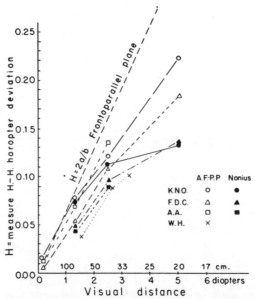

Fig. 18. Empirical results showing the value of H for the Hering-Hillebrand horopter deviation for different observation distances.

the same plane. The actual displacement, the separation of the threads and the observation distance are sufficient for us to calculate the value of H.*

Figure 19 shows graphically the data of Helmholtz[107] and the corresponding values of H computed from them. At all observation distances the center thread was set behind the outer threads.

These data are strikingly similar to those of Fig. 18. Also shown in Fig. 19 are the results of similarly calculated values of H from the data given by Lau[144] and by Liebermann. Only those of Lau suggest any constancy in H with observation distance, and Lau himself was aware of sources of error in his experiments.

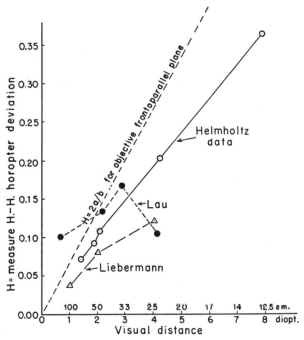

Fig. 19. Calculated values of H from the data of Helmholtz, Lau and Liebermann found in the literature where the three-plumb-line apparatus was used.

The extent to which these data imply a lack of stability of corresponding retinal points cannot be ascertained at the moment. One must take into account the validity of the apparent frontoparallel plane criterion, on the one hand, and the change in the optical distortion of the eye with change in accommodation, on the other hand. Whatever is the cause of the change in H with observation distance, as shown by these experiments, it is a consistent and regular process.

* In equation (2), p. 26, we solve for H after putting $R_0 = 1$, $y = b + c$, where c is the displacement of the central thread from the outer two threads ($+$ = behind), b is the distance of the central thread from the interpupillary base line, and $x = s$, which is one half of the separation of the outer threads. Approximately this reduces to

$$H = (2a) (1 - bc/s^2)/b$$

THE CRITERION OF EQUATING THE PRIMARY SUBJECTIVE VISUAL DIRECTIONS

Before discussing further the results obtained by the criterion of the apparent frontoparallel plane, we should consider those obtained by the criterion of adjusting the threads of rods of the horopter apparatus until the primary subjective visual direction of each will be the same for the two eyes. This criterion is in accord with the basic definition of corresponding retinal points.

The method was that used by Volkmann and by Helmholtz[107] for determining the spatial congruence of corresponding points. Figure 20 shows the type of targets they used in the stereoscope, or haploscope, for determining the spatial congruence of corresponding sections in the vertical meridian. The same method can be used for determining the space values for corre-

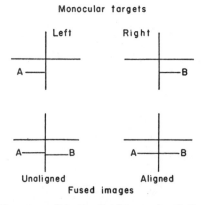

Fig. 20. The type of target used in the haploscope by Volkmann and by Helmholtz to determine the congruence of corresponding sections in the vertical meridian. The eyes fixate the center of the cross.

sponding meridians in the horizontal meridian, as Lau[144] has done. The eyes fixate on the center of the cross, which is identical in the two eyes; the line A is stationary, but B can be displaced vertically. The procedure is to adjust B until A and B appear in alignment. If the separation of the cross and the lines is not too great, this setting of B can be made with considerable accuracy. While this vernier-like device provides one of the most precise methods of testing monocular resolving power (Walls),[244] when used binocularly, as here, the sensitivity is much less.

Van der Meulen apparently was the first to suggest that the same type of visual stimuli employed by Volkmann could be had with vertical threads as used in the horopter apparatus by the placing of suitable screens before the eyes. These screens permitted the top half of the thread or rod to be seen by one eye and the lower half by the other (Fig. 21A). Ames[10] increased the efficacy of these screens by cutting several narrow longitudinal slits in the upper part of each screen so that the wire seen through these would appear as an interrupted line (Fig. 21B). This device was used in the so-called "grid-nonius"* method. However, the screens must be so shaped that both eyes can see the detail for fusion on the central fixation wire. For best results the screen should be illuminated to the same brightness and with the same color as the background.

To ensure a precise fixation point and detail for fusion on the central wire, a small flat thin metal plate, several millimeters square, with a central small hole was set into the central wire so that its face coincided with the center of the wire.

With the eyes fixed upon this object, the movement of any one of the rods along its track on the horopter apparatus caused the upper and lower halves to appear to separate (Fig. 21B), that is, to be seen in different directions.

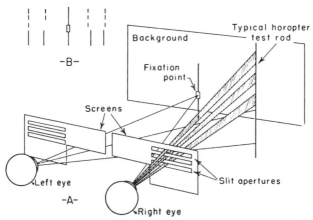

Fig. 21. Perspective sketch of the screens used with the horopter apparatus in the "nonius" method, whereby the longitudinal horopter is determined by the criterion of equating the primary subjective visual directions.

For any one position, a displacement of the images is evidence of a functional disparity between the images in the two eyes. There can be found a position of the rod where the upper and lower halves appear aligned (zero disparity), and for that position we say the rod is seen in the same subjective primary visual direction. By definition the rod then lies on the longitudinal horopter and its images fall on corresponding retinal points.

No stereoscopic sensation of depth is experienced, only the apparent sideways slipping of the upper to the lower parts of a rod. Obviously many retinal elements in vertical meridians come into play, so that this test must be said to determine only corresponding longitudinal meridians. This technic is not an easy one, and some training on the part of the observer is usually necessary. Furthermore, were it not for the backward and forward motion of the rods, with which one sees a varying displacement of the rods in one

* *Nonius* is the Latinized form of Nunes, the name of a Portuguese mathematician, and pertains to a device at one time used in graduating instruments. The device was subsequently improved into the vernier. (From Webster's *New International Dictionary*.)

direction and then in the other, a midpoint could not be easily discriminated. This is especially true the more peripheral are the rods, and beyond a peripheral angle of 12 degrees the data are quite unreliable. In a case in which cyclotropia exists, the two halves of the rod may appear slightly inclined to one another (see for example, Fischer[71]).

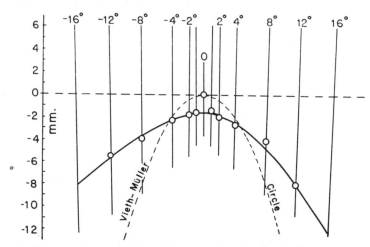

Fig. 22. The spatial representation of the data for the longitudinal horopter as determined by the criterion of equating primary visual directions (nonius method). Data of K.N.O. (esophoria). Observation distance = 40 cm.

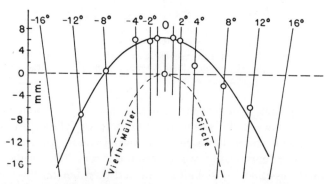

Fig. 23. The spatial representation of the data for the longitudinal horopter as determined by the criterion of equating primary visual directions (nonius method). Data of F.D.C. (exophoria). Observation distance = 76 cm.

Data obtained by two subjects are shown in Figs. 22 and 23. The significant difference between these curves and those found previously is that the entire horopter curve is displaced from the point of fixation. Thus the point of fixation does not lie on the longitudinal horopter, and therefore the images of the fixation point must be disparate. Moreover, this displacement of the curve from the fixation point is in the direction of the lateral heterophoria of the observer, in that in the esophoric case (K.N.O.) the eyes are actually overconverged, and in the exophoric case (F.D.C.) the eyes are actually underconverged in spite of fusion of the images of the fixation object. We can calculate the magnitude of this angular disparity at the fixation point from the amount of displacement of the curve from $\eta = -2a\,\Delta b/b^2$, where η is the disparity, a is one-half of the interpupillary distance and b is the observation distance. For both sets of data we find $\eta = 2.4$ minutes of arc. This phenomenon of the images of the fixation point being disparate will be discussed in considerable detail in Chapter 8.

With the nonius method suggested by van der Meulen, Fischer[71] previously obtained data for the longitudinal horopter by the same criterion of equating the primary subjective visual directions. His results for an observation distance of 30 cm. on the Tschermak apparatus[230] are illustrated in Fig. 24. The two sets of data correspond to the screen adjustment when the right eye sees the upper halves of the threads and the left the lower

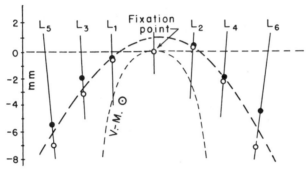

Fig. 24. A plot of the data of Fischer for the longitudinal horopter obtained by a nonius method, whereby one eye sees only the upper halves of the horopter threads, and the other eye the lower halves (Tschermak apparatus). Ordinates magnified tenfold.

halves, and vice versa. Fischer drew lines to connect his data points with the point of fixation. The interrupted curve drawn in the figure through the average positions is that of the writer. Since no data were taken inside the 5 degree lanes, we cannot be positive that Fischer's data actually lie behind the fixation point, but with the magnification of the ordinates in his figure, to connect the 5 degree data points with the fixation point produces far too flat a curve at the fixation point. Fischer was also myopic, with exophoria at near vision.

Data using the nonius method were obtained by three observers[11] for observation distances of 20, 40 and 76 cm. The method could not be used at 6 meters for obvious reasons. In each case the value of H was determined as outlined previously. The results obtained are also shown in Table 3 and illustrated in Fig. 18. From the few data available, conclusive remarks cannot be made, but it would appear that H obtained by the nonius method follows the trend of that for the apparent frontoparallel plane with visual distance, though to a smaller extent, especially for very near visual distances. Since not enough data are available to know the variability of H, especially for the nonius method, we do not know the significance of small differences. We shall discuss these data later.

Tschermak[72] modified the nonius method for use with the horopter apparatus by interposing a small narrow flat screen before each eye so as not to obscure the fixation wire, but so as to prevent binocular perception of a small central portion of each thread. With this screen, when properly illuminated so that it blends into the background, only a small central portion of the wire seen monocularly was compared to upper and lower parts seen binocularly. These parts also appear misaligned except for one position of the horopter thread (rod). This is a "binocular" nonius method. This method was also used by two subjects on the present horopter apparatus, and the results were similar to those with the grid-nonius method. Again the curve was displaced from the fixation point. This device does not make a clear nonius edge between the binocularly and monocularly perceived portions, because of the tendency for fused configurations to carry over a short distance onto similar types of contours the images of which are seen by only one eye. However, the data obtained by the grid-nonius method appear only slightly more precise than those obtained by the binocular nonius method.

THE LONGITUDINAL HOROPTER AND THE REGION OF BINOCULAR SINGLE VISION

The oldest concept regarding corresponding retinal points was that when the images from a point in space fell on corresponding points it would be seen single. Singleness was the criterion for determining the horopter. Wheatstone, however, found with the reflecting stereoscope that configurations of unequal separation in the two targets, which could obviously not stimulate corresponding points, would nevertheless fuse and be seen single. Panum[201] first systematically studied this problem and showed that an image on a retinal point of one eye would fuse with a similar image on the retina of the other eye, anywhere within a small area of the retina. Thus, singleness alone could not be used as a criterion for determining corresponding retinal points. The horopter apparatus can be used to demonstrate and measure this phenomenon of the fusion of disparate images.

Consider the following. Suppose the eyes are fixated on a vertical rod F, at a near observation distance, say, of 40 cm. (Fig. 25). A second vertical rod P is mounted to move in a suitable channel, so that the image of that rod in the right eye always falls on the same retinal elements. One can then observe that when rod P is much further away than the fixation point, say, at P_u, one sees two rods, that is, the rod actually is seen in two different subjective directions. This type of doubling is known as physiologic diplopia. Each of these double images is often called a *half-image* (*Halbbilde*). If the *right* eye is suddenly closed, the *right* half-image of this pair vanishes. Likewise, when P is much nearer than the fixation point, say, at P_c, again one will see two rods. This time, however, when the right eye is suddenly closed, the left half-image of the pair vanishes. In the first case, P_u, the images are said to be uncrossed disparate, because the image on the side of the eye that is closed disappears; in the second, P_c, the images are said to be crossed disparate, because the half-image disappears on the side opposite to the closed eye.

As the rod is moved away from the observer from a position P_c where the half-images are seen in crossed disparity, the apparent separation of these images decreases and finally only one rod is seen. Moving the rod still farther away, one suddenly becomes aware of uncrossed double images, the apparent separation of which increases as the rod continues moving away. There exists an interval between P_c and P_u where no doubling is seen. Such intervals obtained for all visual angles define a region in space which is designated as

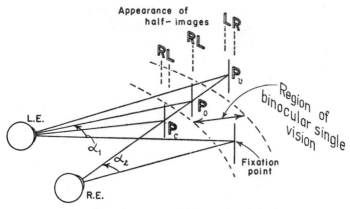

Fig. 25. Perspective drawing of positions of the rods of the horopter apparatus corresponding to the appearance of double images (physiologic diplopia) and corresponding to the region of binocular single vision.

the region of binocular single vision. The images from the two eyes of all points within this region are said to be "fused." The angular extent of this area (to the left eye in Fig. 25) for a given visual angle is a measure of the horizontal dimension of Panum's area (sometimes called also Panum's circle of sensation).

It is clear, however, that if at a near position the images are crossed disparate, while at a greater distance the images are uncrossed disparate, there must be a position between P_c and P_u in the region of single binocular vision where the disparity of the two images must be zero—neither crossed nor uncrossed. This position, P_o, by definition, would lie on the longitudinal horopter—for at this position the *primary* visual directions of the images of the two eyes will be identical. On each side of this position the images are either crossed (rod nearer) or uncrossed (rod farther), even though within a certain region only one image is seen; that is, within this region the two images are fused, although disparate.

The boundaries of the region of binocular single vision are not well defined, and one must consider the limits as being a gradient of some sort where the probable appearance of fusion increases in a statistical manner toward the centers of the areas. Experiment has shown, moreover, that the size of these areas tends to decrease somewhat with training. However, there seems to be general agreement that the training cannot reduce the areas beyond certain limits.

The appearance of double images as the disparities increase is easier to observe when there is movement of the test rods. In the case of stationary objects, one rarely is aware of double images unless the disparities are very great and when one consciously looks for the doubling, as for example, in the apparent doubling of the curtain string on fixating on a distant object through the window. The greater part of this failure to see double images in ordinary life is thought to be due to some form of rivalry and certainly suppression. Nevertheless, the facts of the training effect and the influence of movement on the appearance of double images caused Tschermak[232] to

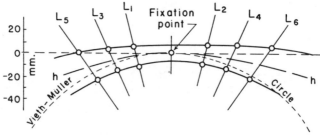

Fig. 26. The region of binocular single vision according to data obtained by Fischer on the Tschermak horopter apparatus.

postulate a relative and an absolute extent of Panum's areas, this extent depending on the experimental circumstances, training and period of observation.

The small involuntary oscillatory movements of the eyes (physiologic nystagmus) also are factors in the extent of Panum's areas. Adler and Fliegelman showed that for monocular fixation there were three types of these movements acting at the same time: (1) rapid shifts of fixation of 12 minutes of arc that occur about once a second; (2) waves, small shifts and recoveries of about 2.5 minutes of arc at the rate of 5 per second, and (3) fine vibratory movements of about 2 minutes of arc at a rate of 50 to 100 per second. These movements would increase Panum's areas only to the extent that they were *not* synchronized for the two eyes.[87] We do not have adequate data on this point. However, the existence of fixation disparity (Chapter 8), of which the displacement of the nonius horopter just described is an example, affords proof that the existence of Panum's areas is *not* a phenomenon of these eye movements, though admittedly they are a factor in the functional effect and in the measurement of the areas. Also, the size of these areas increases toward the peripheral parts of the visual field, whereas they would tend to be constant if the phenomena were due to these eye movements alone.

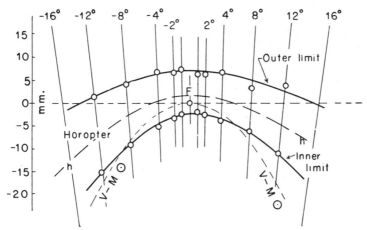

Fig. 27. Region of binocular single vision and the longitudinal horopter. Data of A.A. for observation distance of 40 cm. Ordinates magnified twofold.

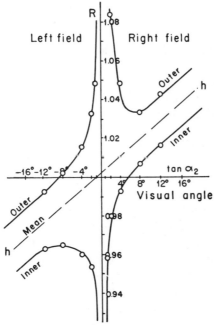

Fig. 28. The analytic curves corresponding to the data of Fig. 27 for the region of binocular single vision.

Fischer[72] obtained data for a visual distance of 30 cm. on the Tschermak horopter apparatus, and his data are redrawn in Fig. 26. This figure differs from the one published by Fischer in that the lines drawn through the points to indicate the boundaries of the region are continued behind and in front of the fixation point. Fischer drew the lines to the fixation point. This would imply there were no fusional areas at the foveas, which is, of course, not true. The longitudinal horopter curve is near the center of this region and is indicated by $h \ldots h$ on the figure. The precise location of this curve is not the spatial geometric center but that corresponding to the center of the visual angle subtended by the inner and outer boundary to one eye for a given ray to the other eye (the center of angle α_1 of Fig. 25, if P_c and P_u were the boundaries of the region of binocular single vision). One can find H and R_0 for these curves as has been done for the data obtained by the other criteria for finding the longitudinal horopter.

Figure 27 shows the data[11] of an observer on the present apparatus for an observation distance of 40 cm. Figure 28 shows the analytic curves for these data. The midline would correspond to the longitudinal horopter. H and R_0 for this line can be readily found from the graph. To be noted here is the displacement of the region of binocular single vision back from the fixation point, which is in agreement with the exophoria of the subject and with the data obtained by the nonius method.

Panum's fusional areas as an aspect of fusion will be considered in Chapter 7.

OTHER CRITERIA

The fourth criterion for the determination of the horopter is that of maximal differential stereoscopic sensitivity. According to this criterion the observer is said to be more keenly aware of small displacements of points nearer or farther away, in the vicinity of the horopter surface than if those points were at some distance from it. In other words, the stereoscopic sensitivity to small changes in the disparity of the images of objects in space decreases with the disparity and therefore is maximal when the disparity is zero. Tschermak and Kiribuchi[229] obtained some measurements using this criterion and reported that the maximal sensitivity was greatest when the threads of the horopter apparatus were in the apparent frontoparallel plane.

The last criterion for the determination of the horopter is that method by which points are arranged in space so that their images are not stimuli for fusional movements of the two eyes. Only when the disparity between the images of all the rods is zero will this be true. To test this criterion presents so many obstacles, such as the ever-present factors of phorias, that as a criterion it is primarily of academic interest only.

COMMENT

Do the empirical longitudinal horopters determined by the three criteria agree, and if not, which is the true horopter?

Tschermak[230] has reported that the curve obtained by the criterion of the apparent frontoparallel plane is different according to whether (1) white threads are seen against a black background, (2) black threads are seen against a white background (as in most of the experiments described previously), (3) red threads are seen against a black background, or (4) blue threads are seen against a black background. The curve of the blue threads was nearest the Vieth-Müller circle; the red showed the greatest deviation. These differences found with variously colored threads were believed to be due to a chromatic difference of magnification of the images in the two eyes.

It has also been shown (Tschermak and Kiribuchi[229]) that when the threads are exposed for very short periods, and set for the apparent frontoparallel plane, the curve also is nearer the Vieth-Müller circle than those

Table 4

COMPARATIVE RESULTS FOR THE H AND R_0 VALUES FOR THE HERING-HILLEBRAND
HOROPTER DEVIATION FROM DATA OBTAINED BY THREE CRITERIA FOR
THE DETERMINATION OF THE LONGITUDINAL HOROPTER

OBSERVER	APPARENT FRONTO-PARALLEL PLANE		EQUAL VISUAL DIRECTIONS (NONIUS)		CENTER OF REGION OF BINOCULAR SINGLE VISION	
	H	R_0	H	R_0	H	R_0
K. N. O. (40 cm.)	0.13 0.12	0.997 0.998	0.125 0.13* 0.08‡ 0.13§	0.998 1.006* 1.008‡ 0.982§	0.13 0.08†	0.996 0.968†
A. A. (40 cm.)	0.14	1.006	0.09	—	0.13	1.004
Fischer (30 cm.)	0.12‖ 0.14¶	1.005‖ 1.004¶	0.11‖	1.006‖	0.12‖	1.006‖
F. D. C. (75 cm.)	0.006	1.000	0.005	1.000	—	—

* +2.00 D. spheres before both eyes
† 3 per cent meridional magnification lens axis 90° before right eye
‡ Tschermak binocular-nonius method
§ 1.5 per cent meridional magnification lens axis 90° before right eye
‖ Black threads seen against white background
¶ White threads seen against black background

set for longer periods of observation. Burian[32] showed that if each of the lateral threads were adjusted alone for the apparent frontal plane, while all the other threads (except the fixation thread) were screened so that they could not be seen, then when each was finally adjusted, the curve representing the positions of all was also found nearer the Vieth-Müller circle than when there was no screening. In spite of the belief that configurations in the background of the apparatus would influence the final settings of the threads, Fischer[72] could not find any such influences. On the other hand, Lehnert found that if the slit aperture before the eyes in the horopter apparatus was not parallel to the interpupillary base line, the horopter curve found would be rotated (skew) slightly about the fixation thread.

Fischer[72] used the Tschermak binocular-nonius method and claimed to have demonstrated by it that the apparent frontoparallel plane, determined by using black threads seen against a white background and red and blue threads seen against black backgrounds, were true horopters; that is, that the positions of the threads satisfied both criteria. The white threads seen against a black background did not give the true horopter. Since his actual data were not given in the paper, his results cannot be studied quantitatively by the method outlined here.

The results of the experiments described are summarized in Table 4, where the H value for the binocular asymmetry between the two eyes and the R_0 value for the ratio of the functional magnifications of the images in the two eyes are given for the three criteria for determining the longitudinal horopter. The values calculated from Fischer's data, while only approximate, are also included.

A study of these results shows that, at least for visual distances of about 40 cm., there is an approximate agreement between the longitudinal horopters as determined by the three criteria: (1) the apparent frontoparallel plane, (2) the equating of the primary subjective directions (nonius) and (3) the center of the region of binocular single vision. This conclusion would be in agreement with those reached by Hillebrand,[114] Tschermak[231] and Lau[144] for small visual angles. This is to say that the criterion of the apparent frontoparallel plane with black threads seen against a white background and observed continuously is valid for the determination of the true longitudinal horopter.

However, the data given previously show that while this is true in degree it is not true as regards the actual space curves, because generally the true longitudinal horopter is displaced in the direction of the phoria of the subject. Hence, as Lau also suggested, the apparent frontoparallel plane which passes through the fixation point is actually a curve, every point of which probably has retinal images with the same disparity with respect to the true horopter curve, and thus is more or less parallel to that curve. On the other hand, observers with large exophoria often tend to set the rods of the horopter apparatus behind the fixation point, even according to the criterion of the apparent frontoparallel plane. If no fixation disparity exists, then the two curves are identical. The value of R_0, which measures the ratio of the regular magnification of the images in the two eyes, and therefore the difference in retinal image sizes, is significantly constant for the same observer.

However, the results (Fig. 18) show a marked discrepancy in the H values between the data obtained by the nonius method and the apparent frontoparallel plane for nearer observation differences, a fact not easy to explain in view of the consistency at distances of 40 cm. and more. We repeat that the H values for the apparent frontoparallel plane at different distances are not constant for the data available. This means that the functional binocular asymmetry between the two retinas increases markedly as the visual distance decreases.

In considering this subject, we must recall that the effective binocular asymmetry as given by H is the sum of the functional asymmetry in the subjective directions correlated with the distribution of receptor elements on the retinas, and the asymmetry due to the optical distortion inherent in the decentered optical systems of the eyes. Hence, even a small change in the effective binocular asymmetry with accommodation does not vitiate the concept of the stability of space values of the retinal elements, for this asymmetry could be due to changes in the optical systems of the eyes. One might even expect such changes to occur with accommodation, or innervations to accommodate. Lau[144] on the other hand did not show any change with increased convergence using the haploscope, and this fact might be considered in studying his data in the three-thread experiment (Fig. 19). It is difficult to account for the difference between the nonius and the apparent frontoparallel plane data for these very near visual distances, however. One must fall back upon the possibility that empirical factors of depth localization become more effective for nearer visual distances, and these tend to cause the apparent frontoparallel plane to become nearer the objective frontoparallel plane.*

From a teleological point of view we might ask why the apparent frontoparallel plane deviates at all from the objective frontoparallel plane. If a binocular asymmetry exists between the two eyes which causes the Hering-Hillebrand horopter deviation and this tends to approximate the objective plane, as is indicated, for example, by Helmholtz' data (Fig. 19), why is it not great enough to make the apparent frontoparallel plane coincide with the objective plane? Under normal surroundings, of course, an extended object in the objective frontoparallel plane has points whose images in the two eyes are vertically disparate (because their distances from the two eyes are different), and it has been suggested that these disparities are a necessary feature to the total conception of the frontoparallel plane. In the horopter apparatus such vertical disparities would be absent, and only that part of the total conception of the plane contributed by the horizontal disparities would be active. However, as Hillebrand[114] has shown, small pieces of paper or beads placed on the rods of the apparatus did not seem to affect the shape of the resulting curve for the rods as determined by the apparent frontoparallel plane. Moreover, when the rods of the horopter apparatus are set for the apparent frontoparallel plane, and then a plane surface with detail on it is placed behind and parallel to the rods, both the apparent plane determined by the rods and the surface appear parallel.

We must agree that more data will be necessary before the matter of the determination of the empirical longitudinal horopter, its functional signifi-

---

* The change in H with observation distance as found experimentally is also too large to be explained by the ingenious hypothesis proposed by Luneburg. In this, a change in the shape of the horopter with observation distance is deduced from a mathematical study on the basis that the visual size of spatial increments is inherently given and constant for all positions in space (Ames), by virtue of which visual space would be non-Euclidean.

cance and the extent to which it does or does not indicate the nature of the stability of the optical spatial counterparts of corresponding points can be known.

SENSITIVITY

Before ending this chapter a mention of the precision of the data for the criterion of the apparent frontoparallel plane and that given by the nonius will be made.

Table 5

MEAN VARIATIONS OF SETTINGS OF RODS OF HOROPTER APPARATUS ACCORDING TO THE CRITERIA OF THE APPARENT FRONTOPARALLEL PLANE AND THE NONIUS HOROPTER. THE ENTRIES ARE SECONDS OF ARC ANGULAR DISPARITY BETWEEN THE IMAGES OF THE TWO EYES

OBSERVATION DISTANCE	CRITERION	OBSERVER*	PERIPHERAL VISUAL ANGLE, DEGREES					
			1	2	4	8	12	16
6 meters	AFPP†	O	—	5	5	11	13	—
		C	3.4	5	9	20	28	—
76 cm.	AFPP	O	7	10	14	35	52	67
		C	14	22	32	61	110	190
	Nonius	O	20	35	50	90	110	—
40 cm.	AFPP	O	12	15	22	46	71	120
		C	20	39	72	170	310	—
	Nonius	O	30	40	70	138	280	—
20 cm.	AFPP	O	—	32	62	89	170	320
		C	—	115	140	220	450	590
	Nonius	O	—	145	290	360	570	670

*O = K. N. O., C = F. D. C.
† Apparent frontoparallel plane

The setting of threads or rods of the horopter apparatus by the criterion of the apparent frontoparallel plane is essentially a task of stereoscopic depth discrimination. The variations, then, in those settings are measures of the stereoscopic sensitivity of the subject not only for central vision but also for the peripheral areas of the binocular visual field. The settings made according to the criterion of equating the primary subjective visual directions of the two eyes, by the nonius method, depend upon direction discrimination, and probably for these experiments upon the motion of the horopter rods.

Table 5 summarizes the results of two observers, the entries being the mean variations of settings of the rods expressed in seconds of arc disparity between the retinal images for the apparent frontoparallel plane and the nonius method for various peripheral visual angles and various observation distances. The observer F.D.C. was the less experienced of the two making these settings. Certainly the mean variation of 3 to 5 seconds of arc for distant vision near the fovea is not unusual for stereoscopic tasks. A striking aspect of this table is the decreased sensitivity (larger mean variations) with the increase in peripheral visual angle and with the decrease in observation distance. The first would be expected because of the known decrease in visual acuity toward the periphery of the retina.

The decreased sensitivity as the fixation point comes nearer the subject may be evidence of a decreased visual acuity at near vision (see Biedermann, and more recently Lehnert), though the decreased mechanical leverage in the experimental apparatus must be taken into account as an explanation. Since a constant stereoscopic acuity would correspond to a depth difference that decreases with the square of the fixation distance, mechanical inertia and so forth of the moving parts of the apparatus could be a contributing factor to the decreased sensitivity.

The precision of the nonius settings appears to be much less than that for stereoscopic vision, the mean variation being of the order of three times as large. This is not too unexpected, because of the difficulty in making the nonius discrimination, especially for the more peripheral visual angles.

CHAPTER 5

The Empirical Longitudinal Horopter
and Monocular Asymmetries

THE FACT that the longitudinal horopter deviates from the Vieth-Müller circle, as has been pointed out, can be taken as evidence that an asymmetry exists between the functional congruities of corresponding retinal elements in the horizontal meridian. It was shown in Chapter 3 that this incongruity is adequately measured by a constant H, and if the magnifications of the images in the two eyes are equal ($R_0 = 1$), the objective visual angles correlated with corresponding retinal elements are described essentially by

$$\tan \alpha_2 - \tan \alpha_1 = H \tan^2 \alpha_2$$

where α_1 and α_2 are the longitudinal visual angles subtended by the fixation point and a given point on the horopter to the left and right eyes, respectively. Thus, for positive visual angles α_2, for points to the right of the fixation point, the angles of the right eye will be larger than the corresponding ones to the left. The difference between these angles is nearly proportional to the square of the peripheral visual angles, H being the constant of proportionality. This shows, in other words, that for points on the curve in the right side of the visual field, the angle subtended by the right eye is larger than the corresponding angle subtended by the left eye. The reverse is true on the left side of the visual field. Tschermak referred to this binocular asymmetry as a *Ziehung*, meaning literally a stretching.

Such a spatial asymmetry between corresponding retinal points, and therefore between subjective directional values associated with those points, leads one to expect these asymmetries to occur in the monocular comparison of distances in the frontoparallel plane.

The reasoning for this expectancy would be as follows. In Fig. 29, suppose P and Q are points on the horopter. The images of P in each eye would therefore be seen in an identical primary subjective visual direction. Similarly, the images of Q in each eye would be seen in another identical visual direction. If, now, we move P so it *always* remains on the horopter, we can adjust it to a position so that the apparent angular distance FP is equal to FQ.* It follows that these angular distances would also appear identical by either of the two eyes. Objectively, however, the angular separations of the points P and Q will be unequal, as long as the horopter does not coincide

---

* Tschermak[233] has suggested a horopter apparatus in which the angular separations of the channels are adjustable, in order that this kind of an experiment could be performed.

with the Vieth-Müller circle. For the point P, α_2 will be larger than α_1, while for the point Q, α_2 will be smaller than α_1.

The binocular asymmetry, of course, would tell nothing about the individual monocular asymmetries of the eyes, but only the relation between them. Thus, a monocular asymmetry in one eye which is equal but just reversed in direction in the other would not affect the shape of the horopter curve. The monocular asymmetries can be measured in a separate experiment by asking the subject, using one eye at a time, to bisect a given horizontal line segment subjectively, while keeping the fixation steadfast on the midpoint. Such procedures are the so-called "partition" experiments.

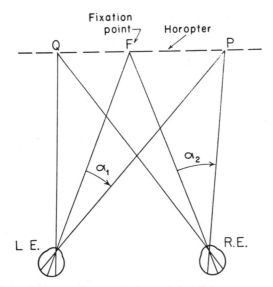

Fig. 29. The relation between the monocular and binocular asymmetries in the functional organization of retinal elements of the two eyes.

Frank, working in Tschermak's laboratory, first showed that the difference of the asymmetry found from bisection of lines measured monocularly for both of the two eyes accounted quantitatively for the binocular asymmetry obtained from the shape of the apparent frontoparallel plane. Monocular asymmetry in which distances in the temporal halves of the fields are overestimated as compared to equal distances in the nasal halves of the field, as is demanded by the horopter experiments, had been reported in the literature by Kundt in 1863, and it was supposed that this was the general type of asymmetry to be found. However, much later Münsterberg reported on individuals in whom the reverse asymmetry was found.

Fischer[71] duplicated Frank's experiments and reported partition experiments on his own eyes in which the Kundt type of monocular asymmetry existed in his left eye and the Münsterberg type in the right. However, the

Kundt asymmetry was the greater of the two, and according to Fischer's results the difference between the two accounted quantitatively for the binocular asymmetry that he found from the curve of his longitudinal horopter. Herzau[110] also reported partition experiments in relation to his horopter studies and showed a small Kundt type in both eyes.

More recent experiments[177] utilized not the simple bisection experiment but one in which seven short vertical rods are adjusted so that all appear equally separated while the fixation is maintained on the central one. These might be called monocular multiple partition experiments. The actual distances, s, of each of the rods from the fixation point are then recorded and from these the degree and direction of asymmetry can be determined. The experiment is conducted for each eye alone.

Table 6

DATA OBTAINED IN MONOCULAR MULTIPLE PARTITION EXPERIMENTS

NUMBER OF SUBJECTIVE UNITS	LEFT EYE					
	Left Field			Right Field		
	$-3j_1$	$-2j_1$	$-j_1$	j_1	$2j_1$	$3j_1$
Mean Setting s mm. from F	−39.82	−25.95	−12.58	12.00	24.10	35.44
Ratio s/j	13.27	12.98	12.58	12.00	12.05	11.81

NUMBER OF SUBJECTIVE UNITS	RIGHT EYE					
	Left Field			Right Field		
	$-3j_2$	$-2j_2$	$-j_2$	j_2	$2j_2$	$3j_2$
Mean Setting s mm. from F	−37.20	−24.23	−12.00	11.26	22.70	33.96
Ratio s/j	12.40	12.11	12.00	11.26	11.35	11.32

The measurements were made for a visual distance of 40 cm. The separation of the central (fixated) rod and the first fixed rod on the left was arbitrarily set for 12 mm. for the left eye and on the right side for the right eye. These were the standard separations to which all the other rods were adjusted. The rods are seen as black lines through a narrow slit in an illuminated screen against an evenly illuminated white background; the observer's eye is entirely shielded from all other objects in the room and from seeing the tops and bottoms of the rods. The plane of the rods was at right angles to the fixation line of the eye in each case. The position of each of the rods could be adjusted by the observer by suitable thumb screws.

The data of one subject (K.N.O.) for an observation distance of 40 cm. obtained in this manner are shown in Table 6.

The measured distances in this table are proportional to the tangents of the visual angles subtended by the several rods when adjusted to the criterion of equal subjective separations. We can assume that the visual angles to any rod can be described by

$$w_1 = \tan \alpha_1 = a_1 j_1 + b_1 j_1^2 + \ . \ . \ .$$

$$w_2 = \tan \alpha_2 = a_2 j_2 + b_2 j_2^2 + \ . \ . \ .$$

(1)

for the left and right eyes, respectively, where j_1 and j_2 are subjective equivalents of the standard separation to which all of the other rods are adjusted for the left and right eyes, respectively. If graphically, instead of plotting the distances from the fixation rod to the other rods, we plot those distances divided by the corresponding multiple of the subjective separation, that is, s/j, the coefficients, a_1, a_2, b_1, and b_2 can be found by inspection

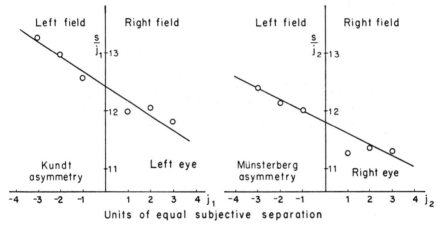

Fig. 30. Method of plotting multiple partition data to determine the constants of the monocular asymmetry of each eye for correlation with the binocular asymmetry found from the empirical longitudinal horopter.

(Fig. 30). We can assume a linear relationship for these data (although there is no reason to believe that the monocular asymmetries cannot be more irregular) according to

$$\frac{w}{j} = a + bj$$

for a is the intercept on the ordinate and b the slope of the best fitting line. One finds from Fig. 30, for these data, $a_1 = 12.45$, $b_1 = 0.260$, $a_2 = 11.83$ and $b_2 = 0.194$.

Equations (1) above can be better utilized in this discussion by considering them as expansions of the expressions

$$w_1 = a_1 j_1 \Big/ \Big(1 - \frac{b_1}{a_1} j_1 \Big)$$

and

$$w_2 = a_2 j_2 \Big/ \Big(1 - \frac{b_2}{a_2} j_2 \Big)$$

where the higher powers in j have been neglected.

Now in order to correlate these monocular measurements with the binocular asymmetry as found from the empirical horopter data, consider the following argument. Let us suppose that units of subjective-directional-differences exist which might be arbitrary ones, or even thresholds. Then, in the partition experiments previously described, j_1 is the number of these subjective-directional-difference units corresponding to the angle $\overline{\alpha}_1$, the arbitrary reference angle for the left eye, and likewise, j_2 is the number of these subjective-directional-difference units corresponding to the longitudinal angle $\overline{\alpha}_2$, the arbitrary reference angle for the right eye. Now, that longitudinal angle of the *left* eye (α_1) which has the same number of subjective-directional-difference units as α_2 of the right eye can be found from the longitudinal horopter equation,

$$1/(w_1) - 1/\overline{w_2} = H$$

(which assumes $R_0 = 1$, which is accurate enough in this case); namely, $(w_1) = \overline{w_2}/(1 + H\overline{w_2})$, where as before $(w_1) = \tan(\alpha_1)$ and $\overline{w_2} = \tan \overline{\alpha_2}$. Thus, there exists a j_0 for the left eye which corresponds to the angle (α_1), and since this will differ slightly from j_1, we can write:

$$j_1 = kj_0 \quad and \quad j_2 = j_0$$

for the reference angle $\overline{\alpha_2}$ used for the right eye partition experiments. We then want to find the value of k from the partition data of both eyes. This follows from three relations given previously in which kj_0 and j_0 replace j_1 and j_2, respectively; namely,

$$w_1 = a_1 k j_0 \Big/ \left(1 - \frac{b_1}{a_1} k j_0\right)$$

$$w_2 = a_2 j_0 \Big/ \left(1 - \frac{b_2}{a_2} j_0\right)$$

$$w_1 = w_2/(1 + Hw_2)$$

Eliminating j_0 and w_1, we find for k:

$$k = \left[a_2 + \frac{b_2}{a_2} w_2\right] \Big/ \left[a_1 + \left(Ha_1 + \frac{b_1}{a_1}\right) w_2\right]$$

Having k, we have tied the two monocular asymmetries to the horopter, and it is only necessary to find the relationship between these and the binocular asymmetry. We have for any value of j now

$$w_1 = a_1 k j \Big/ \left(1 - \frac{b_1}{a_1} k j\right)$$

$$w_2 = a_2 j \Big/ \left(1 - \frac{b_2}{a_2} j\right)$$

and substituting these into the general horopter equation

$$\frac{1}{w_1} - \frac{R_0}{w_2} = H$$

we find upon reducing (and putting $R_0 = 1$)

$$H = \frac{b_2}{a_2^2} - \frac{b_1}{a_1^2}$$

Substituting the values of a_1, a_2, b_1, and b_2, given previously for the data of the table, one finds $H = 0.116$. Comparing this with the results for H obtained from the empirical horopter data for K.N.O. given on page 28, one can say this is an unusual, if not even a fortuitous, agreement.

This result agrees with those of Frank and Fischer and is further evidence that the subjective directional values associated with retinal elements are the same whether they are the result of monocular stimulation or binocular stimulation of corresponding retinal points. As such we have further evidence of the stable character of those local signs associated with corresponding retinal elements, whose psychic correlates are subjective visual directions.

Part II

THE FUSIONAL PROCESSES IN BINOCULAR
SINGLE VISION

CHAPTER 6

The Phenomenon of Fusion

INTRODUCTION

T HE STRIKING FACT of normal vision with the two eyes is that although there are two retinal images, we as individuals experience only a single perception of space. Without implications as to the ultimate nature of this phenomenon, we designate the anatomic, physiologic and psychologic mechanisms responsible as the *fusional processes*. The concept generally held is that normally the neurologic excitations that arise in the two retinas are transmitted to the cortex, where they terminate as "cortical images" in rather localized regions of the occipital lobe. There fusion (unification) either takes place locally as a physiologic process or takes place more diffusely entirely as a psychic response. This unification must occur prior to the conscious awareness of the images in the perceptional experience. In either case the emergent sensation is one of singleness. At the present time we can only conjecture as to the nature of the processes involved.

Much discussion and controversy exists in the literature as to whether there is ever real fusion,[245] whether fusion centers exist in the brain, or whether what appears as fusion is the psychic replacement of one part of the image from one eye by a corresponding part of the image from the other eye. Verhoeff[239] suggested that only one of the corresponding parts of the two retinal images can exist in consciousness at any given moment. The stimulations from certain areas of one eye are said to be replaced in the conscious experience by stimulation from corresponding areas from the other eye, the dominance of one over the other depending upon attention and strengths of the two stimuli. Thus Verhoeff prefers *unification* to *fusion,* and insists that the concept of image replacement makes it easier to understand rivalry, suppression and so forth.

On the basis of binocular flicker experiments, Sherrington expressed the belief " . . . that during binocular regard of an objective image each uniocular mechanism develops independently as a sensual image of considerable completeness. The singleness of the binocular perception results from union of these elaborated uniocular sensations. The singleness is therefore a product of a synthesis that works with already elaborated sensations contemporaneously proceeding." In a similar vein more recently, Neuhaus sought to show that the two retinal excitations are worked up separately and enter the awareness as two different experiences, but only one excitation exerts itself at a time—never both simultaneously. Fleischer[76] rejected the points of view as unproved, and concluded from his own experience that the excitations of the two eyes arrive at a physiologic central cooperation, which follows from the anatomic correspondence of the two retinas.

Until more is known about the neuro-anatomy of the visual areas of the cortex and the association fibers between the two halves of the brain, we must be content to discuss fusion and the fusional processes in phenomenologic terms, leaving in abeyance for the time being the exact meaning of these words.

THE FUSION COMPULSION

If, while one is looking at an object across the room, an ophthalmic prism is suddenly placed in front of one eye, say base-out, one sees momentarily

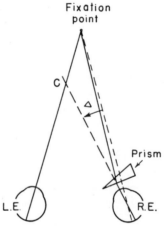

Fig. 31. The compulsion for fusion reflex is demonstrated by placing a prism before one eye.

two objects. These "half-images" (*Halbbilder*), if not too far apart, move rapidly toward each other, the speed of movement seeming to increase as the separation becomes less—as though the two were attracted to each other by a magnetic-like force. They suddenly coalesce, the single impression giving no hint of a dual origin. During this process it can be observed that the eye behind the prism has changed its position from one directed on the distant object to another directed to the optical image of the object formed by the prism. In Fig. 31, the new convergent positions of the eyes correspond to the intersection *C*.

This simple experiment illustrates the gross aspect of a motor reflex known as the *compulsion for fusion*. The movements of the eyes necessary to cause the images to fall again as near as possible to corresponding retinal elements, so that fusion is regained, are known as *fusional movements*. This phenomenon of the visual processes is for the purpose of preventing the appearance of double images (diplopia). The compulsion for a fusional movement in the foregoing experiment is very strong because the entire visual field has been affected by the prism, in that a large crossed disparity is introduced between the images of the two eyes of all parts of the object.

In ordinary surroundings where there may be many objects in the field of view at different distances from the observer, then, there are a multiplicity of horizontal disparities of the images of different objects. While each of these may exert its influence for a fusional movement, attention may be a prerequisite before the reflex goes into action. In any event, once the attention is directed to a given point, although the images are then disparate, the reflex to fusion so directs the eyes that the images on the two retinas fall as nearly as possible on corresponding retinal points. These reflexes cannot be considered as pure reflexes because they first depend upon an attention factor before they become effective. Hofmann has accordingly designated them as *psycho-optical* reflexes.

CONDITIONS FOR FUSION AND RIVALRY

The optical image on the retina is made up of contiguous light and dark areas, the lines of separation being designated as contours. It is these contours, the demarcations between light and less light areas, that provide the pattern of the images and the stimuli for fusion when they exist in both eyes. Hering quoted Panum as saying that "the contours excite the retina to a marked degree, and the nerve stimuli which are engendered by them are of a different nature and much more vigorous than that created by a plainly illuminated surface." Depending on the particular characteristics of the image patterns falling on the retinas of the two eyes, fusion will be complete or partial, or as an antithesis of fusion, the patterns may actually exhibit a rivalry or a resistance to fusion. While it is now believed that the individual's awareness as to whether the images are identical or whether they could have arisen from a single known object in space is not necessary for fusion, yet the strength of the fusion compulsion seems to be enhanced by such identification.

We may review some of the well-known types of configurations conducive to fusion by reference to Fig. 32. Similarity is, of course, the first prerequisite, as in *A*, but this similarity need not be complete as long as certain parts of the figures are the same, as in *B*. Likewise, some fusion can be obtained where the images are defective or fragmentary, as in *C* and *D*. In figures such as *E*, where there is similarity of a type, fusion usually occurs at one of the edges of the wider figure (a fusion of contours), which edge depending for the most part on the extraocular muscle imbalance of the eyes. Entirely unlike images, as in *F*, exert no tendency to fusion or fusional movements. However, it must be kept in mind that some individuals as a result of practice can voluntarily control their eye positions so as to superimpose such unlike figures, but the images themselves exert no tendency to hold the eyes in that position. Images such as *G* which have similarity of a kind readily fuse, if the difference in width is not too great, and then the fused image may be usually seen in stereoscopic depth as a rotated figure in space.

Exact similarity alone, when there is a marked difference in size, as in *H*, will provide at most only a very incomplete fusion and this usually at certain contiguous edges, both figures essentially being seen simultaneously. Likewise, one has the well-known figures of Volkmann in *I* and *J*, where two short parallel lines are presented to one eye and two lines of equal length but with adjustable separation in the other are fused. There is a minimal and a maximal separation, within which two lines are seen binocularly, and outside of which three are seen (two of the lines remaining fused).

Finally we have such configurations as *K* and *L*, taken from Panum's classic work, in which no fusion but actual rivalry between the eyes is experienced. In *K*, the two figures are never seen simultaneously, but either all of one or all of the other, or an interlacing which results in a mosaic-like pattern. This binocular experience is usually unstable and is constantly

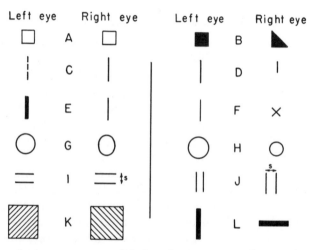

Fig. 32. Types of target contours used before the two eyes to illustrate fusion or rivalry phenomena.

changing. If a symbol (a word, for example) that has meaning to the observer is put on one of the targets, then that target is thought to be more dominant. Figures *L* are widely used to demonstrate not only the phenomenon of rivalry but also the prevalence and conflict of contours, for at the areas where the two bars cross the contours of both "fight" for dominance. We shall omit here the fusion and rivalry of complementary colors, which is, however, a very important aspect of the fusion problem.

FUSIONAL AMPLITUDES (PRISM VERGENCE TESTS)

The usual test for the strength of the fusional attraction or fusional compulsion of the various types of configurations, as well as a measure of the fusional reserve of the observer, consists in forcing the two eyes into greater or lesser convergence until the subject reports a doubling of the targets.

In these tests the eyes of the subject are directed to a target and then forced to converge (or diverge) by means of ophthalmic prisms placed before the eyes (base-in or base-out), or in case the targets are used on a haploscopic type of device, by rotating the arms that support the targets. The degree of the forced convergence (or divergence) is gradually increased until the subject reports the appearance of a blurring or of a confusion of the targets and finally when a complete apparent doubling of the target occurs. The convergence and divergence at the blur and the doubling points are also sometimes recorded. Configurations with small amount of detail result in lower amplitudes. On the other hand, the increase in complexity of detail beyond a certain point has no further influence on the amplitudes. Different results between individuals must then be taken as indications of differences in the fusional and vergence powers of the individual.

Prism vergences are, at least in part, measures of the fusion ability of the subject. The fusion reflex cannot be separated from the convergence mechanisms, because of its definite demand for specific muscular synergies of the oculorotary muscles of the eyes. Fusion power alone, however, is probably not being measured, for in such tests at least three factors are involved: (1) the degree of the forced convergence (or divergence); (2) the strength of the fusion compulsion reflex and (3) the degree to which the otherwise normal accommodation-convergence reflex* is altered or embarrassed.

The stimulus to accommodation (the target distance) is constant throughout the test. The introduction of prism power between the eyes necessarily results in a stress in the normal accommodation-convergence reflex relationship, as long as the images remain fused. An accommodative change demanded by the changed convergence does occur because of the compulsion reflex for clear vision, which is stronger. It has been shown[8, 169] that over fairly wide limits the accommodative change in these tests is small, except near the diplopia point. In the prism vergence test it is this stress which is pitted against the compulsion for fusion with increased prism power. Diplopia occurs either when that stress is so great as to overcome the reflex innervations to maintain single binocular vision or when certain mechanical limits of the oculorotary muscles are reached. There is an expenditure of energy involved, and also a fatiguing of the ocular muscles in the process. Both the magnitude of this stress and the strength of the fusion compulsion will vary from individual to individual.

Fusional amplitudes may also be obtained in the vertical meridians by the use of prisms base-down or base-up before the eyes. Cyclofusional amplitudes can also be obtained on the haploscope, by rotating one of similar targets about the fixation axes of the two eyes.

---

* When the eyes increase their convergence to fixate a near object, the accommodation of the eyes also increases in the interest of maintaining clear vision. A reflex arc is found between the convergence and accommodative functions, which tends to operate even when these functions are disassociated by optical or other means. That this reflex is at least in part not a conditioned reflex is shown in cases of convergent strabismus concomitant with farsightedness, an anomaly that disappears when the farsightedness is corrected by ophthalmic lenses.

CHAPTER 7

Panum's Fusional Areas

W HILE THE binocular processes, through the compulsion-to-fusion reflex, strive to keep the images of objects as near as possible to corresponding retinal points, Panum[200] first showed that the images will, within certain limits, fuse if these images do not fall exactly on corresponding points. Were it not for the existence of these fusional areas (the area between these limits), physiologic diplopia (or doubling, p. 40) would be evident for images of all objects in space not falling precisely on corresponding retinal points.

The phenomenon of Panum's fusional areas can be demonstrated by such target patterns as *I* and *J* shown in Fig. 32 of the preceding chapter. The separation, *s*, of the lines seen by one eye can be changed within fairly definite limits and within these limits only two lines will be seen binocularly. Outside those limits, three lines are seen. One half[*] of the distance between the inner and outer limits where doubling occurs, expressed in angular measure to the eyes, is the dimension of the fusional area in the meridian tested.

In the horizontal meridian, those areas can be conveniently measured on the horopter apparatus, the technic of which has already been described on p. 40 and following pages of Chapter 4. From the data obtained for the outer and inner limiting positions of the region of binocular single vision, the angular extent of the fusional areas can be computed.[†] The results of data for four subjects are shown in Fig. 33 and illustrate well the increase in Panum's areas with peripheral visual angle in the horizontal meridian. The calculation of Fischer's (F.P.F.) data as taken from his paper[72] (see Fig. 26) gives values for these dimensions almost twice as large as those of the other subjects. Why the difference is so great is not clear, though we do not know his exact experimental procedure. He was myopic, with vision uncorrected for these experiments.

The relative proportion of Panum's areas to the peripheral visual angle

---

[*] It is necessary to take one half of the measured range in this type of experiment because usually a fusional movement of the eyes occurs so that images of both lines will become disparate and both will be near the edges of Panum's areas.

[†] We can compute these angles approximately from the formula $\rho = 2ka\ (\Delta b)/b^2$, where ρ is the longitudinal angular extent of Panum's areas in minutes of arc, $2a$ the interpupillary base line in centimeters, b the fixation distance, $k = 3436$ (to convert radians to minutes of arc), and (Δb) is the distance between the outer and inner limits of the region of binocular single vision in centimeters.

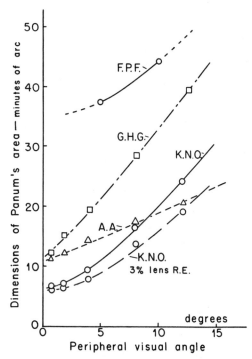

Fig. 33. Data illustrating the magnitude and increase of Panum's fusional areas in the horizontal meridian with peripheral visual angle.

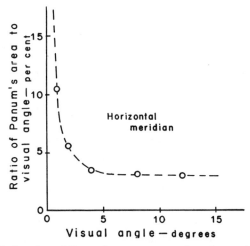

Fig. 34. The relative size of Panum's area compared to the peripheral visual angle. The points represent the ratios expressed in percentage of the horizontal dimension of the area to the visual angle.

is important. Figure 34 shows the curve which describes this relationship, based upon the mean of the data of Fig. 33 (omitting those of F.P.F.). The abscissa is the peripheral visual angle and the ordinate is the ratio, expressed in per cent, of the horizontal dimension of Panum's area to the visual angle. The curve decreases rapidly from the macula to about a visual angle of 4 degrees, and then reaches a nearly constant value of about 3 per cent for visual angles beyond 5 to 6 degrees. Thus beyond 4 degrees, Panum's areas are about 3 per cent of the peripheral angle. This curve will have special significance when we come to discuss the differences in the magnifications of the images of the two eyes.

The vertical extent of Panum's areas has usually been measured on the haploscope, where the separation of the details seen by the two eyes can be easily controlled. Based primarily on the statement of Panum, and the measurements of Volkmann as corrected by von Helmholtz,[107] the vertical extent of these areas is somewhat smaller than the horizontal, so that it would appear that Panum's areas are actually elliptical.

Brecher[28] expressed the belief that the haploscope introduces such unusual (?) fusional demands as to give spurious results. He accordingly set up a suitable target on a track set at a divergent angle to the median plane. As the target figure was moved along the track and observed binocularly, the difference in distance from each of the two eyes became greater and hence the angular sizes of the retinal images became different. The inner and outer positions of the target could be found where double images would appear. He maintains from his experiments that the vertical extent of Panum's areas is identical with the horizontal. There is, however, the possibility that Brecher's calculations are in error by a factor of 2, which would make his data comparable with those of other investigators. Thus, it still appears that the effective horizontal dimensions of these areas are greater than those in the vertical.

Also to be cited in this connection are the results of Verhoeff[237] and of Ames,[3] both of whom found that in measuring cyclofusional amplitudes, horizontal lines usually "doubled" at ±2 degrees, whereas vertical lines would not appear double until the targets had been rotated about ±8 degrees. Too much stress should not be given to these values, however, because of the peculiar relationship between fusion and cyclotorsional movements (Chapter 10).

Table 7 summarizes the results of various experimenters for the dimensions of Panum's areas in or near the maculas. In comparing the results of different investigators, one should take care to note the visual angle at which the measurements were made, because of the rapid increase in size of Panum's areas with peripheral visual angle.

Because of Panum's fusional areas there exists a relatively near fixation distance beyond which all objects will have retinal images that fall within these areas, and there will be no doubling of the images. On the basis of an 8 minute of arc horizontal dimension of Panum's area and average interpupillary distance of 64 mm., this critical distance, which can be computed from $b = 3.2/\tan 4'$, is about 20 meters, or 60 feet.

The implication of Panum's fusional areas to our concept of subjective visual directions must be clearly recognized. Refer to Fig. 25, p. 41, which schematically illustrates the phenomenon of Panum's areas and the region of binocular single vision. Points lying outside this region are seen double, that is, are experienced in two different visual directions. Within the region this doubling is not evident, that is, P is seen in only one visual direction.

Table 7

SUMMARY OF RESULTS FOR THE DIMENSIONS OF PANUM'S FUSIONAL AREAS
AT OR NEAR THE MACULAR REGIONS

INVESTIGATOR		PANUM'S AREA, MINUTES OF ARC		AVERAGE VISUAL ANGLE, DEGREES
		Horizontal	Vertical	
Volkmann	1859	12.1	6.7	2
		25–5*	3–4	—
Fischer[72]	1924	37	—	5
K. N. O.[177]	1932	6	—	1
A. A.	1932	11	—	1
G. H. G.	1932	12	—	1
Lyding	1939	26–44	7–14	7
Brecher[28]	1942	9.0	7.5	2.5
		7.0	7.5	
		6.3	6.4	

* After long practice.

However, it is clear that except when P is exactly at P_0 (on the longitudinal horopter) the images of P in the two eyes must be *physiologically* disparate. But by "physiologically disparate" we understand that the images are seen in two different primary subjective visual directions. This contradiction must be resolved by acknowledging that in the fusion or unification of disparate images, within Panum's areas, one of two things must happen: Either (1) one of the two monocular primary subjective directions must disappear, and the visual direction of the fused image must be that of the other eye, or (2) both of the primary subjective visual directions of the monocular images must lose their fundamental identity and be replaced by a new subjective visual direction, which lies between the two primary monocular directions. The change from the subjective directions of the two monocular images to the subjective visual direction of the binocularly fused image is variously designated as a "directional difference" (Tschermak[231]), a "lateral displacement" (Verhoeff[239]), or a "functional displacement" (Werner*[249]). This displacement must result physiologically if the disparate images of the two eyes can give rise to a perceptual correlate of "singleness." Thus, it is clear that if we are to observe the primary subjective visual directions of images on the retinas we must arrange the instrumentation so as to avoid the possibility of fusion or tendencies to fusion. This is the technic employed in the experiments on the nonius horopter, on fixation disparity (Chapter 8), with the eikonic target (p. 244), and so forth.

* It is believed that the experimental observation of these displacements by Werner is a demonstration of the phenomenon of fusion of disparate images, and is not a phenomenon associated with or necessary to the appearance of stereopsis, as Werner has implied.

Fixation Disparity

INTRODUCTION

THE EXPERIMENTS on the longitudinal horopter as determined by the nonius method (p. 36 and following) show that the horopter may be displaced from the point of fixation when the observer is heterophoric. We concluded that in these cases the retinal images of the fixation point for the two eyes were actually disparate, that the eyes had actually overconverged if the horopter was nearer, or slightly diverged if the curve was farther than the fixation point. Thus, in spite of the fusion compulsion to register the images on the retinas of the two eyes on corresponding retinal elements, an actual small inaccuracy or slipping of those images can exist relative to corresponding elements. Fusion will be maintained with these disparate images by virtue of Panum's fusional areas. That this slipping of the images can also occur even when the images of the entire visual field are involved can be demonstrated.

This phenomenon is easily observed in the stereoscope or, better, in the haploscope where the convergence can be more accurately controlled independent of the object distance. Identical target patterns in these devices will appear single under normal conditions. Dissimilar (and unfusable) details *centered* on each of the *same two* identical patterns will under certain conditions appear decentered, that is, will appear displaced relative to each other, in spite of the fusion of the images of the identical patterns. This displacement is present especially when the observer is heterophoric, or when the convergence and its normal corresponding stimulus for accommodation in the haploscope are altered. This phenomenon has been designated a *fixation disparity*, because the retinal images of the point of fixation and of the entire pattern may be actually disparate.

While this phenomenon must be commonly observed among those who use the stereoscope or haploscope, it was Lau[144] who first described and correctly interpreted it while performing experiments on the horopter problem. In a haploscope he used targets before the left and right eyes as illustrated in Fig. 35A. Each target consisted of a long vertical line in the center and two shorter parallel lines on each side that extended only to the middle of each target. The two short lines on one target could be adjusted laterally by means of a screw arrangement, and their positions could be determined by a scale and vernier. While the observer fixated the central line and its images were fused, Lau adjusted the one pair of lines until they and the two opposing lines seen by the other eye appeared in alignment. In every experiment he found that both lines had to be displaced a small distance in the *same* direction. The magnitude of the displacement was increased somewhat if the

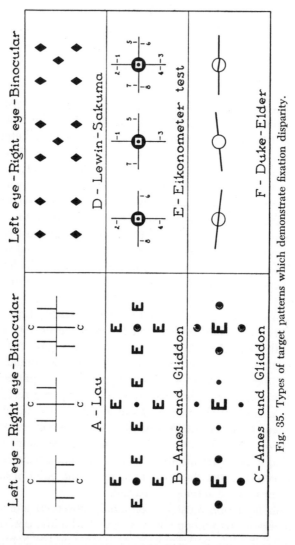

Fig. 35. Types of target patterns which demonstrate fixation disparity.

eyes were forced to converge by turning the arms of the haploscope inward. Lau interpreted the finding to mean that the two eyes were actually fixing slightly behind the geometric position of the fused central line. Hofmann,[118] who had described the lag in the pointing of the eyes in rapid movements of the arms of the haploscope, expressed the belief that the phenomenon shown in Lau's results was associated with an interference in the normal accommodation-convergence reflex.

Lewin and Sakuma mentioned among other experiments the use of a playing card as a target on each side of the haploscope; a four of diamonds before one eye and a five of diamonds before the other, as illustrated in Fig. 35D. On looking into the haploscope the observer easily fused the images of the four outer diamonds. The central diamond seen by only one eye, however, appeared decentered with respect to the outer four, especially as the convergence of the arms of the haploscope and therefore the convergence of the eyes was changed.

In 1928, under the designation of "retinal slip," Ames and Gliddon reported experiments with the haploscope in which targets as shown in either Fig. 35B or 35C were used. They were able to show that the direction of the displacement of the small disks within the larger ones was usually in the same direction as was the phoria of the observer. The data they found are included in the scatter plot shown in Fig. 48, which shows the relationship between the phoria and that convergence position of the arms of the haploscope which centered the small disk within the larger, that is, eliminated the "slipping." This procedure is as though prisms were placed before the eyes, base-in or base-out, as required until the disks were centered. An inspection of this chart suggests some correlation. The nearly identical results from the two types of targets (Fig. 35A and 35B) suggest that the phenomenon occurs irrespective of whether the fusion is in the central or in the more peripheral parts of the binocular visual field.

In the eikonometer when the direct comparison targets[10, 34] (p. 244) are used (Fig. 35E), it is usual for the average patient to see the opposing arrows observed by the left and right eyes displaced in the same direction. In fact, this displacement appears to be a contributing factor to the lowered precision of measurements in the horizontal meridian, as compared with those of the vertical meridian, especially at the reading distance. The apparent magnitude of the displacement cannot be predicted, however, by the magnitude of the phoria.

Duke-Elder illustrated a pair of targets (Fig. 35F) which show that this same effect can also occur as a cyclotorsional displacement of the monocular images compared to the binocularly fused portions of the targets.

This phenomenon rests upon the fact that disparate images in the two eyes can be fused if the images fall within Panum's fusional areas. Thus, in the fusion of disparate images, where a single sense of direction is experienced, that subjective visual direction must be a compromise between the primary directions associated with the two noncorresponding retinal elements upon which the two disparate images are falling. Objects in the binocular visual field which are so arranged (by haploscopic methods) that they can be seen by only one eye are experienced in a subjective visual direction corresponding to the primary uniocular organization of the retinal elements on which the images fall. Care must be taken, however, that these images are not too near other images of binocularly seen contours whose images are fused.[8]

It should be clear, therefore, that if innervations or mechanical stresses exist between the oculorotary muscles of the two eyes demanding an over-convergence or divergence (which if the eyes were disassociated would or-dinarily be manifested as an esophoria or an exophoria), the eyes could ac-tually deviate from exact fixation, so that the images of the point of fixation would be disparate, to an amount not greater than Panum's fusional areas. The actual deviation will be small and measurable only in minutes of arc.

Fixation disparity implies that the cortical images arising from the two eyes are actually slipped or displaced a small amount with respect to each other. The angular value of fixation disparity is a measure of the degree to which the images have slipped, in the same sense that Panum's area, though measured as a retinal dimension, pertains to a cortical area within which disparate images are fused. The processes involved in the compulsion for fusion normally strive to keep the images from the two eyes as nearly as pos-sible on corresponding points, but the fusion is not exact when a muscular imbalance exists. The magnitude of the disparity depends upon the strength of the innervations to the extrinsic muscles of the eyes during fusion, the degree of heterophoria, the strength of the fusion processes themselves and the amount and complexity of the detail in the binocular field of view.

MEASUREMENT

Fixation disparity can be measured (as one method) by the following type of instrumentation,[198] which is suitable for routine testing.*

The Instrument. For the distant-vision measurements at 2.5 meters from a subject's eyes, patterns and special test configurations were projected by suitable lanterns upon an aluminum-coated screen (Fig. 36). The subject observed the screen through a phorom-eter, to which had been attached a pair of Polaroid plates (5 cm. square) before the two eyes with the planes of polarization at right angles to each other. This Polaroid attach-ment could be lowered out of the field of view, and also the two plates could be inter-changed before the eyes if desired. The target for fusion stimuli consisted of Snellen letters projected by a lantern, the total field subtending an angle of about 20 degrees. A small central area, usually about 1½ degrees visual angle, was blanked out at the center of the projected target and hence this would appear black to the subject. With this center, no details for fusion were present within the foveal regions of the two eyes, but details for fusion existed everywhere outside this area.

The test configuration was projected upon this blank square by a second lantern into which a special slide arrangement had been built. The test details (see insert in Fig. 36) consisted of a horizontal bright line and a pair of opposing (vernier-like) short vertical bright lines (arrows). The arrows were polarized in the slide, so that when viewed by the subject through the Polaroid plates, one arrow would be seen by one eye and the other by the other eye. The upper arrow was fixed (stationary), but the lower arrow could be displaced horizontally by means of a special mechanical arrangement in the lantern, operated by a screw and knob. The displacement of the two arrows could be read by the experimenter from an accurate dial indicator on the lantern to an estimated visual angle of 0.2 minute of arc, which is well within the maximal sensitivity found. By means of a shutter, the lower arrow could be occluded or flashed onto the screen at the will of the operator. A light green filter could also be placed over the upper arrow, if needed, for making the identification of the arrows easier for the subject. The long hori-

* This work was conducted under the Mayo Foundation for Education and Research at the Mayo Clinic.

zontal line prevented fusion of the ends of arrows and possibly reduced any vertical deviation.

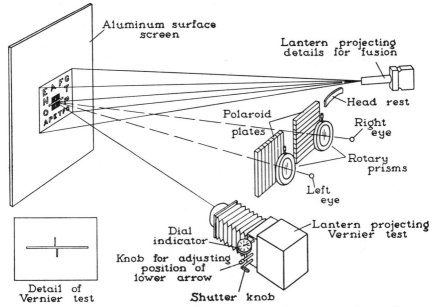

Fig. 36. Perspective drawing of the instrumentation used to measure fixation disparity for distant vision.

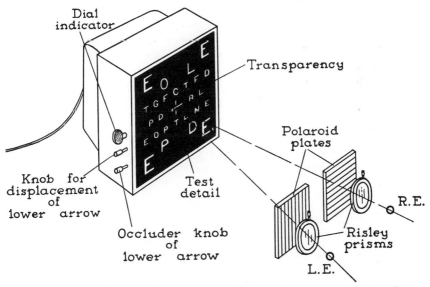

Fig. 37. Perspective drawing of the instrumentation used to measure fixation disparity for an observation distance of 30 cm.

The general illumination of the room was kept low, and the luminosity of the screen and fusion detail were the same throughout the experiments. The binocular visual field was restricted wholly to the details on the screen.

At near vision (30 cm.) a transparency illuminated from behind replaced the lanterns and screen. A carefully made mechanical device provided the two arrows. Figure 37 is a schematic drawing of the instrument used, the features of which are essentially the same as those of the distant test.

The Procedure. The phorometer was adjusted to the subject's head so that the eyes were centered. With the Polaroid plates before the eyes, the visual acuity of each eye was checked. Following this, the phoria was estimated by the Maddox rod or the double prism test, a spot of light being projected on the screen in a room totally dark.

The target and the test arrows were then projected on the screen. With the Polaroid plates *removed* (both eyes observing the target), a dial reading was made when the arrows appeared in alignment, as well as when there was the least perceptible displacement (a measure of the precision) that could be detected. The operator instructed the subject to look at the upper arrow and then he flashed the lower arrow for a fraction of a second, following which he asked the subject whether that arrow was to the right of, to the left of, or directly under the upper arrow. Between flashes the lower arrow was displaced to a new position. By the method of limits, then, the average midpoint and precision were determined. The zero of the dial indicator was then adjusted to that reading for which the subject reported that the arrows were in alignment. This procedure eliminated any constant personal and instrumental errors, although almost no variations were found between subjects for this setting.

The Polaroid plates were then raised and the operator checked that the subject's right eye saw only the upper arrow and his left eye saw only the lower arrow, and finally that ghost images were absent. By means of the shutter the lower line was then exposed for short intervals of about one-fourth second, and the subject was asked to judge whether this arrow appeared to the right or to the left of, or even with, the upper arrow. By adjusting the amount of displacement and obtaining the subject's response, the operator could find the average position and the limits within which the subject reported that the two arrows appeared aligned. The actual displacement of the arrows, which is the degree of the fixation disparity, was expressed by the angle subtended at the eyes of the subject in minutes of arc.

RESULTS

A fixation disparity is measured in the majority of subjects who are heterophoric, regardless of the amount of fusion detail or the size of the central area used on the screen. This means that in these cases the retinal images of the targets on the screen do not fall on corresponding points, because of an overconvergence or underconvergence of the eyes, though the images of the target pattern are fused. The fixation disparity is, therefore, a measure of the muscular imbalance between the two eyes, while fusion is maintained. This imbalance must be the resultant stress not only of mechanical and of tonic neuromuscular factors, but also of functional innervations of a different order arising from fusional stimuli. The phoria which is a phenomenon of the dis-associated eyes may be only a partial indication of those resultant stresses.

In a majority of subjects the direction of the fixation disparity is the same as that of the phoria. The degree or the direction, however, cannot be predicted with certainty on the basis of phoria, for often the fixation disparity is found in a direction opposite to that of the phoria. Figure 38 is a scatter plot of data which indicate the type of association found between phoria and the corresponding fixation disparity for both distant and near vision. An inspec-

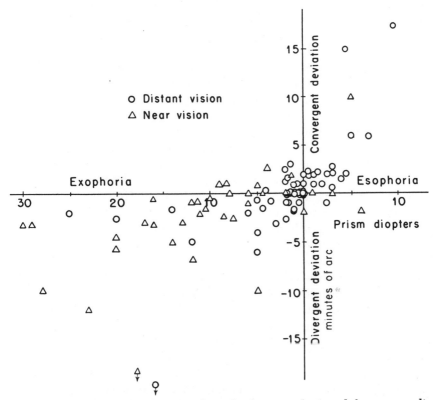

Fig. 38. A scatter plot of data showing relationship between phoria and the corresponding fixation disparity.

tion of this chart bears out the foregoing statements. The phorias were usually measured carefully with the white Maddox rod. Sometimes the cover and the double prism tests were also used to check the Maddox rod measurements. There is, of course, much more uncertainty in the phoria measurements than in the fixation-disparity measurements.

The Precision of the Data. One of the striking aspects of the experiment is the smallness of the quantities being measured and the precision within which they are obtainable. As is the case in many other psychophysical measurements, the observer feels that his judgments are very uncertain, but the actual objective accuracy proves surprisingly great. If the visual acuity is high and the muscle balance is fairly normal, it is usual to find that the limits of disparity within which the two arrows appear aligned are of the order of 1 minute of arc, and often less. The precision decreases with lowered visual acuity. It may decrease considerably when the eyes are forced to converge or diverge through large amounts by prisms, for then the fusion of the images becomes more unstable. It should be clear that the precision as determined by the method of limits here is larger than would be the mean error or the standard deviation if these had been obtained by other experimental technics.

The Fixation Disparity Within Fusional Amplitudes (Prism Vergences). The instrumentation for measuring fixation disparity permits us to study the behavior of the two eyes within the limits of the fusional amplitudes or prism vergence tests. In fact, such measurements can give us a better insight into the fusional processes when a stress induced by forcing the convergence or the divergence of the eyes is introduced. We can then know what the eyes are doing in the process of obtaining prism vergences. Lewin and Sakuma also made some observations of this disparity on the haploscope.

The experiment proceeds in the determination of the fixation disparity as the prism power introduced by the Risley rotary prisms* before the patient's eyes is increased in fixed amounts. For most subjects the prism power was placed alternately base-out and base-in; the base-out (forced convergence) in 4^Δ steps and the base-in (forced divergence) in 2^Δ (4^Δ at near vision) steps. The alternation of base-out and base-in procedure was found necessary to avoid cumulative effects.

The subjects tested seem to fall into four more or less distinct groups according to the way in which the fixation disparity changes with the forced convergence and divergence of the eyes. The results of several subjects have been selected to illustrate these types (see Figs. 39 to 42 inclusive). In these the angle of forced convergence or divergence caused by the prisms and measured in meter angles† is plotted on the abscissa, positive for convergence and negative for divergence. The measured fixation disparity in minutes of arc is plotted on the ordinate, being taken as positive if the deviation of the eyes is convergent (eyes overconverged) and negative if divergent (eyes underconverged).

---

* It is unfortunate that rotary (Risley) prisms introduce optical distortion. However, the advantages of the continuously adjustable prism power over the fixed steps of loose prisms, the axes of which are also difficult to adjust accurately, outweigh the possible disturbing effects of the distortion. Cursory experiments, by using prisms with curved surfaces (p. 131), showed that this distortion seemed to have little effect on the measurements.

† The meter angles are readily obtained by dividing the total number of prism diopters (both eyes) by the interpupillary distance (in centimeters), or roughly by multiplying by $\frac{3}{20}$. At the near distance these values must be corrected for the decreased effect of the prisms, which amounts to about 20 per cent. Correction should also be made for the prismatic effect of spectacle lenses worn by the subject. Meter angles are to be preferred over prism diopters or centrads, for they indicate more clearly the diopters distance of convergence, and the corresponding demand upon the accommodative mechanism through the accommodation-convergence reflex.

Inspection of the graphs shows that points representing the data for each subject describe a sigmoid-like curve, the shape of which definitely varies among the subjects. However, the different types of curves are distinguishable.

Consider for discussion the data for W.A.P. in Fig. 39. This subject was nearly emmetropic, with a visual acuity of 6/6 in both eyes, but was esophoric by 6 to 8 prism diopters for the 2.5 meter visual distance. With no prisms before the eyes (or the rotary prisms set for zero), the two arrows had to

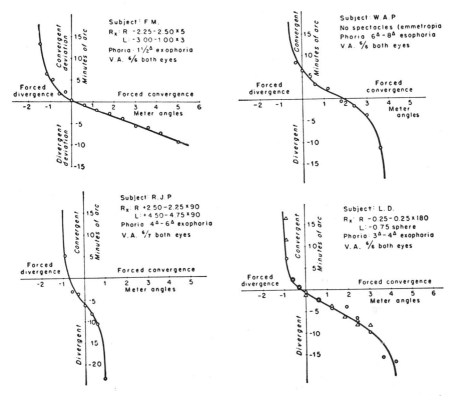

Fig. 39. Typical data of subjects for whom the fixation disparity regularly changes with the forced convergence and divergence of the eyes caused by prisms.

be displaced 6.7 minutes of arc in order for them to appear aligned. The direction of the displacement showed that the eyes were actually overconverged, which is in the same direction as the esophoria. When prisms are placed base-out before the two eyes, a convergence is necessary if fusion is to be maintained. If the convergence-accommodation reflex is active, this forced convergence will be resisted because the accommodation cannot change without blurring the vision. This resistance to the forced convergence would be manifested as an *exophoria* (a decreased esophoria) if the eyes could be disassociated, or as a change in the fixation disparity in the direction of a divergence of the eyes. Such a reaction occurs in this subject. When prisms are placed base-in before the eyes, a divergence of the eyes is forced; the reverse behavior in the fixation disparity is to be expected.

Since the limits of prism vergences base-in at this visual distance are not large, the fixation disparity increases very rapidly as the point of diplopia is reached. Considerable difference between subjects is found in the endpoint of forced convergence (prisms base-out) at which fusion becomes too unsteady for a reliable judgment or diplopia occurs. In several subjects the data could not be obtained to that limit because the extreme blurring, the

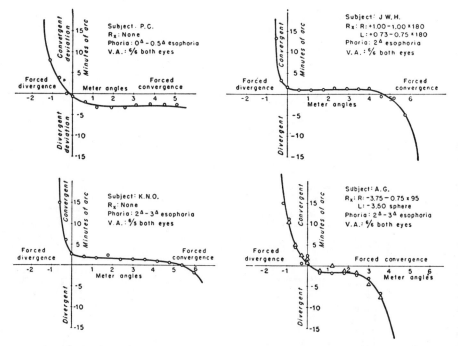

Fig. 40. Typical data of subjects for whom the fixation disparity changes only slightly with forced convergence, except at the limits of the prism vergences.

micropsia and ocular discomfort of sustained convergence prevented judgments, and more especially because of the physical limitations of the prisms.

An inspection of the curves selected shows rather strikingly the manner in which the subjects can be grouped according to the characteristics of the curves. Subjects with intermediate curves occur, however.

In the first group, which is by far the largest (Fig. 39), the fixation disparity increases with the forced convergence (or divergence) of the eyes, and in the middle range the increase is almost directly proportional to the prism power. This suggests that for these subjects the cortical images from the two eyes increasingly slip and the fusion of these images becomes increasingly less exact as the prism power increases, until finally diplopia occurs. Although the rate of change in the deviation suggests itself as a measure of the strength of the fusion reflex, the greater slope indicating a poorer fusional ability, this is not entirely borne out.

In the second group (Fig. 40), which accounts for less than 10 per cent of the subjects tested, the eyes maintain more or less the same degree of fusion, over wide ranges of forced convergence, which is evident in the fact that the fixation disparity changes little between the points where sudden increases are found near the limits of the prism vergences. The fusion of the two images appears to be tightly held in spite of the increased prism power.

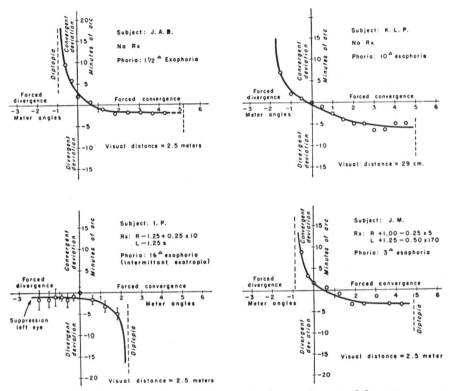

Fig. 41. Examples of data of subjects for whom the fixation disparity did not increase at one of the prism vergence limits.

Even in a wide range of forced convergence, certain of the subjects showed only a small increase in the disparity until the point was reached where abrupt changes would naturally occur.

The third type (Fig. 41), which occurs much less frequently than the second type, is similar to, and in some cases almost indistinguishable from, the second, except in the manner in which the data approach one of the diplopia points. In general the data approach the constant value more gradually than in the second group, but once reaching that, they remain constant until diplopia or extreme blurring suddenly occurs. In most cases the images become very blurred and suppression may set in; yet the fixation disparity, in so far as it can be measured, does not change at the confused endpoint. The precision of the data, of course, is much less in this region.

A fourth type of curve is also occasionally found in which the fixation disparity actually changes with forced convergence only in a very narrow interval, but outside that interval the curve for both increased forced convergence and forced divergence levels off at nearly constant values. Figure 42 illustrates two such cases. The subjects in this group usually appear by ordinary tests to have poorly developed binocular coordination, especially for

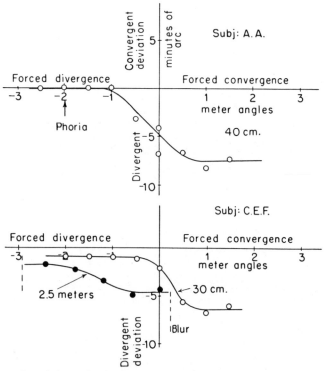

Fig. 42. Examples of data of subjects for whom the fixation disparity attained constant values for both forced convergence and forced divergence of the eyes.

near vision. In each case the constant values were associated with gradual blurring, uncertainty and perhaps some occasional suppression of vision in one eye. Undoubtedly the accommodation is changing in response to the demand of the accommodation-convergence reflex.

The second type of curve is not unexpected, for we might anticipate that the fusional processes would hold the images tightly together during the entire prism vergence test, until at the limits a sudden giving away would immediately occur with the resultant diplopia. However, one would then expect the fixation disparity to be zero between these limits, as is sometimes found (Fig. 43). The anomalous factor in most cases is that an actual more or less constant fixation disparity is maintained between the prism vergence limits. The precaution taken at the beginning of the measurements to determine the "zero" for each observer precludes the possibility that this displacement is a constant personal or instrumental error. The direction of this constant disparity appears (generally, but not always) to be in the direction of the phoria.

The explanation for these results may be that the stress set up in the accommodation-convergence reflex process due to the prisms differs greatly with individuals. On this basis the first two groups could be differentiated. In the first, a real stress is caused by the prisms, and an effort is made to resist the forced convergence and divergence of the eyes. In addition to these stresses, there must be those which are ordinarily manifested by the phoria. In the second group, the disproportion between the accommodation and the

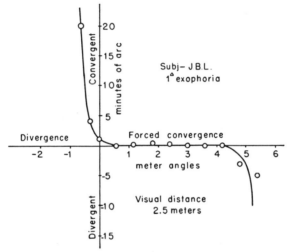

Fig. 43. A curve of the second group in which the fixation disparity is essentially zero for the greater part of the prism vergences.

convergence due to the prisms introduces little or no additional stress at all; there is practically no resistance whatsoever to the prisms, as though the accommodation and convergence relationship was exceedingly elastic, until the degree of convergence or divergence becomes great. Thus, in spite of the prisms and the forced convergence, only those stresses manifested by the phoria remain as the sole source for the ocular deviation. Hence, the fixation disparity would tend to remain constant. It would tend to be constant for a given pattern of fusion detail and only secondarily to be influenced by a change in phoria with convergence.

Peripheral Fusion. It might be argued that the constant deviation in the second group could result from an adapted change in the sensory subjective visual directions, in the same sense as that found in an anomalous correspondence, conditioned by a constant fixation disparity under the influence of a constant neuromuscular tension. However, the increase in the fixation disparity that occurs as the fusion details of the target are confined more and more peripherally shows this not to be true.

If the details for fusion are confined more and more to the peripheral parts of the retinas and fusion is prevented in increasingly larger areas centrally, the fixation disparity curve also markedly changes, though again this is different for the first two groups of subjects. By increasing the size of the blanked-out square in the projected fusion pattern on the screen, upon the center of which the vernier arrows are seen, the fusion of the images is forced more into the periphery. Eye movements do not enter to change the fusion response, for the eyes must be directed to the center of the square to per-

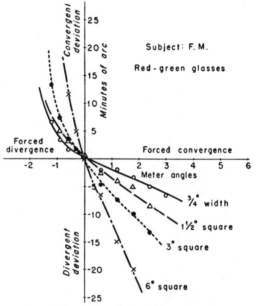

Fig. 44. Data showing the influence of peripheral fusion on fixation disparity for a subject in the first group.

ceive the displacement of the arrows. Squares used to test this effect were of angular sizes of ¾, 1½, 3 and 6 arc degrees subtended at the subject.

The results obtained on two subjects, as examples of the first two groups, are illustrated graphically. In the first case (Fig. 44), for a given convergence the fixation disparity increases rapidly as the size of the blanked-out area increases. Here the change in disparity was enhanced by a red and green glass before the eyes. Since Panum's areas in the periphery are larger than those in the central areas of the retinas, such increased disparity is still possible and fusion can be maintained. The precision of the data decreases also. Figure 45 shows how peripheral fusion influences the fixation disparity of a subject in the second group. The data were obtained for the series of blanked-out areas on the target of different sizes at each prism setting, in the same order as usual. Hence the results found are not cumulative effects of the forced vergences. The fixation disparity increases as the fusion is pushed into the periphery, but here this is evident by a vertical displacement of the curve in the convergent deviation direction (esophoric). As the forced convergence increases, the deviation then changes rather slowly toward the divergent deviation.

From these data we conclude that it is only the average size of Panum's areas that limits the magnitude of the fixation disparity when a muscular imbalance between the eyes exists.*

The Effect of Lenses. The change in fixation disparity that occurs with forced convergence or divergence is probably due in part to disturbances in the convergence-accommodation reflex mechanism. Hence we should expect

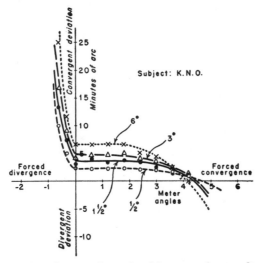

Fig. 45. Data showing the influence of peripheral fusion on fixation disparity for a subject in the second group.

that similar changes might occur when the stimulus to accommodation was also changed by the placing of spherical ophthalmic lenses before the eyes. Certainly the problem being studied would not be complete without such a consideration. Greater changes would be expected for the near visual distance because there the accommodation has greater play.

The procedure is to obtain data for the same type of curves described previously when spherical lenses are placed before the two eyes. Figures 46 and 47 illustrate the results obtained by two subjects as characteristic of the first two groups, for distant and near vision.

In each case the added spheres caused a displacement of the curves. As would be expected, the fixation disparity changes in the divergent direction

---

* Peckham reported the objective measurement of large deviations of the eyes (several arc degrees), with forced convergence experiments, and accordingly concluded that a change in the subjective directional values of retinal elements had occurred to account for "fusion." This conclusion is at variance with the evidence presented here.

with plus spheres, and in the convergent direction with minus spheres, which is the direction in which the phoria would also tend to move. The addition of the plus spheres in both cases, since the accommodation cannot relax

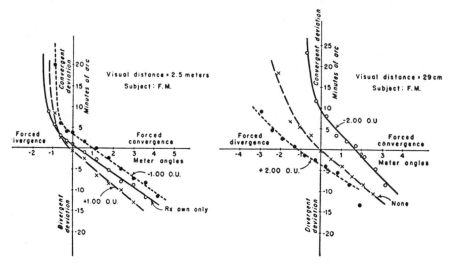

Fig. 46. Data showing the effect of spherical lenses on the fixation disparity-convergence curves with distant and near vision for a subject in the first group.

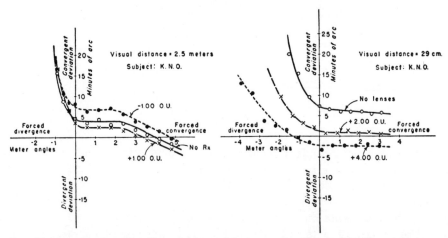

Fig. 47. Data showing the effect of spherical lenses on the fixation disparity-convergence curves with distant and near vision for a subject in the second group.

farther, blurs the vision and reduces the sensitivity, but not sufficiently to prevent data being obtained. In general it appears that the fixation disparity-prism vergence curves are displaced laterally as though the lenses merely added a constant equivalent prism vergence change. The magnitude of this equivalence is about 0.6 meter angle (3.5 to 4 prism diopters) to 1 diopter lens power, though this may vary somewhat between individuals.

Repeatability. Data of the nature of those described in these experiments cannot fail to vary somewhat from day to day, depending upon rather intangible factors associated with the individual. For some subjects the precision of measurements seemed to vary from one day to the next, for no obvious reason, except that fatigue, previous excessive use of the eyes, and even disinterest may have been specific factors. However, in spite of this variation, the curve generally found for a given subject after the lapse of several days agreed remarkably well with that previously obtained. A small training effect is to be expected, but this seems to manifest itself in an increased precision and an increased amplitude of base-out prism vergence, rather than a change in the curve that represents the data. This must not be taken to imply that no changes are found, for frequently the second curve may be displaced from that taken first by a small degree, in the same sense that the phoria will change from day to day.

The small normal involuntary eye movements that are always present, and which appear to increase with the stress, accounted for occasional spurious responses. As the prism vergence approaches the point of diplopia, fusion of the images becomes more uncertain, and here greater discrepancies in the reported data are found. However, the values for the fixation disparity in these regions were already comparatively large, so that the curves themselves were only slightly modified by these variations. Reversing the Polaroid plates before the eyes, so that the arrows would be seen by opposite eyes, had no influence on the data.

It was found that for some subjects the data for a curve repeated immediately following a first were different. A cumulative effect of the sustained use of prisms base-out toward the end of the experiment appeared to leave a residual esophoric stress or a convergent deviation, evident by the vertical displacement of the curve and sometimes also by an increase in the slope (rate of change of the deviation with convergence), especially in the center of the curve. This effect often persisted for several hours after the experiment. Care was necessary not to obtain data for a curve immediately following prism vergence tests or unusual use of the eyes unless the phoria following such tests is the same as originally found. In order to avoid cumulative effects during the experiment, the prisms base-out and base-in were alternated and frequent short rest periods were allowed.

The Prism Vergence for Zero Fixation Disparity. From the curves obtained between the prism vergences and the fixation disparity we can easily interpolate to find the degree of the forced convergence or divergence necessary to give a zero fixation disparity. At that vergence for which the fixation disparity is zero we can say that the fusion of the images from the two eyes is maximal. Curves from subjects in the second group, however, may not permit such interpolation.

It is important to know in this respect the degree to which the correction of heterophoria agrees with the forced convergence necessary to reduce the fixation disparity to zero. Is the phoria alone a measure of the stress in the binocular fusional processes, and does the position of the disassociated eyes represent that position where fusion would be maximal? In alternating strabismus and other tropias this is generally not true.

Figure 48 shows a scatter plot of the data obtained by interpolation on the curves of a number of subjects. Also included are the data obtained by Ames and Gliddon with the haploscope (p. 71). Inspection of this plot suggests a rather imperfect correlation, though in the majority of instances the direction of the phoria and the vergence for no fixation disparity is the same. Especially are the points scattered in the exophoria direction with measure-

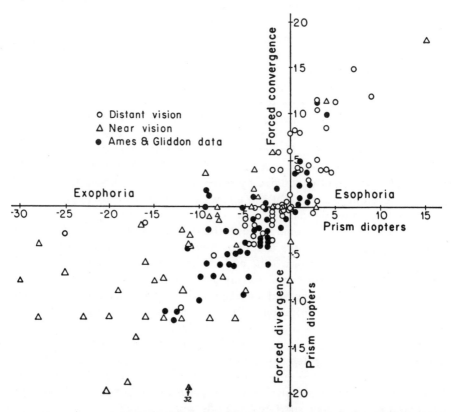

Fig. 48. A scatter plot of the phoria and the corresponding prism vergence necessary to reduce the fixation disparity to zero, for both distant and near vision.

ments obtained at near vision. In part this scattering is probably due to the unreliability of phoria measurements at near vision. We could conclude, however, that the degree to which these data deviate from a close correlation indicates the degree to which phoria alone is not an indication of the true stresses in the binocular fusional processes or a measure of the prism vergences necessary to make the fusion of the images from the two eyes maximal.

THE UNIOCULAR COMPONENTS OF FIXATION DISPARITY

As has been previously discussed, whenever disparate images fall within Panum's areas and are fused, and therefore are seen in one subjective visual direction, the primary subjective visual directions associated with the particular retinal elements on which the disparate images are falling must to some extent be likely to lose, or capable of losing, their primary identity. As discussed before, two possibilities exist: (1) both lose their identity in favor of an emergent compromise visual direction that lies between the two primary directions, or (2) the subjective visual direction of the fused image coincides with the primary direction of one of the eyes, while the other loses its identity entirely. From available data, both can occur, for the phenomenon differs among subjects. The second case probably occurs with individuals who have a marked ocular dominance. In these the subjective direction of the fused disparate images coincides with the primary subjective visual direction of the retinal element on which the image falls in the dominant eye.

To test this phenomenon, a haploscope can be used which has half-silvered mirrors (Fig. 49) and through which a special target can be seen binocularly in front. On each

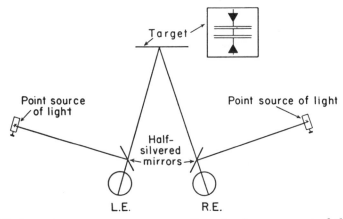

Fig. 49. Haploscopic arrangement to measure the uniocular component of the fixation disparity.

side arm and seen by reflection on the target is a point source of light set up and so arranged mechanically that each can be displaced laterally by a screw. The magnitude of the displacement is measured by a suitable indicator. The left light is seen in the upper gap of the target, the right in the lower. At a given visual distance the instrument is adjusted by means of telescopes, so that each light is at the same distance as the front target from the eyes, and when the scales read zero each light is seen centered with respect to the vertical lines on the target.

The observer adjusts each of the point sources of light so that it appears precisely aligned with the vertical center line of the target. A series of settings is made and the mean values are obtained. Best results will be obtained if the lights can be flashed on between adjustments. The results of a subject for whom the left eye was highly dominant are shown in Fig. 50. The fixation disparity occurs entirely in the right eye, there being no displacement of the light for the left. This was true from 6 meters to 20 cm. Such constancy might not occur in other individuals in whom there is a marked difference in phoria from distant to near vision.

The theoretical basis for this experiment is that the image of each point light source, being isolated from near contours, will be seen in the primary subjective visual direction of each eye. If a fixation disparity is present, then the images of the target are disparate and the target is seen in some subjective visual direction according to the two possibilities listed previously. The point light sources are then adjusted so that their visual directions (primary) coincide with the direction of the fused disparate images. For the preceding subject, the light point seen by the left eye when actually centered (scale zero) coincided with the visual direction of the target. The light seen by the right eye, however, had to be adjusted so that its subjective direction coincided with that of the corresponding point of the left eye, which necessitated a displacement from the center of the target (Fig. 50).

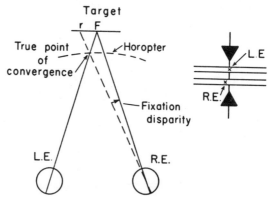

Fig. 50. How an observer with a highly dominant left eye and overconvergence of the eyes (esophoria) adjusts the point sources of light so that each appears centered laterally on the target that is seen binocularly.

If the point light sources on the arms used on the haploscope are mounted on riders that also slide along those arms so that their distances from the eyes can be changed, one can measure the state of accommodation of each eye following the measurement of the fixation disparity. In this test the distance of each point light source is adjusted along the arms until it appears the smallest on the target, that is, in best focus. This is a *stigmatoscopy* method of determining that point in space for which the retina is conjugate, and this in no way interferes with the normal fusion of the two eyes. The reciprocal of the distance when so adjusted is the diopter value of the conjugate point to the retina.

Data have been obtained for both the uniocular fixation disparity and the accommodation by the same observer when the eyes are forced to converge and diverge by prisms. Results of the uniocular fixation disparity and the change in accommodation are shown in Fig. 51, for a normal observation distance of 40 cm. The greater part of the fixation disparity occurs in the right eye, though as the eyes are forced to converge or diverge, both eyes participate in the change in the fixation disparity. These results should be compared with the normal curve for K.N.O. in Fig. 40, the data for which had been taken several years later. For other observers whose eyes have a less pronounced dominance both eyes share more nearly equally in the normal uniocular fixation disparity.

Other things being equal, one would expect that the sum of the deviations of the two eyes would be equal to the total fixation disparity measured by the original method. This appears to be approximately so, although there

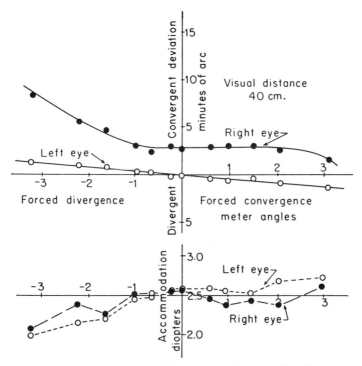

Fig. 51. The uniocular components of the fixation disparity when the eyes are forced to converge and diverge by prisms. The observation distance is 40 cm. The lower data show the state of the accommodation.

is an influence of the fused images of contours near the monocularly seen point light source in the uniocular experiments that seems to interfere somewhat when the displacements are large. Figure 52 shows a scatter plot of data obtained on twenty-four inexperienced subjects for the binocular fixation disparity and the sum of the uniocular deviations under normal conditions. The lengths of the intersecting lines indicate the mean variation of the settings. Generally the uniocular settings are the more precise.

THE UNIOCULAR DEVIATIONS AND PARTITION EXPERIMENTS

Panum's Limiting Case. An unexpected visual phenomenon was reported by Hoefer which may be adequately explained by a fixation disparity. Referring to Fig. 53, the eyes fixate a plumb line F. In line with the left eye and F is placed a second plumb line S, which then cannot be seen by the left eye but is easily seen by the right. This arrangement of lines is that used to illustrate the so-called "Wheatstone-Panum limiting case."[118] A third plumb line at P is adjusted so that not only does it seem to lie in the apparent frontoparallel

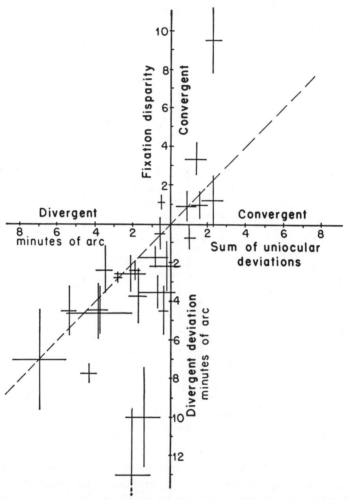

Fig. 52. Scatter plot of data obtained for the binocular fixation disparity and the sum of the uniocular deviations under normal conditions.

plane, but the angular extent $<FS>$ and $<SP>$ appear equal. The left eye is then occluded, and Hoefer found that the line P had to be displaced outward to P' in order to make the two angular separations then appear equal. No adequate explanation has been offered as to why these angular separations should be different in binocular and in monocular observation.

We do not know the ocular characteristics of Hoefer, but if we can make certain assumptions about them, we can account for his results on the basis of a fixation disparity that occurs uniocularly. Most of the data were taken with the right eye making the partition judgments. If he were exophoric and his left eye were dominant, then with binocular fixation of the center thread, the longitudinal horopter would be farther than the point of fixation. The

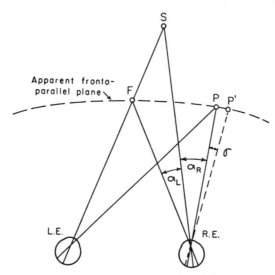

Fig. 53. Hoefer's experiment in which he found a difference in apparent angular separation of vertical threads depending upon whether they were observed in monocular (R.E.) or binocular vision.

subjective direction of the fixated thread would coincide with the primary direction associated with the left eye. The corresponding point for the right eye would be to the right of F, but the cord S would be seen in the primary direction of the right eye, and consequently the angle $<FS>$ would appear

Table 8

THE MAGNITUDE OF THE FIXATION DISPARITY WHICH WOULD ACCOUNT FOR HOEFER'S
RESULTS, AS CALCULATED FROM HIS DATA, ON THE ASSUMPTION
THAT HIS LEFT EYE WAS HIGHLY DOMINANT

Visual Distance, Cm.	15	20	23.2	25	30	40	50
Fixation Disparity in Right Eye Only, Minutes of Arc	13.4	10.2	11.7	7.8	8.8	6.9	3.9

smaller in binocular vision than in monocular, and P would have to be displaced to the right through an angle of twice the fixation disparity. Were there no dominance and were the fixation equally divided between the two eyes, then the displacement of P to the right would be equal to the fixation disparity.

Table 8 shows Hoefer's results as computed according to the foregoing assumptions. The angle of fixation disparity (angular discrepancy between binocular and monocular observation) increases as the visual distance becomes less. This could be accounted for by the exophoria increasing with convergence. Certainly the values computed from his data are of the right order, especially if we assume a complete dominance of the left eye. If the right eye were entirely dominant, then *no* difference between binocular and monocular observation should occur. The assumption that Hoefer was esophoric would necessitate the displacement of P to the left in monocular observation.

The Partition Experiment. That the foregoing explanation of the Hoefer data is reasonably the correct one is shown by a similar experiment on one subject in which partition judgments were made on the haploscope, first in monocular and then in binocular observation of the central thread. Figure 54 shows the scheme of the experiment.

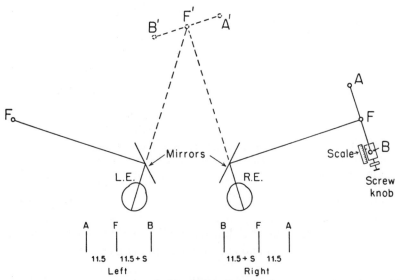

Fig. 54. Haploscopic arrangement used in a uniocular partition experiment with monocular and binocular fixation.

F on each side arm of the haploscope represents vertical black rods used as the fixation targets for each of the two eyes at a distance of 40 cm. Because of the mirrors these are seen by reflection binocularly as one rod at F'. A and B are also vertical black rods seen by reflection at A' and B'. A is fixed at a distance of 11.5 mm. from F, and the distance of B from F is adjustable, its actual distance being read from a suitable scale and vernier. The observer fixates F steadily, first in binocular observation, and secondly with the left eye occluded, and in each case a number of settings of B are made so that the space AF appears equal to FB. The rods are seen against an evenly illuminated white background, and suitable screens and apertures restrict the field of view to the rods. The equipment can be reversed on the two arms so that the partition estimations are made with the left eye instead of the right.

The subject (K.N.O.) whose data are given in Table 9 was highly left-eye dominant. For the left eye there is no difference in the partition settings for binocular or monocular vision, but for the right there is a marked difference. If this difference is due to a fixation disparity that occurs solely in the right eye, as a convergent deviation, the distance AF would appear larger in binocular vision than it would in monocular vision. This follows because the right eye is actually overconverged and the subjective visual direction of F will be functionally displaced to the left in binocular vision, to coincide with the subjective visual direction of the dominant left eye as also indicated in

Table 9

RESULTS OF A MONOCULAR PARTITION EXPERIMENT WITH MONOCULAR AND THEN BINOCULAR OBSERVATION OF THE CENTRAL FIXATION LINE OF THE SPACE TO BE BISECTED

	LEFT EYE	RIGHT EYE
Monocular Setting	1.18 ± 0.04	0.18 ± 0.18
Binocular Setting	1.17 ± 0.15	1.05 ± 0.06
Displacement, mm.	0.01 ± 0.15	0.87 ± 0.18

The deviation between the monocular and binocular settings = 7.5 ± 1.5 minutes of arc. The fixation disparity is then 3.7 ± 1.5 minutes of arc, the right eye being deviated inward.

Fig. 50. Thus the apparent distance of AF will be larger since the image of A is seen only monocularly and is not subject to the displacement. Consequently the distance FB must be made correspondingly larger if FB is to appear equal to FA. The actual displacement of B will correspond quite accurately to twice* the angle of fixation disparity. The result found is in the direction and of about the same order as the normal fixation disparity of the observer at the reading distance.

* Actually the angle of fixation disparity $\sigma = (AF) \, d/(AF + FB)$, where d is the displacement of the line B.

CHAPTER 9

The Fusion from Peripheral Retinal Stimuli

INTRODUCTION

UNTIL RECENTLY only scant attention has been given to a differentiation of the role played by fusion stimuli in the more peripheral parts of the visual field. Customary tests for fusion use targets which are primarily concerned with central stimuli, and most research has involved the use of patterns of this kind. Fusion has usually been thought of in terms of central vision when the acuity is highest, and in the main, fusion in the central parts of the visual field is considered more important and dominant than fusion in the peripheral parts. However, it has been shown (Burian[33]) that under certain circumstances fusion from stimuli in the more peripheral parts of the field plays an important role and can effectively control the orientation of the eyes.

To investigate the strength of peripheral fusion stimuli, an instrument originally devised and used by Ames was set up. This employed Polaroid for disassociating the images seen by the two eyes. Figure 55 illustrates the apparatus schematically.

In a totally dark room various patterns are projected by suitable lanterns upon a screen with an aluminum surface, at a distance of 3 meters from the subject's eyes. The screen can be curved with center at the observer's eyes to reduce distortion in the projected images. Lantern A projects a single long even line, the light from it being unpolarized, and thus the line is seen by both eyes. For experiments testing peripheral stimuli in the vertical meridian, this line is placed vertically and in that position provides fusion for controlling the convergence and horizontal eye movements but not vertical eye movements. Lanterns B and C, with Polaroid attachments, project light squares of equal size on the screen. These are the fusion stimuli and, the light from them being polarized, one is seen by one eye, the other by the second eye. These squares may be projected anywhere on the screen. Lanterns D and E, also with Polaroid attachments, project in the center of the screen short horizontal lines (to be designated as arrows) that are placed on opposite sides of the vertical line but not quite in contact with it to make a nonius test. The light being polarized, the right eye sees the right arrow and the left eye sees the left. Lantern D is so arranged that it can be rotated about a horizontal axis through small angles by means of a tangent screw, and the degree of rotation can be measured by a suitable scale. Such a rotation causes the arrow to be moved vertically on the screen.

With stimuli for fusion projected on the screen, the subject, looking through the Polaroid plates before his eyes, fixates the two arrows. If one is higher than the other, the subject adjusts the tangent screw of lantern D until the two arrows appear level—in line. The actual angular displacement of the arrows when so adjusted measures the vertical divergence of the eyes under the given conditions. Without the stimuli for fusion, the displacement measures the vertical phoria.

The important data to be obtained by this experimental arrangement are the vertical fusional amplitudes (analogous to vertical prism vergences) when the fusion stimuli are placed in a peripheral part of the visual field. A vertical separation of the squares projected by lanterns B and C provides the stimulus for a fusional movement. Figure 56 illustrates the elements of the experiment. If the squares are superimposed at a specified vertical distance from the arrows, and no vertical fixation disparity exists, the exactly

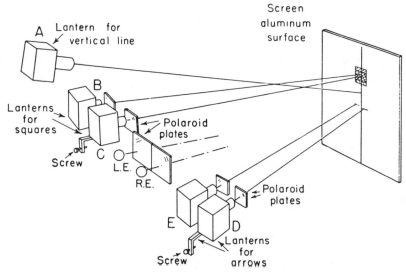

Fig. 55. Perspective sketch of the apparatus used for studying fusion of peripheral stimuli.

opposing arrows should appear to the observer aligned (A in the figure). If the square seen by the right eye is elevated so as to separate the two squares slightly, as in B, and provided fusion of the images is maintained, the fixation axis of the right eye will also be elevated. Accordingly, the right arrow will appear lower than the left and will have to be moved upward if it is to appear aligned again with the arrow seen by the left eye. The reverse displacement of the arrows will occur if the square seen by the right eye is lowered with respect to that seen by the left eye as in C.

The experiment shows that not only central but entirely peripheral stimuli were able to produce fusional movements. The similar but vertically separated images, falling on noncorresponding points of the two eyes in the periphery, provide stimuli for a muscular synergy of the elevator and depressor muscles of the eyes for movements to prevent the otherwise resulting diplopia. The strength of the innervations from the peripheral images for a fusional movement depends on the contrast, size and complexity of the details of the targets and their distance from the foveas. That peripheral stimuli play an important role in fusion is demonstrated by the fact that squares

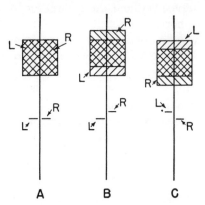

Fig. 56. The displacement of peripheral stimuli for fusion can cause a fusional movement of the eyes. Here the arrows are shown as adjusted by the subject to appear aligned. The hatched lines indicate only the direction of the reflected polarized light, and are not contours.

subtending a visual angle of ½ degree at an angular distance of 12 degrees from the foveas are capable of producing definite and measurable fusional movements.

Table 10

DATA WHICH SHOW THAT SMALL PERIPHERALLY SEEN TARGETS ARE SUFFICIENT TO CONTROL THE POINTING OF THE EYES—IN THIS CASE A VERTICAL DIVERGENCE[*]

PERIPHERAL ANGLE, DEGREES	DISPLACEMENT OF ARROWS, MINUTES OF ARC	
	Below Fixation Center	Above Fixation Center
2	21.7 ± 0.3	17.6 ± 0.3
4	22.3 ± 0.5	18.7 ± 0.5
8	20.0 ± 0.8	19.6 ± 0.4
12	20.0 ± 0.4	20.9 ± 0.5

[*] Since the observer (H. M. B.[33]) for these data had a small right hyperphoria, these data may include a small vertical fixation disparity.

It was possible to obtain the data in such experiments with considerable accuracy, and it is not unusual to find that subjects with high visual acuity can adjust the arrows with a mean variation in settings of about 20 seconds of arc, provided of course the vertical separation of the squares is not too great.

Table 10 illustrates the fact that peripheral stimuli consisting of 1½ degree squares separated about 15 minutes of arc (¼ arc degree) above or below the foveas are sufficient to control the pointing of the eyes out to 12 degrees. The mean deviations of settings are also given.

VERTICAL DIVERGENCE AMPLITUDES

In order to measure the complete cycle of response of the eyes to vertical divergences and shorten the time for the test, an automatic arrangement was constructed so that a continuous record could be taken of the displacement of the two arrows when they appeared to the subject as being aligned.

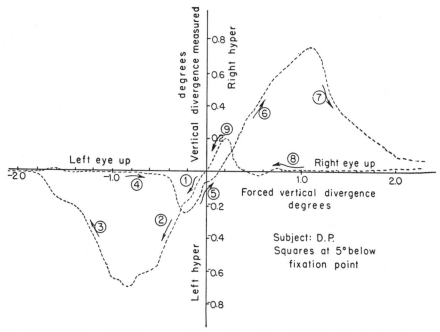

Fig. 57. Typical vertical divergence fusion curve obtained by a normal observer as a response to a divergence of peripheral stimuli.

A moving horizontal platen was linked by a cam to the lanterns B and C, whereby a given lateral movement of the platen resulted in a proportional separation of the fusion patterns as projected on the screen. A pencil support was mounted over the platen and linked by levers to the lantern E which controlled the vertical position of the arrow seen by the right eye. The task of the subject was to adjust continuously the position of the pencil (which left a mark on a paper attached to the platen) so as to keep the two arrows apparently aligned. With the platen in the middle of its travel, the two squares were superimposed at a desired vertical peripheral angle. The platen was then set into motion by an electric motor, and the two squares slowly separated vertically until the platen reached the end of its travel. Then it was automatically reversed and the squares moved toward each other, superimposing at the center, and then separating in the opposite direction. At the end of the travel it was automatically reversed again, and the platen returned to the center. During this procedure a continuous record of the response of the eyes to the separating fusion stimuli was obtained.

Figure 57 shows a typical curve obtained on a subject with normal eyes and no vertical muscle imbalance. The abscissas are the vertical separations of the squares, and the ordinates are the corresponding vertical divergences made by the eyes. For this curve, squares of 1 arc degree on a side were used at a peripheral angle of 5 degrees below the fixation area. The squares were separated first so that the image in the left eye was lowered. The dashed lines in the graph indicate the mean position. The order in which the data were obtained is indicated by the arrows numbered in sequence.

As the squares are separated, nearly exact superposition of the retinal images on corresponding points is maintained (1 and 2), for the curve shows that the vertical divergence of the eyes bears a 1:1 correspondence to the separation of the squares. At a separation of about 0.6 arc degree, the images start slipping, for the vertical divergence of the eyes no longer keeps pace

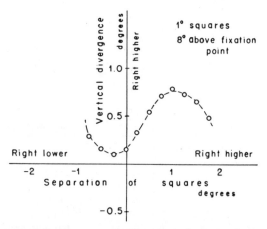

Fig. 58. A simple vertical divergence curve illustrating the fusional response to peripheral stimuli, for a subject with a vertical fixation disparity and vertical phoria.

with the separation of the images. Finally, a maximal divergence of the eyes is reached at about 1.1 degrees and then the subject reports that the targets appear double. However, as the squares continue to separate, the vertical divergence of the eyes does not return immediately to zero but falls rather slowly (3).

When the platen reverses and the separation decreases, the vertical divergence of the eyes remains nearly zero until at a particular separation the fusion is suddenly recovered and a divergence occurs at once, which of course slowly decreases in proportion to the decreased separation of the squares. When the latter are superimposed, there remains a small vertical deviation, probably the residual effect of the tonic state of the elevator and depressor muscles. The other half of the cycle then follows immediately as the squares separate in the opposite direction. Considerable differences in the amplitude of the vertical vergence curves are found between subjects.

When the subject has a vertical phoria initially, the curve may be found displaced vertically on the graph, because a vertical fixation disparity will exist even when the squares are superimposed. An example is shown in Fig. 58. The data for this curve were not obtained on the automatic device, but the displacement of the arrows was measured in each instance for a sequence of different separations of the targets.

Subjects have been found for whom the magnitude and direction of the fixation disparity when the targets are superimposed was different for different positions in the peripheral parts of the field (Ames). This might be taken as indicating an irregular functional asymmetry of some type between the images of the two eyes. It is evident that such individuals will be subject to different innervations for fusional movements from images falling on different parts of the retinas of the two eyes.

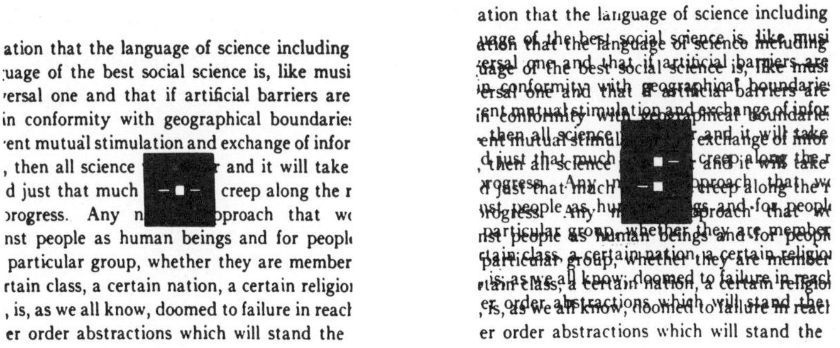

ation that the language of science including :uage of the best social science is, like musi 'ersal one and that if artificial barriers are in conformity with geographical boundarie: 'ent mutual stimulation and exchange of infor , then all science ▮▮▮ r and it will take d just that much ▬▪▬ creep along the r progress. Any n pproach that we nst people as human beings and for peopl particular group, whether they are member rtain class, a certain nation, a certain religio1 , is, as we all know, doomed to failure in reacl er order abstractions which will stand the

ation that the language of science including :uage of the best social science is, like musi 'ersal one and that if artificial barriers are in conformity with geographical boundarie: 'ent mutual stimulation and exchange of infor , then all science ▮▮▮ r and it will take d just that much ▬▪▬ creep along the r progress. Any n pproach that we nst people as human beings and for peopl particular group, whether they are member rtain class, a certain nation, a certain religio1 , is, as we all know, doomed to failure in reacl er order abstractions which will stand the

A   B

Fig. 59. Illustration of the figures that can be used with a Polaroid technic to demonstrate that vertically disparate patterns which stimulate fusion in the peripheral parts of the retina can actually cause a breaking of fusion of images falling on the macular areas of the two eyes.

CENTRAL AND PERIPHERAL FUSION

One of the important results of these experiments with peripheral fusion is that under certain conditions peripheral fusional stimuli are strong enough to break the fusion of images falling on the macular areas of the two eyes.

Two identical patterns (print, for example) as shown in Fig. 59A, which subtend a visual angle of 12 arc degrees, are projected from two lanterns (as B and C of Fig. 55) and, first, superimposed and carefully registered. In the center of these patterns a central area is blanked out so as to appear black on the screen. Projected by a lantern (A) in the center of this area is a single small square pattern of light (unpolarized) which is seen by both eyes. The two test arrows (polarized) from lanterns D and E can also be projected on this black area. When the print pattern from one lantern (say, B) is elevated slightly on the screen so as to separate the two patterns vertically (Fig. 59B) the central object suddenly appears double and at the same time the two test arrows will also be separated vertically. At this moment the eyes have made a vertical divergence movement such as would tend to keep the peripheral image patterns falling nearly on corresponding retinal points, and as a consequence central fusion is broken. This fusion on the maculas can be broken even when the center squares are as large as 1 arc degree and when the central black area is as large as 5 arc degrees. Furthermore, if all but a quarter of the peripheral patterns is blanked out, the effect can still be demonstrated.

The whole problem of peripheral fusion has only been touched in these experiments. Nevertheless they show that peripheral stimuli actually play a significant role in the fusional processes by which the eyes are directed so that images on the two retinas fall as near as possible on corresponding retinal points. The functions of the peripheral areas of the retinas, to which scotopic vision and the perception of motion have been ascribed, play an important part in the processes of fusion.

The fusional movements due to peripheral stimuli are most easily demonstrated in the vertical meridian, but they can also be demonstrated in the horizontal. The difficulty in the horizontal meridian is that the displacement of the peripheral targets may be experienced stereoscopically and seen in depth compared to the approximate convergence point of the two eyes at the position of the arrows. Whether horizontally disparate images when seen in stereoscopic depth also are stimuli for fusional movements remains to be studied.

CHAPTER 10

The Cyclofusional Eye Movements

INTRODUCTION

WHEEL-LIKE rotations of the eyes about their lines of fixation are known as cyclotorsional movements. These rotations can occur in the normal use of the two eyes in the interest of maintaining binocular single vision and then are called *cyclofusional* movements. In this respect their behavior corresponds to that of other types of fusional movements of the eyes.

Nagel[173] was the first to report that the eyes make cyclofusional movements in the stereoscope when horizontal lines are rotated in opposite directions. Von Helmholtz[106, 107] replaced the stereoscope with an arrangement of prisms before the eyes and found similar evidence. The results of Nagel and von Helmholtz were later verified by Hering.

The classic experiments which demonstrate that cyclofusional movements can be enforced optically are those of Hofmann and Bielschowsky. Cards of identical print are mounted on the two side targets of a haploscope. Above the center of one card and below the center of the other, horizontal lines are drawn. An observer sees in the haploscope a single card of print with two horizontal lines that appear parallel. When the cards are slowly rotated in opposite directions about their centers, these lines continue to appear parallel until the cards have been rotated as much as 5 to 8 degrees and then they slowly deviate from parallelism. Finally the print appears a confused jumble of characters, and is then recognized as being double. The range of angular torsions through which the targets can be rotated and the print appears single are called "cyclofusional amplitudes." It is clear that during the time the lines appear parallel the eyes must have been making cyclotorsional movements at the same rate as the rotation of the targets.

Hofmann and Bielschowsky's experiment was repeated by Verhoeff[238] with improved instruments and he verified their results completely. Verhoeff had at first denied the possibility of cyclofusional movements on neurologic grounds and attributed cyclofusional amplitudes entirely to Panum's fusional areas. These areas are a factor in all fusional amplitudes, and this has been generally recognized (Tschermak[232]).

Brecher[27] reported that cyclorotations of the eyes had been actually observed with a telescope and distinctive markings on the iris in haploscopic cyclofusional amplitude tests. Both eyes make essentially equal but opposite cyclotorsions even though only the image of one eye is rotated,[119] a fact indicating that the innervations leading to those movements are supplied equally to the two eyes. Herzau[111] showed, moreover, that the cyclofusional movements as measured by amplitudes were unaffected by a vertical divergence of the two eyes enforced at the same time. This fact is taken to indicate that these movements arise through an independent muscular synergy. That parallel or conjugate torsional movements (as against the contra-, or disjunctive, torsional movements involved in cyclofusional amplitudes) can, under appropriate conditions, be induced optically[176] and even optokinetically[27] has also been reported. These studies do not include the well-known parallel compensatory cyclotorsions of the eyes that accompany changes in head and body positions.

Apart from the control of the torsional eye movements according to Listing's law, or those parallel reflex cyclotorsional movements that tend to compensate for changes in head and body inclinations, or those changes in torsion associated with convergence, and elevation and depression of the eyes, one concludes that the external muscles of the eyes can cooperate to provide cyclotorsions about the visual axes which themselves may remain fixed in the interest of maintaining binocular single vision. These movements fall into the category of reflex movements characterized by Hofmann as "psycho-optical" reflexes in that they do depend upon the attention of the observer, yet when that attention is given, they act as reflex movements, and can neither be induced nor suppressed spontaneously.

All experiments dealing with enforced cyclofusional movements necessitate similar patterns in a stereoscope or haploscope, or with prism and mirror devices by which the image seen by one eye can be rotated about its visual axes with respect to the image seen by the other eye. The pertinent facts regarding these movements may be summarized briefly as follows: Cyclotorsions of the eyes lag slightly behind the actual torsions of the images, and hence these movements are considered to be delayed and relatively slow movements. The range within which the cyclofusional movements of the eyes can follow the torsions of the targets varies greatly with the amount of detail in those patterns, being least for a single horizontal line and greatest for print or for greatly detailed stereoscopic pictures. A vertical line has not proved suitable because stereopsis makes it appear inclined toward or away from the observer and this seems to delay the appearance of doubling. Cyclofusional movements, like the other fusional movements, are subject to training, have residual tendencies following a movement in one direction, show varying reaction times, vary with the individual, and so forth.

The evidence[194] reviewed in this chapter shows that cyclofusional movements of the eyes take place more readily than has been indicated by previous experiments. In fact, these movements probably are continually being made in everyday life, as demanded by changes in the orientation of objects in the visual field and especially by contours inclined to the visual plane.

Suppose the eyes are fixating a line which is perpendicular to the visual plane (Fig. 60), and suppose further that this line (in the absence of all

other special localization clues) appears precisely vertical to the observer—
vertical in the sense that all parts of the line appear the same distance from
him, the top neither nearer nor farther away than the bottom. The images
of this line on the two retinas, then, fall on meridians of the retinas which
are on the average stereoscopically zero; that is, the average of the horizontal disparities of the retinal images of all parts of the line is zero. These
retinal meridians in the strictest functional sense are corresponding meridians.

Now, if the line is inclined with the top (say) farther from the observer,
each of the retinal images will no longer be vertical, for each will have been
rotated slightly about the foveas in directions opposite to each other (Fig.
60). This rotation follows geometrically because each of the two eyes has
a slight side view of the plane of inclination of the line. An angular deviation
between the images in the two eyes will then exist and they will fall on noncorresponding meridians. If we denote the total angular deviation between

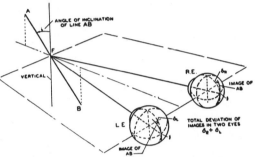

Fig. 60. Perspective drawing showing the rotary deviation of the images on the retinas
of the two eyes of a line inclined to the visual plane.

the images by δ, and the angle of inclination of the line by i (measured from
the vertical), δ and i are related with sufficient accuracy[196] by

$$\tan \delta = \frac{2a}{b} \tan i$$

where as usual $2a$ is the interpupillary distance, and where b, which is large
compared to a, is the observation distance. Table 11 gives the approximate
values of δ for various inclinations of the line, computed for several observation distances, and for an average interpupillary distance of 64 mm. It will
be seen that relatively large angles of inclination (i) correspond to small
deviation angles (δ). At an observation distance of 2 meters an inclination
of 10 degrees will be associated with an angular deviation of the retinal
images of only 0.3 degree. The magnitude of the inclination for a given deviation will increase markedly with the observation distance.[165]

The retinal images of the inclined line (or more generally, the images
of any extended spatial configuration so inclined to the visual plane), by
virtue of their rotary deviation, provide stimuli not only for a stereoscopic
perception of the inclination of the line but also for a cyclofusional move-

ment; that is, they tend to compel cyclotorsions of the eyes so that the images will then fall as near as possible on corresponding retinal points (meridians). Under circumstances where no actual cyclotorsion can occur, the inclination of the line is perceived by stereoscopic perception correctly inclined. If, however, owing to the compulsion for fusion, cyclotorsional movements of the eyes do take place (in the figure an excyclotorsional movement), the images of the line will fall nearer corresponding retinal meridians. The *functional* rotary deviation between the images, which depends upon the relationship of images to retinas, will then be reduced or even eliminated and the line would appear or would tend to appear normal. As far as the eyes are concerned, the images then fall on retinal meridians corresponding to

Table 11

THE ANGULAR ROTARY DEVIATION BETWEEN THE IMAGES IN THE TWO EYES AND THE CORRESPONDING INCLINATION OF A LINE IN THE MEDIAN PLANE IN SPACE, FOR VARIOUS OBSERVATION DISTANCES

INCLINATION OF LINE, DEGREES	ANGULAR DEVIATION BETWEEN THE IMAGES IN TWO EYES, DEGREES			
	Observation Distance			
	6 meters	2 meters	60 cm.	30 cm.
0 (vertical)	0.00	0.00	0.0	0.0
10	0.09	0.32	0.9	2.2
20	0.22	0.67	2.2	4.5
30	0.35	1.06	3.5	7.1
40	0.51	1.54	5.1	10.3
50	0.73	2.19	7.3	14.3

those of the line perpendicular to the visual plane with no cyclotorsion of the eyes.

This last phenomenon can be demonstrated when a long white thread uniformly illuminated is inclined in the median plane of the subject and is observed through unlike apertures in an otherwise totally dark room where no empirical clues or motives for spatial localization from other objects can be seen. The thread appears vertical. Only when the inclination is large will the thread appear inclined, and even then only to a small degree.

If, however, a *horizontal* white thread also is brought into the field of view and placed nearly in contact with the center of the inclined thread, the latter then will actually appear inclined, though perhaps not to its full extent to be expected. The explanation of this change in apparent inclination with the addition of the horizontal line readily follows. A cyclotorsional movement of the eyes would in one direction reduce the rotary deviation between the retinal images of the inclined line, but such a cyclotorsion would then introduce a rotary deviation between the retinal images of the horizontal line. The images of the horizontal line in turn would exert a compulsion for a cyclotorsion in the direction opposite to the first. Thus, the addition of the horizontal line dampens the degree to which a cyclofusional movement can overcome the functional deviation between the retinal images of the inclined line.

A clear distinction must be made between the geometric rotary deviation between the images and the functional rotary deviation of the images on the retinas in the two eyes. The first is a space phenomenon determined solely by the geometric position of the line relative to the positions of the optical centers of the two eyes, and is then independent of any movements the eyes may make. The response of the observer to the deviation of these images will depend upon their *functional* deviation, that is, the deviation of those images relative to corresponding retinal meridians. The term "declination," originally introduced by Stevens,[222] can be used appropriately to describe this functional deviation. The declination will be equal to the geometric deviation less the torsional position of the eyes measured from the position where the corresponding retinal meridians are vertical to the visual plane.

The wholly subjective experiments just described are very unsatisfactory; it is almost impossible to eliminate the empirical space factors of varying brightness and change in angular size with distance which increase the more the line is declined. Furthermore, one is restricted in the degree of inclination that can be obtained, without the subject seeing the frame which supports the line. To overcome these difficulties all configurations used in the field of view can be fixed, and the rotary deviations between the images can be introduced optically.

EXPERIMENTS FOR DETERMINING EXISTENCE OF SMALL CYCLOFUSIONAL MOVEMENTS

Instrument. The rotary deviations between the images in the two eyes can be introduced with great precision by means of meridional afocal magnification lenses (see p. 122). Such a lens magnifies the image seen through it in one meridian only, and consequently images of all lines in space not parallel or perpendicular to the meridian of magnification will be deviated in a rotary sense toward the meridian of magnification. When the axis of the lens is placed obliquely, as in Fig. 61, the images of vertical and horizontal lines will always be deviated almost equally but in directions opposite to each other (a scissors effect). The magnitude of the total deviation angle, δ, of the images of the vertical lines (and of those of the horizontal lines, though this will be in an opposite direction) will be related to the meridian angle θ, measured from the horizontal, by $\tan \delta = (M - 1) \sin 2\theta / (M + 1)$, where M is the magnification of the lens (p. 307).

Geared Lens Unit. The optical device, called the geared lens unit, placed before the two eyes consists of two of these lenses matched for power and magnification mounted in special geared rings. Figure 149 is a drawing of the unit. The dimensions of the two rings are such that when the teeth mesh, the separation of the lenses (which are 44 mm. in diameter) will correspond to an average interocular distance. When activated by a small pinion meshed to one of the rings, the two lenses will then rotate equally but in opposite directions. A suitable drum attached to the shaft of the pinion is calibrated to read directly the rotary deviations of the images of vertical (and horizontal) lines seen through the device, in tenths of degrees. The drum reads zero when the axes of the lenses are parallel and vertical, and accordingly there is no deviation of the images.

With lenses having a 2 per cent magnification, the rotary deviation, δ, produced by the device, which is the sum of the deviations of the two lenses, is approximately 0.034 degree per degree θ, for small angles of rotation, with a maximal δ when $\theta = \pm 45$ degrees of about 1.1 degrees. If the lenses are rotated in the sense of an incyclotorsion (axes of the lenses converging up-

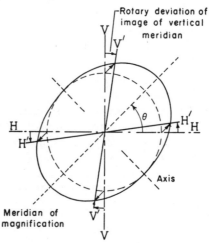

Fig. 61. The images of the vertical and horizontal meridians of the two eyes undergo a rotary deviation when the visual field is magnified in an oblique meridian.

ward), the deviation of the images of the verticals (δ_V) will be taken as positive; if in the sense of an excyclotorsion (axes converging downward), as negative. No differences between the magnifications of the images of the two eyes will be introduced by the unit in the vertical or the horizontal meridians, for all angles of θ. This unit was calibrated very carefully on a special lens-testing instrument[191] for the distance at which it was to be used before the eyes, and for the particular viewing distance.

Apparatus. Directly in front of the observer at a distance of 3 meters a rigid wooden square frame (Fig. 62), 1.5 meters on a side, was set up vertical, with its plane at right angles to the median plane of the observer, and was centered with respect to that plane and at the eye level of the observer. The various test configurations employed in the experiments were supported within this frame. Suitable fluorescent or Lumiline lamps, screened from the observer, illuminated the configurations uniformly. The test elements were seen against a uniform black shadowless background made by black velvet cloth stretched tightly over a frame. Suitable screens and apertures restricted the field of view of the subject to the area of the fixed frame. The geared lens unit was suitably mounted before the eyes. In all cases the head of the observer was held fixed by a suitable head-rest and usually by a wax bite, which prevented depth discrimination by the parallax associated with head movements.

The Basic Experiment with Inclined Line. Within the supporting structure, an inner wooden frame was mounted which could be rotated about a horizontal axis in the plane of the frame and on the eye level of the subject. A suitable scale and pointer indicated the inclination of the inner frame. A white cord was stretched between the centers of the top and bottom members of this frame, and hence the cord always lay in the median plane of the observer for all inclinations of the frame. A second white cord was also stretched to coincide with the axis of rotation of the frame. The configuration was then a pair of intersecting lines, and the one in the median plane could be inclined to any angle from the vertical. The inclination of the frame could be adjusted by the subject by means of a handwheel and cord attachments.

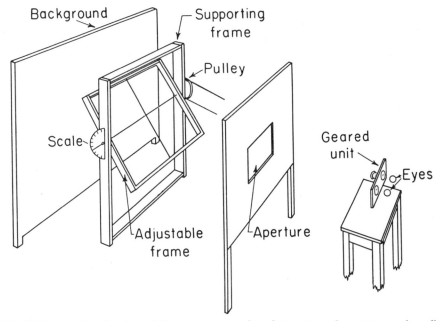

Fig. 62. Perspective drawing of the apparatus used to demonstrate the existence of small cyclofusional movements of the eyes.

The geared lenses would be set to introduce a given rotary deviation of images of the vertical and horizontal cords, this deviation being in directions opposite to each other for the two cords. Stimuli for a cyclofusional movement would exist for each of the lines, in opposite directions. The images of the vertical line would be disparate and by stereoscopic vision it would appear inclined in space. The subject then adjusted the inclination of this line until it appeared vertical, that is, until the upper and lower halves appeared the same distance away. This adjustment was made slowly. It is even preferable to interrupt binocular vision by means of a shutter before one eye during any movement of the frame, the judgments being made when the cord is stationary. The angle of inclination of the cord for the settings made by the subject was recorded by an assistant. From the inclination measured, the corresponding deviation, δ_b, between the images in the two eyes for this inclination was then calculated from tan $\delta_b = 2a$ tan i/b, where again i is the angle of inclination, $2a$ is the interpupillary distance and b is the visual distance.

Figure 63 illustrates typical data obtained for δ_b calculated from the inclination of the line which appears vertical, for various deviations δ_u introduced by the geared unit. In the figure the deviation measured is plotted on the ordinate, and the deviation of vertical images introduced is plotted on the abscissa. The significant fact from these data is that the deviation determined from the adjusted inclination of the line is *twice* that deviation introduced by the lenses. This constitutes proof that a cyclofusional movement of the eyes must have occurred which eliminated entirely the declination between

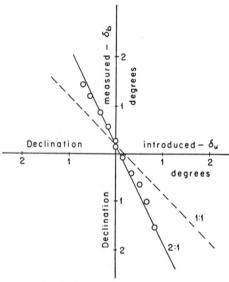

Fig. 63. The 2:1 ratio of the declination measured to that introduced by the geared lens unit shows that a cyclofusional movement has occurred to eliminate completely the declination between the images of a single horizontal line.

the images of the horizontal line. Moreover, when the central line was finally adjusted so that it appeared vertical, there would also be no declination between its images in the two eyes either. Obviously, as the line is inclined to appear vertical, the declination between its images decreases and the only compulsion for cyclofusional movements is exerted by the images of the horizontal cord. A cyclofusional movement which eliminated the declination of the images of the horizontal cord would make the declination between the images of a vertical cord twice as large. One would anticipate therefore a 2:1 ratio between the deviation measured and that indicated by the drum on the geared unit.

The Relative Strength of Stimuli from Different Types of Spatial Configurations. This apparatus is too limited if we want to measure the relative amounts of cyclotorsion when stimuli for cyclofusional movements are antagonistic. The problem in instrument design was to find a device with which we could determine the declination, δ, for the apparent stereoscopic vertical (stereovertical) in a given experiment without the stimuli from that device itself introducing a measurable cyclofusional effect. It was found that two points of light separated vertically could be used.

The Instrument. To the apparatus described previously an attachment was added so that a pair of beads would be seen by reflection from a large half-silvered mirror set up in front of the geared unit (Fig. 64). The beads were supported on a black thread attached to the top and bottom of a narrow wooden frame, and separated 50 cm. The frame was pivoted so as to rotate about a horizontal axis at the eye level of the subject. The distance of this frame was such that the images of the beads were seen stereoscopically at the same distance as the frame which supports the test elements. The beads were independently illuminated and seen against a black background. If the experiments were

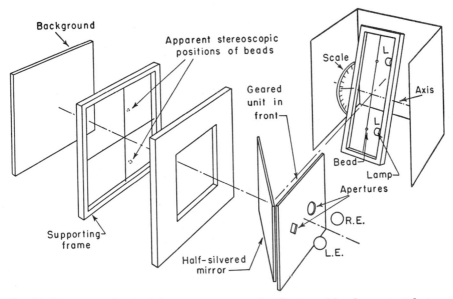

Fig. 64. Perspective sketch of the apparatus using the illuminated beads as a test device.

conducted in a dimly lighted room, the thread supporting the beads could not be seen. Compared with most of the test configurations used, the beads themselves exerted only an insignificant compulsion for cyclofusional movements. To reduce further a possible compulsion to fusion by them, a timing device was hooked in the electrical circuit of the lamps so that the beads would be seen intermittently for only a second at a time with a one second "off" interval.

By means of a hand wheel and cords, the subject could adjust the inclination of the frame and therefore the difference in relative distance of the two beads. As before, the angle of inclination was taken as positive when the beads were inclined back (away) at the top, in order that the corresponding deviations of the images for the two eyes would be positive. The test configurations themselves (except where noted) were then fixed vertically in the central frame.

The procedure in a given experiment was simply to introduce a deviation between the images of the two eyes by means of the geared unit, and instruct the subject to turn the hand wheel to adjust the orientation of the beads until they appeared vertical (or what is better, equally distant from him). The actual inclination of the cord supporting the beads was then read from the scale attached to the frame. From this measurement the equivalent rotary deviation was then computed as indicated previously.

The Fundamental Experiments. The suitability and precision of the technic of using the beads in this modified apparatus is shown in three fundamental experiments, when (1) only a single horizontal white cord is used, (2) only a single vertical cord is used, and (3) when white cords are arranged to form an oblique cross. The results are illustrated in Fig. 65. In this graph, the deviation angle introduced by the geared unit δ_u is plotted on the abscissa, while along the ordinate axis are plotted the corresponding rotary deviations between the images of the two eyes δ_b computed from the

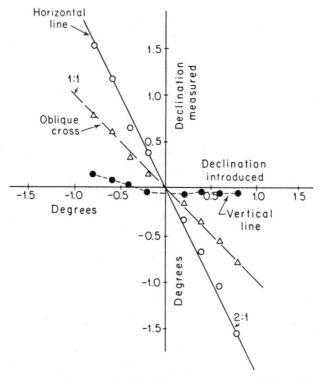

Fig. 65. Typical results using the bead technic to measure cyclofusional movements in the three fundamental experiments described in the text.

actual inclination of the beads when they appeared vertical. In these experiments it must be remembered that the geared unit introduces equal rotary deviations, though opposite in direction, between the images of the vertical and of the horizontal meridians.

First, a single horizontal line only was used. If no cyclofusional movement occurred to reduce or eliminate the declination of the images of this line, then the actual inclination of the cord supporting the beads should be such as to offset twice the declination between the images for the vertical meridian. Figure 65 shows that a cyclofusional movement has occurred which has substantially eliminated the declination of the images of the horizontal cord introduced by the geared unit.

Second, only a vertical cord was used as the test configuration. Again the beads, whose images were a little to one side of the line, were adjusted by the subject so that they appeared the same distance away. The actual inclination of the beads will be different depending on whether or not a cyclofusional movement has occurred. If no fusional movement has taken place, the line should appear inclined in space because of the vertical declination that has been introduced. The inclination of the beads should then be such as to offset the vertical declination introduced. On the other hand, if there has been a cyclofusional movement which eliminates entirely the vertical declination introduced, then the line should appear vertical and the actual inclination of the beads should be zero. The latter is shown to be the case, except for a suggestion that when negative declinations are introduced, the cyclotorsional movement is not quite complete.

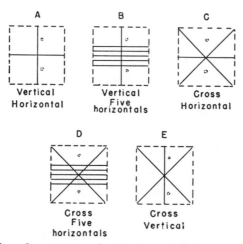

Fig. 66. Types of configurations used with the geared lens unit for studying cyclo fusional movements. The small broken circles indicate the approximate positions of the illuminated beads that are observed stereoscopically.

Third, an oblique cross consisting of white cords attached to the corners of the frame was used as the test configuration. With this, a 1:1 ratio would be expected between the measured δ_b from the setting of the beads and the vertical deviation δ_u introduced, because the geared unit will not itself affect the apparent orientation of the oblique cross[189] (p. 323). As shown by Fig. 65, the measured declinations associated with the inclination of the beads are substantially equal to the declination introduced by the geared unit.

The precision of these data in terms of the mean variation of the settings of the inclination of the beads, expressed in declination angle, was of the order of 0.03 degree or about 2 minutes of arc. For subjects with high visual acuity and some experience in stereoscopic judgments, this is not unusual. This value corresponds to an angular retinal disparity between the images of the beads in the two eyes of approximately 10 seconds of arc, which is not unusual.

Antagonistic Stimuli. More important now is the answer to the question of how the eyes respond to antagonistic stimuli for cyclofusional movements. The five configurations as shown in Fig. 66 were studied.

Vertical and Horizontal Lines. This configuration (Fig. 66A) consists of both the vertical and horizontal strings attached to the sides of the central frame. A setting of the geared unit will introduce equal but opposite rotary deviations between the images of the two eyes for these contours. Each cord in this configuration will accordingly provide a stimulus for a cyclofusional movement, but these will be in directions opposite to each other. If each exerted the same degree of compulsion, no cyclotorsion of the eyes would result. The degree to which the inclination of the beads when they appear to be the same distance from the observer is actually greater or less than that caused by the rotary deviation of the unit on the beads themselves is a measure of the amount of cyclotorsion that has occurred.

Hence if δ_u degrees are the rotary deviation of the images of the vertical introduced by the geared unit, and the eyes make a disjunctive cyclotorsional movement of τ degrees, the resultant vertical declination (functional) between the images would be $(\delta_u - \tau)$. Here τ is taken as positive if the torsion of the eyes is an outward rotation of the upper parts of vertical meridians. When the two beads are set to appear vertical (the same distance from the observer), their actual inclination must be such that the corresponding vertical declination δ_b would be equal to $(\delta_u - \tau)$. Thus the cyclotorsion of the eyes would be $\tau = \delta_u + \delta_b$.

Table 12 shows the degree of cyclofusional movements that occur with a horizontal and a vertical line when equal but opposite rotary deviations are introduced between the images of those lines. All the data are in degrees.

These data show that in spite of the two sets of antagonistic stimuli for a cyclofusional movement, a movement does occur which reduces the declination of the images of the vertical line by about 40 per cent. Thus the compulsion for cyclofusional movements from stimuli from the vertical appears to be greater than that from the horizontal. The resultant declination of the images of the horizontal cord will actually be increased to $(\delta_u + \tau)$. Moreover, if a number of horizontal cords replace the single horizontal cord (as in Fig. 66B), the response is about the same. The compulsion from the images of the vertical cord is still strong enough to determine the direction of the cyclofusional movements. Concentration of the attention of the subject on the vertical or the horizontal elements made no significant differences in the results.

There was other evidence that the compulsion for a cyclofusional movement exerted by the vertical contours was not only stronger than that exerted by the horizontal, but very much faster. A series of settings of the beads made at intervals of about fifteen seconds showed that in the beginning the cyclotorsion was actually greater for the vertical line (almost complete at times) and that as the settings were continued, the magnitude of the cyclotorsion in that direction decreased; that is, a cyclofusional movement toward the horizontal increased, finally reaching a stable value. Even these might vary somewhat over a prolonged period of observation.

This phenomenon of a stronger and faster compulsion to fusion caused by declinations of the images of vertical contours as compared to horizontal, in spite of stereopsis, is noteworthy not only for its own sake, but because it is not consistent with accepted notions, at least regarding fusional movements in the visual plane.

A Horizontal Line and an Oblique Cross. When an oblique cross made by cords stretched between the corners of the frame is used with a hori-

Table 12

TYPICAL DATA SHOWING THE DEGREE OF CYCLOFUSIONAL MOVEMENTS ASSOCIATED
WITH A VERTICAL AND A HORIZONTAL CORD CONFIGURATION WHEN
EQUAL BUT OPPOSITE DECLINATIONS ARE INTRODUCED
BETWEEN THE IMAGES OF THE TWO EYES

VERTICAL DEVIATION INTRODUCED δ_u	INCLINATION OF BEADS i	CORRESPONDING DECLINATIONS δ_b	CYCLOTORSION OF EYES τ
$+0.80$	-15.1	-0.45	$+0.35$
$+0.60$	-7.9	-0.24	$+0.46$
$+0.40$	-5.5	-0.17	$+0.23$
$+0.20$	-2.8	-0.09	$+0.11$
-0.20	$+0.1$	$+0.01$	-0.19
-0.40	$+3.2$	$+0.12$	-0.28
-0.60	$+8.9$	$+0.26$	-0.34
-0.80	$+12.4$	$+0.36$	-0.44

zontal cord (Fig 66C), the stimulus for a cyclofusional movement can arise only from the horizontal contour (since any change in the images of the cross caused by the geared unit is the same in both eyes). The settings of the beads in this experiment proved unusually difficult as compared to the previous experiments because of the subjective uncertainty of each setting.

If a cyclofusional movement does occur which decreases or eliminates the declination between the images of the horizontal cord, then rotary deviations between the images of the oblique cross will be introduced, with the result that the cross should appear stereoscopically inclined in space[189] (p. 319). For a series of declinations introduced by the geared unit, the two beads were adjusted so that they appeared the same distance from the observer; the data showed that little or no cyclofusional movements would occur.* Obviously, the images of the cross would tend to counteract any cyclofusional movement that might be started by the declination of the images of the horizontal line.

If, however, five horizontal heavy white ropes are substituted for the single horizontal cord (Fig. 66D), significantly large cyclofusional movements do occur which for the small declinations introduced are sufficient to eliminate completely the declinations of the images of the horizontals. Thus, as soon as the number and contrast of the horizontal contours are increased, the compulsion arising from the declinations of these becomes great enough to offset entirely the opposing compulsions that arise from the oblique cross, and then a torsion does take place.[194]

A Vertical Line and an Oblique Cross. Consider, now, an oblique cross in combination with a vertical cord *in the plane of the cross* (Fig. 66E). When the geared unit is now used to introduce deviations, the cross itself will not be affected but declinations will be introduced between the images of the vertical line. The extent to which a cyclofusional movement will now occur depends on the relative compulsion strength from the vertical contours as opposed to those of the oblique cross which would exist when a cyclotorsion occurred. Following the procedure outlined previously, data were obtained which show that cyclofusional movements *do* occur. We must conclude that the stimuli from vertical contours predominate over stimuli from contours located otherwise.

However, if the central vertical elements are placed *in front* of the plane of the cross so that their images, compared to the images of the cross, now have *horizontal* disparities in the two eyes, the cyclofusional movements are greatly reduced. Much depends upon whether the fixation is maintained on the cross or allowed to wander continuously from the vertical cords to the cross. As might be anticipated, with constant fixation on the plane of the cross the compulsion for cyclofusional movements resulting from declinations of the images of vertical contours is reduced if horizontal disparities are also introduced between their images in the two eyes. If pairs of vertical cords are placed both before and behind the plane of the cross (as in the configuration used in the space eikonometer, p. 249), and wandering fixations are made, cyclofusional movements do occur.

THE DEPTH CONTRAST PHENOMENA AND CYCLOFUSIONAL MOVEMENTS

Cyclofusional movements also occur to compromise the declinations of the images of vertical and spatially inclined contours when both are present in the binocular field of view.

If the outer two of three vertical lines (in the objective frontoparallel plane) in space are inclined with their tops *nearer* the observer, and the en-

---

* The degree of cyclotorsion in these experiments can also be determined by adjusting the beads so that they appear to lie in the plane of the cross,[194] and data so obtained were entirely in agreement with those taken by adjusting the beads so that they were apparently the same distance from the observer (vertical).

tire binocular visual field is restricted to these lines, the central line, instead of appearing spatially vertical as it is, appears inclined somewhat *back* at the top. Nagel[173] first described this phenomenon with figures drawn on targets and observed in a haploscope. Werner[250] designated the effect, the "binocular depth contrast" phenomenon. Because of the declination between the images of the two outer lines as they fall on the retinas of the two eyes, one would expect to see, stereoscopically, a single vertical line between two lines that are inclined in space with their tops nearer to the observer than the vertical line. Actually the central line also appears inclined in the direction opposite to that of the outer lines, and thus farther away at the top. The phenomenon is best observed when the configurations are seen through suitable apertures which prevent the ends of the lines being seen, and which themselves do not provide contours the images of which provide stimuli for fusional movements. It can be demonstrated on nearly all observers, though its apparent magnitude varies with the individual.*

To test the phenomenon quantitatively the apparatus described previously, in which the beads are used, can be modified and employed. Within the supporting frame, a second frame is mounted that can be rotated about a horizontal axis as that shown in Fig. 62. A scale is attached for indicating the inclination of this frame. Various numbers of cords can be stretched in both the movable and the fixed frames. Five configurations were used; namely, (1) two separated cords, one vertical and the other which could be inclined (the configuration used by Nagel), (2) one central vertical cord and two outer cords that could be inclined (the configuration used by Werner), (3) two vertical cords and a central cord which could be inclined, (4) a central vertical cord and eight cords, four on a side, which could be equally inclined, and (5) eight vertical cords and one which could be inclined. The geared unit *was not* used throughout the tests. Obviously, the purpose of these different configurations was to obtain various degrees and types of compulsions for cyclofusional movements. Throughout the experiments the beads were used to determine that inclination which corresponded to the criterion of the subjective equal distance (vertical). The inclination of the beads when the two appeared vertical would give a direct measure of the degree of cyclotorsion the eyes had undergone, since the geared unit was not used.

A study of the data[190] obtained with these five configurations shows that in every case a small cyclofusional movement occurs which reduces the declination of the images of the inclined line or lines. The degree of cyclotorsional movement depends upon the relative number of the inclined to the vertical cords; in the case of the eight vertical cords and one inclined cord,

---

* Werner ascribed the phenomenon to "a change in the correspondence within the particular visual field." The nature of this "change in correspondence" is not clear, but in view of the other experiments reported in his article, a sensorial change seems to be implied. The experiments described here make clear that there has been no change in the sensorial (or anatomic) correspondence between the retinas of the two eyes, but only a change in cyclotorsional positions of the eyes.

practically no cyclofusional movement occurred. We must conclude that in a binocular visual field with objects at various inclinations, cyclofusional movements of the eyes do occur in an effort to compromise the various declinations of the images—especially those of vertical or near vertical configurations.

COMMENT

To measure the actual cyclotorsional movements of the eyes in these experiments directly by a telescope or similar device, as Brecher[27] had done, would have been desirable. The movements reported here, however, are small, and when divided between the two eyes, each is so small as to preclude practically such objective measurements. The precision to which Brecher could measure the cyclorotations was of the order of $\frac{1}{2}$ to 1 degree, which obviously is not accurate enough here. Observing the displacements of blood vessels near the limbus would also demand great precision since a 1 degree cyclorotation of the eye would give a displacement of only about 0.2 mm.

Under the controlled conditions described previously, where empirical factors and motives for depth perception are, so far as possible, eliminated, it is demonstrable that the eyes are capable of making cyclofusional movements of great precision. Thus, a standard deviation of ± 0.07 degree declination was not unusual. Such precision should be compared with stereoscopic thresholds of 5 seconds of arc, which is significant in view of the small involuntary eye movements (physiologic nystagmus) that are constantly present.

Under controlled conditions it has been shown that the eyes respond to stimuli from contours in either the horizontal or vertical meridian for an actual cyclofusional movement. The compulsion to cyclofusional movements arising from vertical or near vertical contours is much greater than that from other contours and especially horizontal ones. This difference found between the vertical and other meridians is surprising and difficult to explain satisfactorily.

However, the declinations between the images of vertical or near vertical contours also result in a stereoscopic perception of depth, while those of horizontal contours cannot. The facts that the processes of stereoscopic vision are rapid processes (of the order of several hundredths of a second, according to Langlands), while the cyclofusional processes with horizontal contours are slow (of the order of one-half second, according to Verhoeff[238]), may hold the key to the explanation. Certainly, there exists a basis for suggesting, as Fleischer,[77] for example, has done, that, in general, stereoscopic perception results from the compulsion stimuli to fuse disparate images. In this sense, the processes of stereoscopic perception and those of the compulsion for fusional movements are interrelated and concomitant. In that case, the cyclofusional movements compelled by the declinations of the images of vertical contours should be faster than those of horizontal contours, and, in being faster, should accomplish the cyclotorsion before the compulsions from the horizontal contours get under way.

The difference between the compulsions to fusion arising from vertical and horizontal contours cannot be associated with a sensorial difference in the perception of direction. It has been shown that lines can be set for the apparent vertical or horizontal meridians with considerable precision, with no significant difference between the two.[204] However, the precision is much poorer for oblique contours.[118] The results described previously show that the cyclofusional movements are roughly proportional to the declination introduced. This would not be true when the declinations approached the limits of the cyclofusional amplitudes, where the amount of cyclofusional movement would be affected by cyclophorias and cyclotropias.

The degree of the cyclofusional movement varies not only with the configuration in the binocular field of view but also with the contrast and relative weights of antagonistic declinations. This is to be expected on the basis of earlier works on the problem of fusion. Moreover, horizontal disparities between the images decrease the compulsion for cyclofusional movements. This may also be expected.

In this discussion should be mentioned the experiments of Hofmann and Bielschowsky,[120] which showed that a background of inclined contours affected the setting of the subjective vertical (not the stereoscopic vertical) to the right or to the left in the frontoparallel plane. Similarly, the experiments of Vernon and also of Gibson[89] showed that a prolonged observation of an inclined line (right or left) subsequently causes a vertical or a horizontal line to appear inclined in the opposite direction. These effects are considered to be the result of experiential adaptive processes and are not concerned with eye position at all. However, all these results should be considered in the light of the experiments of Noji and Brecher,[27] which certainly suggest that cyclotorsions can, under certain conditions, follow the influence of external stimuli. The famous case of Sachs and Meller is often quoted to show that the subjective vertical can be adapted to new retinal meridians in the case of pronounced cyclotropia, possibly in the same sense that an anomalous "correspondence" can develop in squint. Recently, similar aftereffects have been demonstrated (Köhler and Emery) in the third dimension. These effects would certainly need to be considered in experiments which depend exclusively on the absolute criterion of the stereoscopic vertical.

While the nature of these effects is outside the scope of this discussion, they would seem to imply that the retinal meridians which correspond to the subjective vertical are variable and subject to previous experience. The crux of this problem is whether the retinal meridians corresponding to the subjective stereoscopic vertical can be the same meridians as those of the monocular subjective vertical. Certainly the experiments described here, where the visual plane of the observer is horizontal, suggest that the subjective stereoscopic vertical agrees accurately with the objective stereovertical. The angle V (of von Helmholtz,[107] Volkmann,[242] and so forth) between the meridians of the apparent subjective verticals of the two eyes, if maintained in binocular vision, would make this result impossible. It is probable, however, that the measurements of this angle, like the majority of those dealing with torsions of the eyes with convergence, elevation and depression of the eyes[109] are made with targets which permit the eyes to slide into a cyclophoric position.

The results of the experiments described here would provide evidence for the discussion of Hering concerning enforced cyclofusional movements, to the effect that the eyes can make adjustments which tend to keep the images of vertical contours in space on the retinal meridians for the stereoscopic subjective vertical, irrespective of eye movements. These cyclofusional movements probably occur, however, in any complex visual field where certain contours are inclined fore and aft with respect to the visual plane, in an effort to compromise the disparities in the interest of a single binocular vision.

From the point of view of a functional and stable binocular stereoscopic localization we might anticipate that near vertical contours would play an important role in the compulsions for cyclofusional movements. In order that vertical objects such as walls, trees and so forth may maintain their orientation as one raises or lowers the eyes to look at various parts, a cyclofusional movement is a necessity.

Part III

THE PROBLEMS IN BINOCULAR VISION WHEN
CHANGES ARE MADE IN THE RELATIVE
MAGNIFICATIONS OF THE IMAGES
OF THE TWO EYES

CHAPTER 11

Optical Means for Changing the Magnification of the Retinal Image

W E SHALL BE CONCERNED in this section with those phenomena which occur in binocular vision when a change is made in the magnification of the image of *one* of the two eyes, or when unsymmetric changes are made in the magnification of the images of both eyes. First, however, it is necessary to review the concepts of magnification and of changes in magnification, and then to describe the various optical means for effecting such changes.

GENERAL CONCEPTS AND DEFINITION OF MAGNIFICATION

In any optical system which forms an image of an object, the true magnification is defined as the ratio of the size of the image to the size of the corresponding object. In symbols, $M = I/O$, where M is a number, the magnification, and I and O are the sizes (say, in centimeters) of the image and object, respectively. Often this magnification is designated the linear magnification, to distinguish it from longitudinal and from angular magnifications. If the system exhibits no distortion, the magnification is the same for all sizes of the object, and the size of the image will always be proportional to that of the object, or, $I = M \times O$. In the following discussion regarding the eyes we shall refer to the magnification of the images rather than to the size of the images. This eliminates the size of the object as a variable. Because most optical systems have some distortion, the linear magnification may pertain only to objects of small size and those which lie close to the axis of the system.

Suppose the distances of the object, O, and of the image, I, from the lens are given as u and v (in centimeters) from a simple lens, or from the principal planes of a more complex lens system. The elementary theory of image formation relates u and v to the power (the reciprocal of focal length, f) of the lens by $uv + f(u + v) = 0$. The magnification is given by $M = I/O = v/u$. In the case of the human eye, v will be about 1.7 cm., and we have for the magnification, approximately, $M = 1.7/u$, u being the object distance measured in centimeters. An object 1 cm. high at a distance of 100 cm. from the eye will have an image on the retina about 0.17 millimeters in extent;

at 50 centimeters, the image will be about 0.34 millimeters in extent, and so forth.

The magnification and therefore the size of the image depend on the object distance and the power of the system. We cannot pick up a lens or an instrument at random and speak of its having a specific magnification, except if that instrument has no power, such as a telescope or afocal lens, but even then we imply that the instrument has no power and that the object (and also its image) lies a considerable distance away.

The magnification of the retinal image of the eye can be altered first by changing the object distance u and, second, by placing before the eye a suitable lens or lens system. The first is not usually feasible or possible, except under special conditions, as for example when the haploscope is used. Any lens or lens system introduced before the eye modifies the magnification of the retinal image, and it is convenient to discuss the magnitude of this effect from the point of view of *afocal* lenses first, and then the part played by the power. Finally special purpose lens systems will be described.

It is convenient often to designate the change in magnification as the per cent change, m per cent $= 100(M - 1)$, where M is the magnification of the lens system. Thus, if $M = 1.03$, m will be 3 per cent. Again, if $M = 0.97$, $m = -3$ per cent, a diminution of the image.

LENSES

Afocal Lenses. The afocal type lens is the simplest lens and the lens preferable for experimental and general use when one wishes to change the magnification of the image in a given eye. Such a lens is substantially without power, so that the image of a distant object seen through it coincides (more or less) with the object itself. The lens does not change the optical distance of the object seen by the eye through the lens, and hence the stimulus to accommodation remains unchanged (Fig. 67).

The afocal lens is a little Galilean telescope in that it consists of positive and negative surfaces, analogous to the objective and eye lenses. The powers are related by $D_1 + D_2 - D_1 D_2 t/n = 0$, where D_1 and D_2 are the powers of the front and back surfaces in diopters ($D = (n - 1)/R$, where n is the index of refraction of the glass and R is the radius of curvature in meters), and t is the actual thickness again expressed in meters. In all cases the back surface power will be a little more negative than the power of the front surface. The magnification can be computed from any one of the three formulas; namely, $M = -D_2/D_1 = 1/(1 - D_1 t/n) = 1 + D_2 t/n$. Since the per cent magnification, m, will be $100 \times (M - 1)$, the per cent magnification, m per cent $= -D_2 t/n$, and approximately m per cent $= D_1 t/n$, if D_1 and D_2 are diopters surface power, and the thickness t is in centimeters. Because there are three parameters, D_1, D_2 and t for each lens, there are many lenses of different dimensions which will give the same magnification. The magnifying effect of an afocal lens is practically independent of the distance at which the lens is placed before the eye, provided of course the object is distant.

The specifications for a set of afocal type of magnification lenses are given in Table 13. These lenses have essentially a uniform magnification and power for visual angles up to 20 degrees. Beyond 20 degrees a small but increasing magnification—a pincushion distortion—will be found.

Afocal lenses used for near vision tests of the eyes, say, 40 cm., a reading distance, then have a small power error and also a slightly reduced magnification.

Afocal type magnification lenses of two kinds are used—*overall* and *meridional*. The overall lens has spherical surfaces and the lens therefore magnifies to the same degree in *all* meridians. The meridional lens has cylindrical surfaces with parallel axes, and therefore magnifies in only *one meridian*, that perpendicular to the axes of the surfaces. The meridional lens has no magnifying effect in the meridian corresponding to the axes of the cylinders, except when used for a near observation distance, when the lens in this meridian acts as a plane sheet of glass (see later).

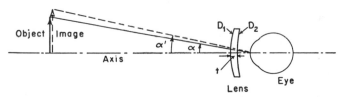

Fig. 67. An afocal type lens that magnifies the image without introducing power.

The total magnification of two (or more) lenses used in sequence is, of course, the product of the separate magnifications. For small magnifications, the resultant per cent magnification will be the sum of the per cent magnifications of the separate lenses.

Power Lenses. In general when an ophthalmic (power) lens is placed before the normal eye, the magnification of the retinal image is also changed.[*] Such a lens, however, reduces the distinctness of objects seen through it because the retinal image is blurred—out of focus. The visual acuity of the eye may be only slightly impaired if the power of the lens is weak, and then the magnification effect can be more easily observed. We can calculate the magnification to be expected by finding the *angular magnification* of the lens referred to the entrance pupil of the eye (Fig. 68). This construction follows because only that ray of light that is aimed at the center of the entrance pupil falls in the center of the blur circle on the retina (p. 24).

The formula for the angular magnification can be simply derived as follows: In Fig. 68B, all distances and the power of the lens are taken positive. Let α and α' be the angles subtended by the object and by the image as seen

[*] This discussion does *not* apply to the correction of refractive errors of the ametropic eye by an ophthalmic lens, because an entirely different problem is then involved (see Chapter 20).

Table 13

Specifications and Characteristics of a Set of Terrascopic Lenses for an Observation Distance of 75 Cm. and Nearly the Same Angular Magnification When Used for All Other Observation Distances. Lenses to be 25 Mm. From Entrance Pupil.

MARKED PER CENT MAGNIFICATION	FRONT CURVE*	BACK CURVE*	THICKNESS, MM.	PER CENT MAGNIFICATION AT		EFFECTIVE POWER IN DIOPTERS AT		PER CENT MAGNIFICATION IN AXIS OF MERIDIONAL LENSES AT	
				6 m.	40 cm.	6 m.	40 cm.	75 cm.	40 cm.
0.50	4.99	−5.00	1.4	0.50	0.52	+0.01	−0.01	0.06	0.12
0.75	4.98	−5.00	2.0	0.76	0.73	+0.01	−0.02	0.09	0.17
1.00	9.94	−10.00	1.4	1.02	0.98	+0.03	−0.02	0.06	0.12
1.25	9.91	−10.00	1.8	1.27	1.23	+0.02	−0.04	0.08	0.15
1.50	9.90	−10.00	2.1	1.53	1.47	+0.03	−0.04	0.10	0.18
1.75	9.88	−10.00	2.5	1.79	1.71	+0.04	−0.05	0.11	0.21
2.00	9.87	−10.00	2.8	2.04	1.96	+0.05	−0.05	0.13	0.25
2.25	13.75	−14.00	2.3	2.33	2.16	+0.04	−0.07	0.11	0.20
2.50	13.73	−14.00	2.6	2.60	2.39	+0.05	−0.08	0.12	0.22
2.75	13.71	−14.00	2.8	2.85	2.66	+0.06	−0.07	0.13	0.25
3.00	13.68	−14.00	3.1	3.10	2.89	+0.06	−0.09	0.14	0.27
3.50	13.63	−14.00	3.6	3.63	3.35	+0.07	−0.11	0.17	0.31
4.00	13.58	−14.00	4.1	4.18	3.84	+0.09	−0.12	0.19	0.36

* Diopters for glass of index 1.523

through the lens, at the entrance pupil of the eye. Then the angular magnification $M_a = \tan \alpha'/\tan \alpha$. But $\tan \alpha' = I/(v - h)$ and $\tan \alpha = O/(u + h)$, where h is the distance between the lens and the entrance pupil. Assuming a thin lens, we also have the elementary paraxial ray relations

$$u + v = V\,u\,v \quad \text{and} \quad I/O = v/u, \text{ where}$$

as before v and u are the image and object distances (in meters), and V is the *vertex* power of the lens in diopters. Eliminating v from these expressions, we have for the angular magnification $M_a = 1/(1 - Vh)$, if u is large compared to h.

Thus, the angular magnification of a thin power lens, before a normal eye and for a distant object, depends only on the power of the lens (V) and its distance from the entrance pupil of the eye (h). For low powers, and an

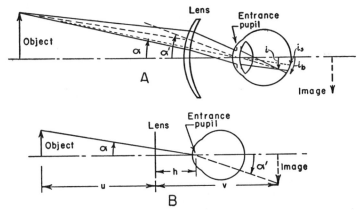

Fig. 68. Figures used to derive the formula for the angular magnification of an ophthalmic lens before a normal eye.

average distance of h of 15 mm., the per cent angular magnification caused by the lens is about 1.5 per cent per diopter. For negative lenses, there is a diminution in the size of the retinal image; M is less than unity.

We can consider a thick lens as composed of two separate lenses in contact. The first is an afocal lens, with the dimensions determined by the front curve (D_1) and the thickness (t); and the second lens is an infinitely thin lens of power V diopters in contact with the back surface of the afocal lens. The combined magnification for a distant object of this pair would be

$$M = \left[\frac{1}{1 - D_1 t/n}\right] \left[\frac{1}{1 - Vh}\right]$$

where D_1 is the front surface power (diopters), t is the thickness of the lens (meters) and n is the index of refraction. The per cent magnification with sufficient accuracy will be m per cent $= D_1 t/n + Vh$, where t and h are in centimeters and D_1 and V in diopters.

Thus one can use low powers of spherical lenses to obtain overall magnifi-

cations and low power cylinders to obtain meridional magnifications. It must
be remembered, however, that there is a loss of acuity with these, and a
changed stimulus to accommodation is introduced which not only may be
objectionable but may introduce errors.

There is one important aspect in any discussion of the angular magnification of the images introduced by lenses, and this concerns the relationship to prismatic deviation. In a real sense, an angular magnification corresponds to a prismatic deviation that is proportional to the visual angle. In
application to the eye, there is a difference in magnitude of these quantities
because the angular magnification must be referred to the entrance pupil if
we are concerned with the effect on the retinal image, whereas the prismatic
deviation in which we would be concerned with eye movements must be
referred to the average center of rotation of the eye. Prismatic deviations so
defined will thus be larger than the corresponding angular magnifications.

The Plane Parallel Plate. A sheet of plate glass will introduce an angular
magnification when used before an eye for objects at a near observation

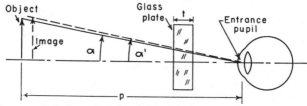

Fig. 69. A plane parallel plate of glass used before the eye observing a near object introduces an angular magnification of the image.

distance.[246] This follows because the image of the object is displaced toward
the eye a distance $(n - 1)t/n$, where n is the index of refraction and t is the
thickness of the plate (Fig. 69). The displacement of the image is therefore
about one third of the thickness of the plate. The angular magnification
would be $M_a = 1/[1 - (n - 1)t/pn]$, where p is the distance of the object
from the entrance pupil of the eye.

Terrascopic Magnification Lenses. Just as it is possible to design an afocal
lens for which the image coincides with the object at a great distance, one
can also design a lens such that the image can be made to coincide with the
object for a given near observation distance. Such a lens might be called
a "terrascopic" lens to distinguish it from the telescopic or afocal lens. In
either case the vergence of the rays of light leaving the lens is the same as
though the lens were not there.

Terrascopic lenses are necessary in precise experiments where the visual
task is nearer than 60 cm. A set of these lenses designed for an observation
distance of 40 cm. has been used (Chapter 16). The meridional magnification lenses of such a set involve a special problem in that an angular magnification is introduced in the meridian of the axes of the cylindrical surfaces,
because in that meridian the lens acts as a plane parallel plate of glass. To
eliminate this magnification, the surfaces in these meridians are ground con-

vex to the observer, with radii of curvatures equal to the distance of the lens from the object. This design requires the surfaces of the lens to be "saddle-shaped"—convex in one meridian and concave in the meridian at right angles—and this presents a difficult lens-grinding problem.*

Constant Angular Magnification Lenses. It should be clear that a lens designed for one observation distance will have a small effective power when used for any other observation distance (and also for different distances of the lens from the eye). This power will change the angular magnification from that specified. One can, however, design a terrascopic or telescopic (which is the special case) lens that will have a specified magnification for one observation distance, and the same angular magnification at all observation distances.[178] This is possible because the increase in angular magnification, due to the small effective power that enters with a decrease in object distance, can be made to offset the decrease in the magnification due to lens thickness. The dimensions for a lens which is to be afocal (distant vision) but with a constant angular magnification, M, for all observation distances can be computed from

$$D_1 = (n - M)/(M + 1) M h$$
$$D_2 = -D_1 M$$
$$t = n h (M^2 - 1)/(n - M)$$

where h is the distance from the vertex of the lens to the entrance pupil, n is the index of refraction of the glass, and, as before, D_1, D_2 and t are, respectively, the dioptric power of the front and back surfaces, and the thickness of the lens (meters).

Table 13 (p. 124) gives an example of the specifications and properties of a set of lenses of this type originally designed, however, to be terrascopic for an observation distance of 75 cm., and to have the same angular magnification at all observation distances. Compromises have been made in the calculated specifications in order to reduce the number of tools necessary to grind the lenses for the set.† The errors introduced by these compromises are below the precision to which the lenses can be ground.

Brewster Prisms. Meridional magnification without effective power for distant vision can also be obtained by the device known as an "anamorphoser," the simplest of which is the Brewster prism unit.[95] This device consists of two identical prisms placed base to apex, and hinged at the base of one and apex of the other so that the angle between the prisms may be changed. The degree of meridional magnification which occurs in the base-apex meridian varies with the angle between the prisms. For large prisms (10 degrees apex angle), magnifications up to 20 per cent can be easily obtained. There is very little chromatic error at the edges of images, and the pincushion distortion is small within visual angles of ±15 degrees.

An Adjustable Magnification Unit. A useful optical device[185] that can be

---

* Much credit is due the American Optical Company for its willingness and ability to adapt its shop facilities so as to grind these lenses with the precision required.

† Anyone desiring a set of these lenses should communicate with the American Optical Company, Southbridge, Mass.

used with the eyes to obtain a continuous range of magnifications consists of a telescope-like combination of plus and minus lenses, the separation of which can be adjusted. The component lenses of the unit are so dimensioned and mounted that, when the separation is changed, the virtual image of an object observed through the unit remains substantially at the position of the object, and the magnification of the object depends upon the prevailing separation.

The device is most satisfactory when designed for use for reading distances, that is, an object distance of about 40 cm. or less from the eyes. The unit is based on several facts of geometric optics as illustrated in Fig. 70.

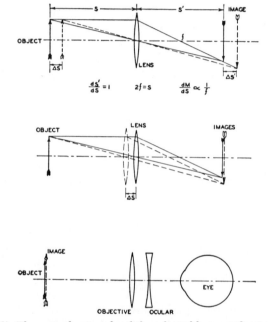

Fig. 70. The optical principle of the adjustable magnification unit.

When an object is at a distance from a converging lens twice its focal length, the real image formed will also be at the same distance from the lens on the other side. The size of the image will be the same as that of the object, and a *small* displacement of the object along the axis results in an equally small displacement of the image in the same direction, but now the image is changed in size. Obviously, if the position of the object remains fixed, and the lens is displaced slightly along the axis, under the same conditions, the position of the image remains substantially fixed in space, though magnified. This magnification is approximately proportional to the power of the lens and to the displacement.

A negative lens of proper power used with the positive objective lens will make the final virtual image seen through the two lenses at the same position as the object itself. Thus when the axial separation of the lenses is changed and the ocular (negative) lens is fixed, the combination (unit) is essentially without power error, yet has a variable magnification approximately proportional to the separation of the component lenses. For the observation distance of 40 cm. from the eyes, a change in separation of the lenses from contact to 10 mm. changes the angular magnification by 5 per cent, with a power error at any separation not exceeding 0.01 diopter. This unit is ideal for use in the laboratory, for near vision work. In the actual design of the units, the factors introduced by the thicknesses and shapes of the two lenses must also be taken into account. All units show more or less pincushion distortion that increases with the separation. Within the 16 to 20 degree field, however, this distortion either is generally not important or can be allowed for.

Obviously, a unit designed strictly on these principles, for greater visual distances, would not give a sufficient range of magnification. In order to obtain a 5 per cent range, larger errors in power must be admitted. A unit can be designed for the observation distance of 6 meters, however, which will have the 5 per cent range in magnification and yet have a power error

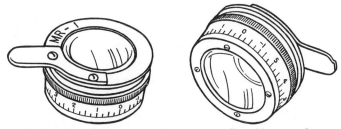

Fig. 71. Sketches of the unit for obtaining an adjustable magnification.

not exceeding 0.10 diopter for any given separation of the elements. Such an error would generally be permissible in ophthalmic practice. Of course, more complicated lens systems can be designed which will eliminate even this power error.

In one sense this system is an ordinary Galilean telescope. However, the changes of separation of the components in the Galilean telescope, where the powers of the elements are relatively large, are specifically for the purpose of changing the power of the system, whereas here a change in magnification with little or no change in power is desired.

The component lenses are mounted in an aluminum cylinder; the ocular lens is fixed at one end, while the objective lens is propelled in a sleeve along the cylinder by pins in a helical groove actuated by a ring on the outside of the unit. A scale attached to this ring is engraved to read per cent magnification (Fig. 71). These units are made for overall (spherical lens components) and meridional (cylindrical lens components) magnification. Considerable care must be taken in aligning the cylindrical component lenses in order to avoid, finally, the presence of astigmatism in the unit.

The units are measured for accuracy in power and are calibrated for magnification on a special ophthalmic lens instrument.[191]

NONUNIFORM MAGNIFICATION

Ophthalmic Prism. An ophthalmic prism placed before the eye, in addition to causing a general prismatic displacement of the image toward the apex, also introduces a distortion of that image. This fact is discussed in the literature[102] and is fairly widely known, being specifically apparent in the Risley rotary prisms. In one sense this distortion is an unsymmetric prismatic effect that varies with the different parts of the prism. In general, this distortion is apparent because from any point in space the cross-section of the cone of light (which is determined by the size of the pupil of the eye)

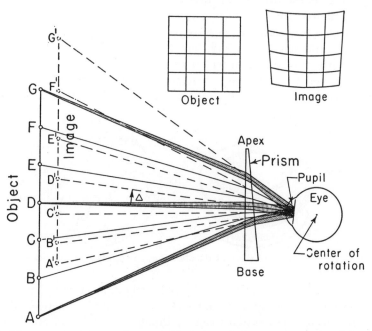

Fig. 72. The unsymmetric angular magnification and distortion introduced by a flat ophthalmic prism.

is small when it passes through the prism. Hence the optical effect will be substantially different for every part of the prism, owing to the differences in angles of incidence and the corresponding differences in the length of the glass light path. The distortion (Fig. 72) is essentially characterized by (1) an increasing angular magnification of the image toward the apex in the base-apex meridian,[11] (2) a curvature of the images of lines perpendicular to the base-apex meridian, and (3) an increased slanting of the images of lines parallel to the base-apex line. In this diagram the image points $A' \ldots G'$ must not be taken literally but rather to indicate the direction of the images of points $A \ldots G$ from the entrance pupil of the eye. The distortion increases proportionately with the increase in prism power.

As illustrated in Fig. 68, the angular magnification of a lens was defined as $M_a = \tan \alpha'/\tan \alpha$. Now replacing the lens in this figure by a prism, as in Fig. 73, and confining our discussion to the base-apex meridian of the prism, it is found that M_a, the angular magnification, will itself vary with the visual angle α. The rate of that change, $\triangle M_a / \triangle \alpha$, where $\triangle M_a$ is the change in angular magnification corresponding to small changes in the visual angle, defines the distortion in the base-apex meridian for a given value of α. It has been further found that this distortion is nearly constant for visual angles within ± 15 degrees, so that we can describe the angular magnification at any visual angle α as

$$M_a = B \, \alpha + A_0$$

where B specifies the distortion or unsymmetric magnification, and A_0 is the paraxial angular magnification, or that magnification near the visual axis.[11, 191]

The prisms to be found in ophthalmic trial cases usually have flat (plano) surfaces, but, in general, ophthalmic prisms are ground with spherical sur-

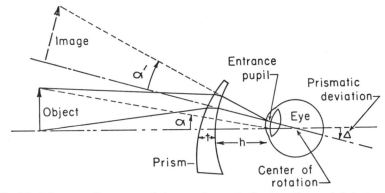

Fig. 73. Schematic illustration of the angular magnification of an ophthalmic prism.

faces, varying from 3 to 16 diopters surface power. The distortion of these prisms varies with (1) the surface curvature (base-curve), (2) the distance from the eye, (3) the prism power (angle of prismatic deviation), (4) the thickness of the prism, and (5) the orientation of the prism before the eye. For the purpose of this discussion, only the variation of the distortion with surface curvature need be considered. Though depending somewhat on the distance of the prism from the entrance pupil, the distortion decreases with increase of surface curvature (decreased radius). An idealized graph showing this relationship as well as that to prism power is illustrated in Fig. 74, when the prism has been placed 23 mm. from the entrance pupil. The dioptric surface curvature D in diopters, defined as usual by $D = (n-1)/R$, where n is the index of refraction and R is the radius of curvature in meters, is plotted on the abscissa, and the distortion, B, as change in per cent magnification per degree visual angle, is plotted on the ordinate. For a base-curve near 9 diopters (for the 23 mm. distance of the prism from the eye) the unsymmetric magnification is zero. Still higher base-curves result in a negative distortion, that is, the magnification increases toward the base of the prism. Associated with the increased base curve and thickness is an increase in overall magnification—an increase in the value of A_0 in the foregoing equation.

It is not possible to eliminate the curvature of the images of lines perpendicular to the base-apex meridian by change in base-curve, though it becomes less as that curve increases. Thus, although a prism may have no unsymmetric angular magnification, it is not possible to eliminate all optical distortion. The farther the lens is from the eye, the lower must be the base-curve necessary to obtain no unsymmetric magnification.

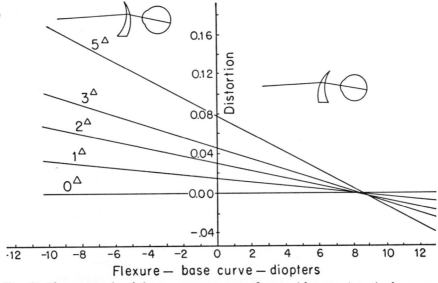

Fig. 74. The magnitude of the unsymmetric magnification (distortion) in the base-apex meridian of ophthalmic prisms with base curve and prism power (idealized chart).

A combination of two prisms which has a specific unsymmetric magnification without prismatic deviation can be readily obtained. A prism on a 9 diopter base-curve is combined with a flat prism of equal prism power, the apex of one being placed opposite the base of the other, the flat prism being toward the eye (Ames, Gliddon and Ogle[12]). The front prism eliminates the prism power but leaves the unsymmetric magnification of the flat prism next to the eye. Greater unsymmetric magnification can even be obtained by placing the second prism convex to the eye. Such units, however, exhibit considerable power (especially astigmatism) and the concomitant distortion toward the periphery, which may be quite objectionable.

The Hinged Unit. This same type of unsymmetric magnification with much less power aberration can be obtained especially at a near visual distance, by using the adjustable magnification unit described previously, but hinging the two component lenses so that the separation is zero on one edge and a given separation at the other.

CHAPTER 12

Spatial Localization and Stereoscopic Vision

INTRODUCTION

PROBABLY IN NO OTHER aspect is the study of binocular vision more concerned than that of the role played by the two eyes in spatial localization. Certainly so far as the light sense is concerned, the sensation of brightness in binocular observation is only slightly greater than that in monocular observation.[207] Nor is visual acuity of both eyes greatly superior to monocular acuity.[14] In spatial localization, however, through vision with both eyes there emerges an entirely new sensation not even suggested through monocular vision; namely, *stereopsis*. As a background for the researches to be described, a review of the facts of spatial localization in general and of stereoscopic perception in particular will be given in this chapter.

In discussing space perception we must distinguish between the perception of depth differences, or relative depth—the extent to which one object appears nearer than another—and the perception of absolute distance, in which the actual distances of objects from the individual are experienced and estimated (egocentric localization—Hofmann).

We can attribute the visual localization in space, on the one hand, to certain factors which are primarily empirical and for the most part monocular in origin, and on the other hand, to stereopsis, the unique sensation of depth which is solely binocular in origin. The phenomenon of stereopsis provides the most vivid and accurate relative depth discrimination. Absolute localization probably results from a more complex psychic integration of empirical and stereoscopic stimuli.

EMPIRICAL FACTORS

The empirical factors of spatial localization as motives for depth localization (sometimes referred to as secondary factors) must be considered psychologic conceptions of depth obtained from experience.[93] The characteristics of the patterns of the retinal images are constantly being related to the characteristics of objects in space learned by association through the impact of all the senses.

The more important of these psychologic motives for visual space localization are:

(1) *Overlay* (interposition),[93] the mechanism by which near objects overlap and tend to hide the more distant objects.

(2) *Perspective,* which depends upon the fact that the farther away objects of equal size are, the smaller are the retinal images. Linear perspective relates to the apparent convergence of parallel lines that recede into the distance (for example, railroad tracks). Details within known objects are more readily seen when near than when distant. Thus, the size of the retinal image related to known size provides a clue for the estimation of distance.

(3) *Aerial perspective,* which results from the fact that the edges of distant objects are less clearly defined than those nearby, owing primarily to atmospheric haze. The more distant objects also for the same reason appear cooler (bluer) in color. Nearer objects appear to have higher saturations of color and greater contrast with respect to neighboring objects when compared to those of more distant objects.

(4) *Light areas and shadows,* which provide spatial clues by virtue of their shapes, intensities and especially their relationships to other objects and to each other.

(5) *Parallax,* which results from the change in the relative alignment of objects with head and body displacements. The apparent movements of more distant objects are less than those for near objects. This clue provides a strong and highly developed response in spatial localization, and the precision of depth estimation by it is quite comparable to that of stereoscopic acuity.[94, 234]

(6) *Height,* whereby objects seen above others are also judged as being more distant.

(7) *Accommodation and convergence,* through a myosensory clue arising from the muscles of the eyes, or better through an awareness of the strength of the innervation going to the accommodative and convergence musculature,[44] *may* provide data by which an awareness of *gross* differences in depth can be had.

BINOCULAR SPATIAL LOCALIZATION

Binocular space perception and the stereoscopic perception of depth in particular exist by virtue of the fact that the two eyes are separated in space. Each, therefore, views the three dimensional world of objects from a slightly different point of view. As a consequence, the "patterns" or the internal arrangements of the images of separate object points in the total dioptric images which fall on the retinas of the two eyes will be slightly different. The perspective and the relative alignment of objects in space will be unlike in the two images, and this dissimilarity will be greater the nearer are the objects to the observer. As those objects recede into the distance, the two images gradually become identical.

It should be clear that the dioptric retinal image patterns falling on the retinas are approximately fixed in space, and therefore are independent of the eye movements. This would be exactly so were the entrance pupils and centers of rotations of the eyes coincident. One can say (Ames) that for a given head position the dioptric images are fixed in space and during eye excursions the retina sweeps over that image.

Thus we can specify the geometric angular disparity of the retinal images of objects in space on the basis of geometry alone, as was done in Chapter 3 and illustrated in Fig. 4. The *functional* disparity, however, as was pointed out, is a more elusive quantity to specify, because it depends on the location of the horopter.

Stereopsis. The stereoscope reveals the essential difference between the monocular and the binocular perception of depth. By means of suitable figures drawn on targets, disparities of the images of the two eyes can be introduced, almost entirely free of empirical clues. The observer experiences at once an obvious and striking sense of plasticity or of depth which is not evident when either target is viewed by one eye alone. This phenomenon of stereopsis is unique and cannot be described adequately to a person who has not experienced or cannot experience it. We seem to "see" actually the empty space between objects, an aspect of relative depth perception that cannot be experienced in monocular vision. Even when every psychologic motive to depth perception is absent, the equality or inequality of the separation of boundary lines as viewed by the two eyes is recognized binocularly and not monocularly.[77] Stereopsis is therefore said to be a specific experiential response—a sensation—directly arising from physiologic stimuli, in the same sense that the color red is an experience arising from the excitation of the retina by light of a particular wavelength.

Upon this theory, stereoscopic vision would have a physiologic basis founded on the anatomic organization of the visual apparatus, would afford a direct perception of the depth relationships between objects at different distances and would be unequivocal. The empirical factors (the secondary motives of depth localization—Tschermak[231]) are psychologic and result from an interpretation or conception of the depth relationship stemming from experience, and by their nature may be equivocal. Stereopsis is assumed to be innate (that is, acquired phylogenetically), whereas the judgments of space based on monocular depth clues would be empirical, acquired by an individual's past experience.

In contrast to this dualistic conception of space perception, unitary hypotheses have been proposed from time to time (for example, Trump), and especially by some Gestalt psychologists (for example, Dahlmann). More recently a similar concept has been elaborated by Ames,[7, 196] according to which there is no room for a fundamental difference in the nature of monocular and binocular factors to space perception. The subjective appearances of objects in space and their orientation, whether observed by one eye or by both eyes, are essentially of the same inherent nature and have the same origin in past experience, individual and phylogenetic. Both monocular and binocular space perceptions are based on relationships to an innately fixed organization in the anatomy of the retinas. Both are related to psychologic and physiologic processes. According to this point of view, the dual concept outlined previously is artificial.

However, for present purposes no exceptions need be taken to these two points of view, for their exact natures are not of immediate importance here as long as one recognizes that the monocular and binocular factors are to some extent independent, but on the other hand, that a significant interdependence between the two exists in the total processes by which spatial localization is made possible. Both the empirical and the stereoscopic processes to spatial localization are important for man's personal subjective orientation in space and there must be a constant interaction and integration of both factors. However, even a person who has but one eye learns to localize objects with considerable facility, and performs tasks that demand a visuomanual coordination. Such a person is, however, handicapped in fine tasks involving critical judgments of depth.

The principal facts in stereopsis may be summarized briefly as follows:

(1) Stereopsis necessitates simultaneous vision in both eyes and bifoveal fixation on the same object.

(2) Stereopsis occurs over the entire binocular visual field and is not a phenomenon confined to regions about the point of fixation; it has been demonstrated in very low illumination with only rod vision.[99, 170] Stereoscopic acuity is usually measured in or near the macula because there the keenest discrimination of depth would be found.

(3) Stereoscopic acuity is related generally to the monocular visual acuity of the two eyes,[105] though for high visual acuities there appears to be some variation in stereoscopic acuities. Occasionally stereopsis may be entirely absent, though the visual acuity is high in each eye. Stereoscopic acuity will also depend on those factors, such as illumination, which affect visual acuity.

(4) Stereoscopic acuity varies with the duration of the stimuli. For central vision a maximal acuity is found when the duration is three seconds and longer, while for shorter durations down to 0.2 second, there is a fourfold to fivefold decrease in acuity. The threshold then remains nearly constant for durations less than 0.2 second (the instantaneous threshold—Langlands). That stereopsis exists for very short durations was first shown by Dove and has been repeatedly verified. There has been one criticism of these experiments, however, in that the subjects used had been acquainted beforehand with what to expect from the test objects.

(5) If by stereoscopic vision one is to obtain the correct estimation of depth for all visual distances, then additional information must come to the individual from some other source. It is easily shown that the actual depth difference between two objects corresponding to a given angular disparity is nearly proportional to the square of the visual distance, and therefore the estimated depth difference between two objects would have to vary not only with the angular disparity but also with the actual distance of one of the objects. This is a complex problem and no satisfactory answer has yet been found. One must assume that (*a*) the additional information comes from a

myosensory influence of the external muscles of the eyes which informs us of the convergence and therefore the absolute distance;* or (b) the estimation of depth difference always depends on there also being other objects in the field of view that provide empirical clues for space localization, or (c) there is innately (so far as the individual is concerned) associated with every pair of points of an object in space a subjective estimate of size, and this together with the disparity gives the clue as to the spatial depth (Ames).[7, 159] It is highly probable that the stereoscopic sensation of depth is only roughly quantitative, and when estimates of depth have to be made, the judgment does depend upon empirical factors.

(6) As discussed previously, the disparity of images in the two eyes provides stimuli not only for a stereoscopic sensation of depth, but also for fusional movements which, if made, would eliminate that disparity. The extent to which the two processes, stereopsis and compulsion for fusional movements, are related is not entirely clear, for while it is usually assumed that stereopsis occurs only so long as the disparate images fall within Panum's fusional areas and are fused, evidence exists (for example, Burian[32]) that a stereoscopic-like perception occurs even if the disparity is so great that images are actually seen double. In fact, Hofmann suggested that absolute spatial localization rests on some type of stereoscopic perception that relates a part of the body (nose, hands, and so forth) with the objects in space. In that case the successive angles of disparity between the images would be quite large.

(7) The threshold value of disparity for stereopsis implies geometrically that there exists a critical visual distance beyond which stereopsis no longer provides information as to spatial depth. Beyond that distance all space perception becomes monocular or empirical. We can calculate this critical distance, b, approximately from the formula $b = 2a/\tan \eta_0$, where $2a$ is the interpupillary distance and η_0 is the threshold of disparity of stereopsis. Now η_0 is a statistical quantity and will vary somewhat with the conditions of observation. Taking it as 10 seconds of arc, however, and an average interpupillary distance of 65 mm., b is about 135 meters, or a little more than quarter of a mile. The threshold value of η_0 also increases with peripheral visual angle, so that this critical distance becomes much nearer peripherally from the fixation point. It must also be borne in mind that when the eyes are converged for a very distant object, the limiting distance beyond which there is no stereopsis may be the 135 meters, but there will also be an interval of nearly 67 meters nearer than this critical distance within which there cannot be a stereoscopic perception of depth, because that interval will again correspond also to the stereoscopic threshold. In fact there will be a sequence of these "dead" intervals, each decreasing in depth extent as it is nearer the eyes. Small variations of fixation nullify these dead intervals.

Pure Stereopsis. That stereopsis exists under the elemental conditions

---

* A review of the literature shows that little evidence for a proprioceptive sense from the external muscles exists at all.[124] See also, however, Bair.

devoid of all empirical motives for depth localization is shown by the following experiment.[195] In this the threshold of disparity necessary to give rise to a stereoscopic response was determined with two separated point sources of light.

In a totally dark room three point sources of light were mounted horizontally 3 meters from the observer. The center light was fixed in the median plane of the observer; the separation of the outer two could be changed as desired, but they were always kept equally separated from the center light. By means of a suitable tap key, when the center light would be on, the two outer lights would be off and vice versa. The center light provided a point of fixation in the plane of the test lights when judgments were not being made. The outer test lights would be exposed only for durations approximating two seconds of time.

A horizontal disparity between the retinal images in the two eyes of the two test lights was introduced by an adjustable magnification unit (p. 127). Increasing the magnification of the image of the right eye would introduce an uncrossed disparity in the images of the right test light and a crossed disparity in the images of the left (see Fig. 79), so that the right light would appear farther away than the left. This optical method of changing the angular disparity between the images of the two eyes eliminates empirical factors that would be associated with actual movements of the test lights in space, such as a change in brightness, a change in angular separation, and so forth. The smallest degree of magnification that could be detected in the apparent difference in distance of the two point sources of light would be the threshold and a measure of the stereoscopic sensitivity.

Stereoscopic thresholds, like those of other physiologic processes, are a statistical matter. A stimulus will not always evoke a response, or at another time even a smaller stimulus will cause a reaction. The problem is to determine the percentage of times that a given change in magnification will be recognized in the apparent difference in distance of the two point light sources, for a number of different changes. This means the determination of the psychometric curve, and care must be taken in the procedure to ensure meaningful results.[193] The standard deviation (σ) was again taken as the threshold measurement, and this corresponds to that change in magnification for which about 68 per cent of the judgments were correct. The threshold in angular disparity will be the product of the change in magnification and the angular separation of the outer point light sources.

The results of three observers, whose visual acuity in both eyes was 20/15, for various separations of the point sources of light are shown graphically in Fig. 75.

Empirical Factors to Space Localization in Vision With Two Eyes. While stereopsis is the essential phenomenon of binocular vision and binocular space perception, we must not lose sight of the fact that dissimilarities between the two retinal images for a field of objects at near vision, which may or may not give rise to a stereoscopic response, nevertheless provide empirical clues to spatial localization. These binocular empirical factors fall roughly into four groups which are not, however, independent, and, moreover, stimuli for stereoscopic vision are also usually present.

Binocular Differences in Perspective and Visibility. At near vision, objects may be so oriented that the perspective pattern of the two retinal images may be greatly dissimilar. As a limiting condition, whole boundaries

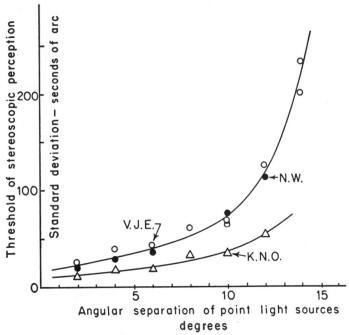

Fig. 75. Stereoscopic thresholds for horizontally separated point light sources.

seen by one eye may be hidden to the other. In Fig. 76 is illustrated a cube so located with respect to the two eyes that the left eye sees two surfaces, the right eye only one.

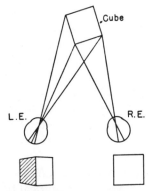

Fig. 76. Binocular differences in visibility and perspective.

Binocular Parallax. While intimately associated with the disparities of the retinal images that give rise to a stereoscopic perception, objects may be so arranged at near vision that the overlay of one object upon another more distant object may be greatly different as seen by each of the two eyes. In Fig. 77, needles at *A* and at *B* are located at different distances in front of a ruler. The needles then overlie different positions on the ruler as observed by each of the two eyes. This difference in overlay or occluding positions on the ruler as seen by the two eyes constitutes a true visual *parallax*. Stereoscopic depth perception is undoubtedly a significant factor in the depth localization in this case, also, for the parallaxes also constitute disparities between the images of the needle and those of the markings on the ruler, but this case must be distinguished from *pure* stereoscopic perception in the experiment just described for point light sources, where binocular parallax was not present.

Binocular Differences in Image Size Due to Spatial Location. In normal vision, only objects located in the median plane can have retinal images the

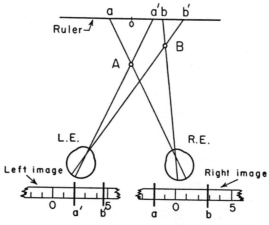

Fig. 77. Binocular parallax.

same size. The images of those located any distance from the plane will be of different size because the distance of the object (the distance factor in the magnification) from each of the two eyes will be different. In Fig. 78, a pencil is observed in asymmetric convergence to the right. The image in the left eye will be smaller than that in the right because the corresponding distance is larger. The vertical difference constitutes, of course, a vertical disparity and while this probably does not give rise to an experience of depth, it cannot fail to be an empirical clue to spatial localization. The difference in size of the retinal images of extended objects in the horizontal meridian will also depend on their orientation in space in the sense of a rotation about the point of fixation.

The Binocular Difference in Image Gradient in Known Object Patterns. This constitutes a more elusive type of empirical factor of spatial localization than the foregoing three. It rests upon the fact that a regular and consistent gradient in the disparities and pattern shapes between the images in the two eyes exists geometrically with certain kinds of object patterns. This gradient is larger, the nearer is the pattern to the eyes. The magnitude of this change is associated empirically by the observer with the object distance of that known pattern.

All of these binocular empirical factors for space localization become less and less effective as the visual distance increases, until gradually at the limit of the range of stereoscopic vision all depth perception becomes monocular.

Under normal surroundings the psychologic depth motive and the processes of stereopsis aid, confirm and correct one another in one's perception of space. They normally do not conflict in one's familiar surroundings, for both means for space perception are associated with the same depth rela-

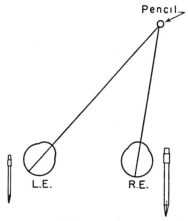

Fig. 78. Binocular differences due to spatial position.

tionships between objects in the field of view. If the empirical motives are ambiguous or weak, as they might be in certain surroundings, the stereoscopic sense may provide the basis for the resultant interpretation of space. Again, it may be possible that the stimuli for stereoscopic perception of these depth relationships may not conform to more powerful empirical motives, in which case the stereoscopic perception may be ignored.

Many other factors well known to psychologists exist in the perception of space. These are especially demonstrable in certain illusions. Attention is called to the *size-constancy* phenomenon,[25] by which the apparent visual size of an object is also dependent on its apparent visual distance, and not wholly on the size of the retinal image. In fact, there is an approximate proportionality between apparent size and object distance (Emmert's law). For a retinal image of a given size, the apparent size will, within certain limits, increase with the distance.

The Distortion in the Stereoscopic
Perception of Space

INTRODUCTION

IT IS A STRIKING experience to observe for the first time the apparent distortion of space that results when the retinal image of one eye is magnified by a suitable lens worn before that eye. This phenomenon is due, of course, to the stereoscopic perception of the disparities between the images of the two eyes that have been changed by the introduction of the lens. Especially convincing is the effect in surroundings where the empirical motives to space localization are relatively few as compared to the extent and number of stereoscopic stimuli. An apparent distortion of space will occur with any change in the normal magnifications of the retinal images of the two eyes, but it is especially vivid when the changes in those magnifications are in one meridian only—for example, that introduced by a meridional magnification lens before one eye. Actually, changes introduced by an overall magnification, that is, a uniform magnification in all meridians, cause little or no distortion, a fact that will be discussed at some length later.

That the distortions are caused only by the changes in the disparities between the images of the two eyes is clear because the magnifications involved are small, usually less than 5 per cent, and as such would have little or no influence on the empirical clues to the spatial localization. The keenness of our stereoscopic perception, on the other hand, enables us to recognize the changes in image disparities introduced by lenses with magnification as low as 0.12 to 0.25 per cent.

The simplest and yet most common type of the apparent distortion of space is that caused by a meridional magnification lens placed before one eye so that the magnification is in the horizontal meridian only. In Fig. 79 the case is illustrated. The eyes are fixating a point F. Points P and Q equidistant from the fixation point in the frontoparallel plane would, were the lens not present, have retinal images as points p and q on each of the two retinas. The lens increases the magnification of the retinal image of the right eye, that is, it increases the size of the image on the retina, and consequently the images of P and Q will now fall more peripherally on the retina, on points p' and q'. The disparities of the images between the two eyes have now been changed by the lens, and the corresponding stereoscopic response would be one as though the objects P and Q were now located at points P' and Q' in space.

Thus those points which were in the frontoparallel plane have been displaced apparently in space as though rotated about the point of fixation (which in this case is the only point not affected by the lens). However, in addition to this rotation, there is also a spatial distortion, in that the equal distances PF and FQ appear now as unequal distances, $P'F$ and FQ', respectively. Objects on the right-hand side of the field have been enlarged and pushed away, while those on the left have been made smaller and

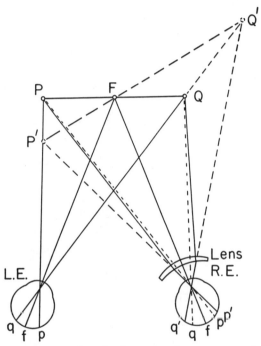

Fig. 79. Geometric optics involved in the distortion of space as perceived in stereoscopic vision when a lens is placed before one eye.

brought nearer. This description may be taken as a basis for the apparent distortion of space by stereoscopic perception when the image of one eye has been magnified by a suitable lens.

The apparent distortion in space perception caused by unequal refractive corrections before the two eyes has, of course, been discussed in the literature from time to time since 1876, when Wadsworth first reported on a patient with high astigmatism who complained of this distortion. Culbertson also wrote that objects were distorted with astigmatism but that he was able to correct this by a shift in axes of the astigmatism. Later Lippincott[151] roughly described spatial distortion due to astigmatic lenses when placed at various axes before an eye, but he attributed the phenomena to changes in accommodation. It was Green who first correctly interpreted the phenomenon as being due to the stereoscopic perception of the changed relationships between the retinal images. Friedenwald[80] elaborated on this explanation and reported patients with anisometropia who reported such spatial distortions. Koller[133] and, again, Lippincott[153] and von Rohr[211] at later times discussed and confirmed the stereoscopic explanation. Even at a somewhat earlier date, Hillebrand[114] had reported that at near vision a thick plate of glass before one eye caused a skewed orientation of the apparent frontoparallel plane horopter. That prisms could cause an apparent distortion of binocular perception had been discussed even earlier by Nagel[173] and by Maddox.

One is handicapped in making a systematic study of the apparent distortion of space if ordinary ophthalmic lenses are used. To avoid the blurring of vision the powers of those lenses must be weak, but then the effect on

Fig. 80. The leaf room.

stereoscopic vision will also be small. In addition to the variation of the magnifying effect that would occur with changes in distance of the lenses from the eyes, the blur of the image itself would interfere with accurate estimation of the extent of the distortion. The afocal type of lenses described in the preceding chapter, however, provides a means for a comprehensive description of the distortions (Ames[6]) and a precise study of the relationships between magnification change and the corresponding effect.

THE LEAF ROOM

The device admirably adapted to a qualitative observation and description of the types of distortion experienced with different types of changes in the relative magnification of the images of the two eyes is the so-called "leaf room," devised by Ames. This room (Fig. 80) is a rectangular box about 7 feet (about 213 cm.) on an edge, open at one end, with the walls vertical and the floor and ceiling level. The observer views the room from the center of the open end, with the head held in position by a chin cup. To the inside surfaces of the room (painted black) are stapled many artificial vines which literally cover those surfaces. The leaves are adjusted individually so that they stand out from the surface but are not parallel. The rough edges of the leaves and their haphazard orientation under good illumination provide many contours to stimulate stereopsis. Yet these leaves would introduce only a minimum of empirical clues to depth perception, clues which might otherwise tend to inhibit the binocular perception. The features, especially the corners of the room, outline the definite cubic shape that is readily observed in binocular vision, and yet have only slight perspective. In fact, with a continued monocular observation (one eye occluded) the room appears to lose its shape entirely, for the corners tend to blend with the walls into a uniform shapeless concavity covered with leaves. The cubical aspect of the room in stereoscopic vision makes for an easy description of its appearance on the part of the observer, for he needs only to describe the apparent positions, shapes and sizes of the walls, the ceiling, the floor and the individual leaves themselves.

TYPES OF DISTORTION

The particular distortions can be reduced to four basic types corresponding to their respective causes.

1. The image of one eye is magnified in the horizontal meridian, as by a meridional lens, axis 90 degrees.

2. The image of one eye is magnified in the vertical meridian, as by a meridional lens, axis 180 degrees.

3. The images of both eyes are magnified in oblique meridians, as by a meridional lens at axis 45 degrees before one eye and a second at axis 135 degrees before the other, or vice versa.

4. The images of both eyes are magnified unsymmetrically by ophthalmic prisms (or an asymmetric prism combination) placed before the eyes base-in (toward the nose) or base-out (toward the temples).

The effects produced by these lenses must be experienced to be fully appreciated. Descriptions of the spatial distortions, such as will follow, generally prove inadequate, even when accompanied with drawings.

A Magnification of the Image of One Eye in the Horizontal Meridian (a Meridional Lens at Axis Vertical, Axis 90 Degrees). This is the case considered previously for points in the visual plane. It will be well to refer to that account as well as to Fig. 79, in the more detailed description for the whole of visual space which follows. The apparent distortion characteristic of an increase in the magnification of the image of (say) the right eye in the horizontal meridian by a meridional magnification lens (3 per cent) placed before it is as follows (Fig. 81):

(1) The floor appears no longer level but on a slant, up on the left side, down on the right, as though it were on a side hill.

(2) The ceiling appears slanted in the opposite direction, higher on the right, lower on the left.

(3) The side walls remain substantially parallel to their original position, but that on the right appears much farther away, the one on the left much nearer. A corresponding change in the sizes of the leaves appears; those on the left are small, those on the right large.

(4) The front wall appears more or less vertical but considerably skew (rotated), the right side appearing farther away, the left side nearer. The objects on the right appear enlarged, those on the left shrunken. The shape of the wall now appears trapezoidal, the larger dimension being on the right.

Objects held in the room also appear distorted, swollen on the right and compressed on the left. Squares become trapezoids, and even if they are rotated so as to look frontoparallel, their shape remains distorted.

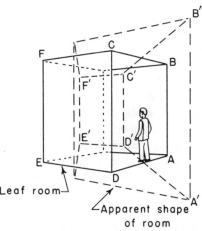

Fig. 81. Diagrammatic representation of the apparent shape of the leaf room when a meridional magnification lens is placed before the right eye so as to magnify the retinal image in the horizontal meridian only.

The many characteristics of this distortion due to a lens which magnifies the image of one eye only in the horizontal meridian can be predicted on the basis of the geometry involved. Accordingly this phenomenon is referred to as a *geometric effect*.[180, 192]

A Magnification of the Image of One Eye in the Vertical Meridian (a Meridional Lens at Axis Horizontal, Axis 180 Degrees). If the meridional magnification lens is placed before the right eye with its axis at 180 degrees, so as to increase the magnification of the image of that eye in the vertical meridian only, the overall appearance of the leaf room is much the same as that described in the preceding section, except that the direction of the distortion is reversed, actually as though the lens had been placed before the *left* eye with axis at 90 degrees. This apparent distortion is *not* predictable on the basis of geometry as was the previous case, and as such it constitutes a unique phenomenon in binocular vision.[180] It has been called the *induced effect* from the fact that the type of apparent distortion of space is the same as though the lens at axis 180 degrees before one eye *induced* an increased magnification in the horizontal meridian of the other eye. The effect is a complex process and will be considered in some detail in subsequent chapters.

The Overall Magnification of the Image of One Eye. Because of the induced effect, when the magnification of the image of one eye is increased by an overall magnification lens, little or no apparent distortion of space occurs. The induced effect acts to offset the geometric effect that would be caused by the horizontal components of the magnification of that lens.

A Meridional Magnification of the Image in Both Eyes in Oblique Meridians. The third type of the stereoscopic apparent distortion of space results when images in one or both eyes are changed by meridional magnifications introduced at oblique meridians. A meridional lens before one eye that introduces a meridional magnification at an oblique axis has components of that magnification in the horizontal and vertical meridians. Hence the

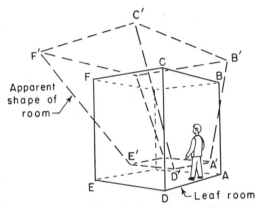

Fig. 82. Diagrammatic representation of the apparent shape of the leaf room when meridional magnifying lenses are placed before the eyes so as to magnify the retinal images of the two eyes obliquely: in this case, R.E. 2 per cent at meridian 135 degrees and L.E. 2 per cent at meridian 45 degrees.

disparities between the images of the two eyes are changed in those meridians, with the resultant effects described in the preceding paragraphs. To remove this complicating effect, equal meridional magnification lenses are used with meridians symmetrically located before the eyes. A maximal effect is obtained when these are placed at 45 degrees before one eye and 135 degrees before the other. The vertical and horizontal components of the magnifications for both eyes offset one another. There remains a torsional (scissors) effect which is the principal cause of the characteristic spatial distortion experienced; namely, an inclination of vertical surfaces.

Lenses in spectacles which introduce magnifications of the image of the right eye in the 135 degree meridian* and of the left in the 45 degree meridian (axes of the lenses in upper nasal-lower temporal directions—see Fig.

* In ophthalmologic practice the meridian as well as the axis of a lens is designated by the angle measured counterclockwise (0 to 180 degrees) from the horizontal, as one faces the wearer of the lens. The designation is the same for both eyes.

100) cause a spatial distortion of the leaf room with the following characteristics (Fig. 82):

(1) The floor appears more or less level but much nearer the observer,
and upon his looking down, his legs appear short, his feet small. All objects
on the floor appear to have become smaller.

(2) The ceiling likewise appears more or less level, but much farther away,
and the leaves upon it appear quite large.

(3) The side walls appear more or less flat, but slanting in space, outward
at the top and nearer at the bottom.

(4) The frontal wall appears flat, but also greatly inclined in space with
the top much farther away, the bottom nearer. Leaves at the top appear
larger than those toward the bottom.

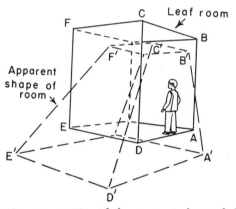

Fig. 83. Diagrammatic representation of the apparent shape of the leaf room when
meridional magnifying lenses are placed before the eyes so as to magnify the retinal
images of the two eyes obliquely: in this case, R.E. 2 per cent at meridian 45 degrees
and L.E. 2 per cent at meridian 135 degrees.

Objects held before the eyes above the eye level appear large, those below
small. Square objects appear trapezoidal with the upper dimension being
the longer.

If the lenses before the two eyes are interchanged, so that the axes of the
lenses are in the upper temporal-lower nasal meridians, the direction of the
entire distortion is reversed, as suggested by Fig. 83.

In this case a circular disk or any other object moved vertically from the
floor toward the ceiling appears to undergo a gradual but marked decrease
in size. Ames[7] has suggested that this phenomenon be considered in any
study of the "moon illusion" (the apparent enlargement of the moon or sun
at the horizon compared to its apparent size in the zenith), for which no
entirely satisfactory explanation has yet been found (Boring[26]).

The characteristics of this type of spatial distortion can also be predicted
on the basis of the geometry involved and the optical imagery produced by
the lenses. The phenomenon of the apparent fore-and-aft inclination of lines
or surfaces in space caused by the small rotary deviations of the images in

the two eyes has, of course, been known since the invention of the stereo-scope by Wheatstone.

A Magnification of the Images of the Two Eyes Unsymmetrically in the Horizontal Meridian. A pair of identical prisms (for example, 3^Δ on flat surfaces) or prism combinations (see p. 132) placed before the eyes, with their bases toward the nose (base-in), introduces increasing magnifications of retinal images of the two eyes toward the temporal halves of the visual field. The disparities of the images are accordingly changed unsymmetrically. The characteristic apparent distortion of space caused by these lenses is the convexity of all flat surfaces. The convexity in the vertical meridian is, of course, due to the curvature of the images of all lines perpendicular to the base-apex meridian of the prisms.

In certain surroundings, however, the motives from a binocular empirical localization from pattern recognition on surfaces affect the sense of absolute distance. The pattern gradient (p. 140) of horizontal disparities between the images in the two eyes will have been changed by these prisms in the direction corresponding to that of a surface much nearer the eyes. Consequently a familiar frontoparallel surface may actually appear nearer and the details on it accordingly smaller.* Accompanying this are the corresponding changes in the distances of side walls, the ceiling and the floor.

If the prisms before the eyes are now interchanged, so that the bases are temporal (base-out), the direction of the apparent distortion is reversed from that just described.

Comment. Under more everyday surroundings these same types of apparent distortion of space occur,[6] though often the empirical motives to spatial localization, especially rectilinear perspective, may dampen or even inhibit the phenomenon. The degree to which the distortions will or will not appear varies greatly with individuals.

Also, the lapse of time between the moment when the observer puts on the magnification lens and that when the distortion appears varies with individuals. With some it appears almost instantly, with others the development is slow and gradual, taking from ten to fifteen seconds for the distortion to appear. This delay must be attributed to several factors, among which are attention, keenness of stereoscopic perception, visual acuity, and the degree to which the individual tends to rely on empirical stimuli for his spatial localization. Usually some strong stimulus for the response of stereopsis is a necessary prerequisite. For example, a grass lawn may not appear to slant in space until a small branch or twig from a tree, or similar object with details above the surface of the lawn is stuck into the ground fairly near the observer.

Many bizarre and irrational spatial effects can be secured with suitable surroundings when observers wear these lenses.[6] Water may appear to run

---

* If absolute distance were determined by a proprioceptive influence of the external muscles of the eye, these surfaces should appear *farther* away, for the prisms have necessitated a relative divergence of the eyes.

uphill, moving objects appear to change size with motion; one misjudges the position and orientation of objects, such as dishes on the dining table; one stumbles on the grass in walking, and so forth.

The apparent distortion of space that occurs with suitable lenses before the eyes can be used as a test for stereopsis and stereoscopic acuity, as was earlier suggested by Lippincott.[152] The leaf room is particularly suited for such a test because of the characteristic distortion it assumes when a given lens is placed before one eye. A meridional afocal magnification lens in a trial frame can be placed before the right eye, and the examiner can determine after a few questions whether the subject is responding stereoscopically, for if he is, all his answers will be consistent with the characteristic distortion. With no stereoscopic vision the subject reports the room unchanged in shape; no distortion is apparent. The smallest magnification to which the subject responds would constitute a measure of his stereoscopic acuity, and this for a person with high visual acuity in each eye will be as low as 0.25 per cent magnification. Often subjects are found who fail to show stereoscopic vision in the ordinary tests for stereoscopic acuity but who will respond quickly in the leaf room. Likewise subjects in whom normal binocular vision is suspected as being absent can be quickly tested by this method. Such a test has the advantage of causing the images of the whole visual field to enter into the stereoscopic perception, whereas most tests simply involve the macular perception.

THE DEGREE OF DISTORTION

In general, because of the subjective nature of the phenomenon, we cannot determine the degree of this stereoscopic distortion of space caused by a lens. Certainly empirical factors can dampen or inhibit the actual perception of distortion. Consider, however, the following experiment which is nearly devoid of empirical clues.

The Plumb-line Square. At a distance of 3 meters from an observer a pair of plumb lines separated 50 cm. are suspended in the objective frontoparallel plane and equidistant from the median plane of the observer (Fig. 84). A second pair equally separated are suspended 50 cm. farther from the eyes. The observer, whose head is held by a suitable headrest and chin cup, views the plumbs against a uniform black background and through appropriate apertures in screens which restrict his vision entirely to the lines. By means of an adjustable magnifying unit, that increase in magnification of the image of the right eye which is necessary to cause the front right line to appear the same distance as the left rear line can be easily found.

From the dimensions of the arrangement and the interpupillary distance of the eyes (p. 162), we can compute the value of this necessary magnification that would theoretically cause this effect. This turns out to be $M = 1.020$, or 2 per cent. The mean variation of settings for three observers, after correction for initial errors in image magnification, agreed to within 0.2 per cent magnification of this value. In this experiment we are *perhaps* measuring the degree of stereoscopic distortion introduced by the magnification of the lens.

The simplest approach to a measurement of the stereoscopic distortion with a lens before one eye consists in one's placing a series of objects in such an arrangement in space that they appear normally oriented and spaced, according to some reproducible subjective criterion. We then measure the dimensions of the actual arrangement and from these deduce the amount of distortion. Examples of this procedure may be found in the experiments with the horopter apparatus, various types of "tilting planes," and Ames's "distorted rooms."

The Horopter Apparatus. In the horopter apparatus (Chapters 3 and 4), settings of the rods for the criteria of the apparent frontoparallel plane, the

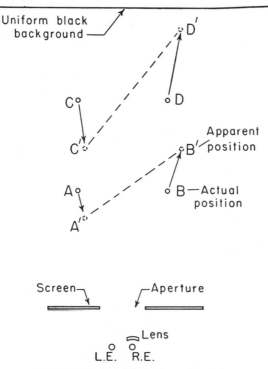

Fig. 84. Four plumb lines experiment.

center of the region of binocular single vision, and by the nonius method have been made with the afocal type of magnification lenses. The effect with this apparatus is entirely due to changes in the horizontal disparities between the images of the two eyes, because the wires are smooth with no details. Empirical factors to spatial localization are minimal. With a lens before one eye, the wires will have to be adjusted to lie on a skew curve about the point of fixation. The extent of this skewness or rotation can be determined immediately by the analytic procedure previously described. The data for the apparent frontoparallel plane show that this rotation is quite exactly that to be expected from the magnification difference introduced between the images of the two eyes (p. 29 and following).

Similarly when the image of one eye is magnified in the horizontal meridian, the entire region of binocular single vision will be skew about the point of fixation. Figure 85 shows the typical results for one subject when a 3 per cent meridional afocal magnification lens is placed before the right eye. The region of binocular single vision has been rotated so that the right side is *nearer*, the left farther away than the point of fixation. The analytic transformation of these data shows that the degree of rotation agrees quite accurately with that to be expected.[177]

These data are important in showing that when a subject is given a difference in magnification between the images of the two eyes, only those objects near the fixation point will have images that always fall in the region of binocular single vision. With the 3 per cent lens, points in the objective frontoparallel plane only inside of 2 to 3 degrees on each side of the fixation

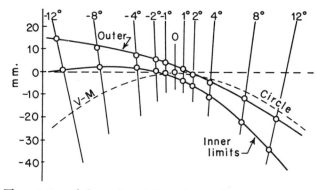

Fig. 85. The rotation of the region of binocular single vision about the fixation point when the image of the right eye is magnified by 3 per cent. The observation distance is 40 cm.

point are in the region of binocular vision. The images of all other points would be or tend to be double, uncrossed disparate on the right side, crossed disparate on the left. The larger the magnification difference, the smaller is the region in the normal plane about the point of fixation where binocular single vision is possible, although probably it never is less than a visual angle of about 1 degree (the fovea).

We should therefore always expect to find fusion for small objects near the point of fixation, irrespective of the magnitude of the magnification difference. This was substantiated by the experiment of Erggelet[65] who wore a +13 diopter ophthalmic lens before one eye to correct a farsightedness caused by a contact lens, and who thus introduced a marked difference in the magnifications of the images of the two eyes (p. 258). He reported that the images of small objects, such as door knobs, when fixated were readily fused, but those of more extended objects were seen confused or their edges tended to appear double. We similarly should not expect any change in the stereoscopic acuity of the eyes for a small region about the point of fixation when a difference in magnification of the images of the two eyes exists.[16]

The Tilting Plane. The "tilting plane" apparatus consists of a plane surface which can be turned about an axis in the median plane of the observer and can be adjusted by him. The observer, whose head is held by a suitable chin cup (occasionally a wax bite) and forehead rests, views this plane at a fixed distance with the eyes symmetrically converged (Fig. 86). A protractor and a suitable indicator permit an assistant to record the degree through which the plane has been turned from the objective frontoparallel position. An illuminated screen with a suitable aperture restricts the vision to the surface and prevents the edges from being seen regardless of the orientation of the plane.

Care must be taken to exclude, so far as possible, empirical factors which might interfere with the stereoscopic perception. Recognizable geometric forms that will appear deformed when the plane is rotated can provide such inhibiting clues. Squares, symmetrical triangles or large circles and similar geometric patterns should be avoided. Adjustment of the plane during observation should be made quickly and judgments made preferably when the plane is not in motion. Generally the observer seems more sensitive in his judgments if there is some detail with depth for stereoscopic stimulus

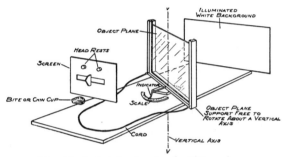

Fig. 86. A sketch of a simple tilting plane.

near the center of the surface. With strict attention at the center of the surface when the observer is adjusting it to appear frontoparallel, the empirical clues often become of less importance, especially as he gains experience.

A satisfactory surface consists of a sheet of plate glass, with details on its surface consisting of a large number of small India ink spots irregular in size and scattered indiscriminately. On the back side several spots of ink are also placed near the center. The details on this surface are seen silhouetted against a large sheet of white cardboard that is uniformly illuminated. Such a pattern provides fusion stimuli, as well as stereoscopic stimuli over the whole of the restricted binocular visual field, and yet avoids obvious geometric patterns.

After his head is adjusted in the headrest, the observer adjusts the plane about the vertical meridian until it appears frontoparallel to him, the right and left sides of the plane appearing equidistant. The actual angular position indicated on the scale is recorded. A number of such settings are made, and the mean position is found. Then a meridional magnification lens, the magnification of which is accurately known for the particular observation distance of the test, is placed at axis 90 degrees (axis vertical) before the right eye. The observer is again asked to adjust the plane by the identical criterion, and the mean setting of the plane is again determined. Now a meridional magnification lens at axis 90 degrees before the right eye would cause the frontal wall to appear skew with the right side farther away. Consequently, to make the plane appear "normal," it will actually have to be turned so that the right side is nearer than the left side. By a sequence of lenses of different magnifications, placed first before one eye and then before the other, complete data for the corresponding rotations of the surface are obtained.

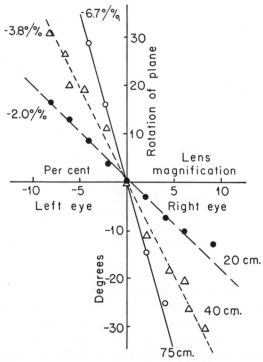

Fig. 87. The degree of rotation of the tilting plane about a vertical axis, corresponding to a given magnification of the image in one eye in the horizontal meridian, for three observation distances.

Typical results[180] are shown in Fig. 87, in which the abscissas are the per cent magnification of the lens, taken positive when the lens is before the right eye, and in which the ordinates are the degrees of turning necessary for the plane to appear normal, taken positive when the right side is farther away.

Within the range of magnification used, the data fall on straight lines, indicating a linear response. The greater the visual distance, the greater is the rotation for a given magnification. The differential response, that is, the degrees rotation corresponding to a 1 per cent magnification change, can be measured by the slopes of these lines. In Fig. 87 these slopes, G, are —6.7, —3.8 and —2 degrees per 1 per cent for observation distances of 75, 40 and

20 cm., respectively. Now, we can predict this differential response from the geometric relationships involved (p. 162) and for small magnification this is given by $G = -0.29b/a$ degrees per 1 per cent, where b is the observation distance and a is one half of the interpupillary distance. One finds for the observer whose data are given in Fig. 87 that the differential responses are -7.2, -3.7 and -2 degrees per 1 per cent, for the same observation distances respectively. For an observation distance of 40 cm. the mean variation in settings for a large number of subjects lies between 0.2 and 1.4 degrees with a median of about 0.6 degree. This corresponds to a magnification difference between the images of the two eyes of less than 0.1 per cent. The agreement of the data with theory is satisfactory in this case.

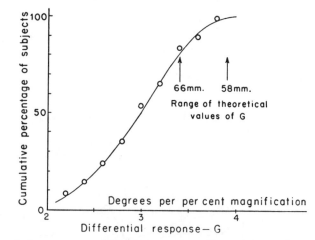

Fig. 88. Cumulative percentage of subjects corresponding to given values of the stereoscopic differential response of the tilting plane.

For a majority of untrained observers, the differential response is lower than that which might be expected on the basis of the theory, even as much as 20 per cent less. This deficiency varies among observers and with the type of details on the test surface, and even at different times. The cumulative distribution of the G-differential responses for a large number of observers is shown in Fig. 88. The test pattern was the field of ink dots observed at a distance of 40 cm. The results of these observers have been lumped together in spite of the variation that would be expected owing to the variations in interpupillary distances among them. However, the range of values that would be expected on the basis of geometric theory is near the top of the graph. Clearly the range of experimental values is considerably lower and only 15 per cent come within the expected range.

We probably shall have to account for the deficiency in the experimental values upon the basis of the individual variation in response to the empirical factors associated with the particular pattern used on the plane. No such deficiency has been found with a limited number of subjects on the horopter apparatus where empirical clues are certainly at a minimum. However, it is not clear how the dampening effect of the empirical clues can be proportional to the magnification introduced or, as more probable, even to the correspondingly rotated position of the plane.

With test planes which are inclined to the visual plane, data can be obtained in two ways: (1) rotations about a vertical axis, as in Fig. 89, or (2) rotations about an inclined axis in the test and median planes, as in Fig. 90.

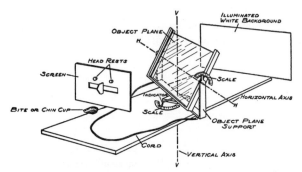

Fig. 89. Sketch of the inclined tilting plane apparatus with rotation about a vertical axis.

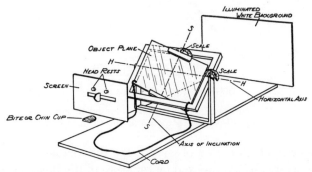

Fig. 90. Sketch of tilting plane apparatus in which the plane can be turned about an inclined axis.

In the first case—a rotation of the surface about a vertical axis—data show that the rotation of the plane corresponding to a given magnification of the image of one eye in the horizontal meridian is independent of the inclination; the same rotation is found irrespective of the inclination of the plane. This result is of course what is expected, for all objects in the binocular visual field will appear skew in one sense about a vertical axis (or more accurately, about an axis perpendicular to the visual plane), the degree depending on the difference in magnification between the images of the two eyes.

In the second case, in which the axis of rotation necessary for the plane to appear normal lies in the plane itself, the effect with meridional lenses at axis 90 degrees before one eye decreases as the inclination increases, being greatest when the plane is vertical. Now according to geometric theory

(p. 165) this rotation should decrease with the inclination proportionally to the cosine of the angle of inclination from the vertical (to the visual plane). The stereoscopic differential responses from typical data[182] are shown in Fig. 91. Here they are plotted against the cosine of the angle of

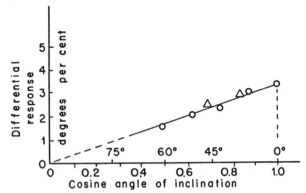

Fig. 91. The linear relationship between the differential response measured about the inclined axis and the cosine of the angle of inclination of the tilting plane, for magnifications of the image of one eye in the horizontal meridian.

Fig. 92. Large horizontal tilting plane devised by Ames.

inclination. Because the points approximate a straight line through the origin, the results can be said to agree with the geometric theory, except in absolute magnitude, because of the same type of deficiency described previously.

So much, then, for the measurements of the magnitude of the distortion of that space perceived by stereoscopic vision when the relative magnifications of the images of the two eyes in the horizontal meridian are altered by magnification lenses. Certainly tests of this kind are useful in detecting unsuspected differences of the magnifications of the images of the two eyes, but not a measure of the magnitude unless the differential response is known.

A larger type of tilting test plane was once employed, the surface of which was more or less horizontal (Fig. 92). The test surface could be adjusted for any lateral or fore-and-aft inclination about a pivot at the center.[4, 112] The observer looked down at the surface at an angle of about 30 degrees. Thus, the plane would be inclined to the visual plane by 60 degrees. Hand wheels and attached necessary cords and pulleys permitted the observer to adjust the board so that it appeared horizontal. This apparatus proved helpful for a study of the distortion of space due to lenses but proved unreliable for measuring or analyzing the unknown differences in magnification between the images of the two eyes.

A simple demonstration tilting table also devised by Ames is shown in Fig. 93.

Distorted Rooms. A distorted room is a large wooden box, the shape of which corresponds to one of the four types of apparent shapes of the leaf

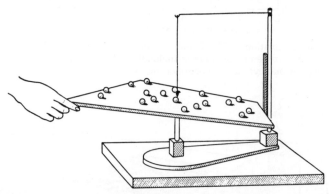

Fig. 93. Sketch of simple demonstration tilting field designed by Ames.

room when the corresponding lens (or lenses) is placed before the eyes. Referring to Fig. 81, one can build a box of the shape A', B', C', and so forth, in dimensions corresponding to calculations (p. 161), or from drawing-board layouts, making sure that the angular sizes of the various details to the observer are the same as those for the original cubical room. Such a distorted room will appear cubical when viewed through the appropriate magnification lens placed before the other eye, so as to produce a distortion in the opposite direction. In these rooms, features such as windows, baseboards, and so forth, all with dimensions corresponding to the distortion, may also be incorporated, without significantly affecting the appearance. The more details which constitute empirical factors to spatial localization included in the room, however, the less critical is the percentage magnification of the lens needed to make the room appear cubical. Otherwise that lens needed agrees well with theoretical values. Monocularly the room appears cubical. Many bizarre and confusing experiences can result with such distorted rooms while the observer is wearing the correcting lens.[149]

CHAPTER 14

The Analytic Discussion of the
Distortion in Stereoscopic
Perception of Space

INTRODUCTION

T HIS CHAPTER[*] will be devoted to a mathematical theory of the apparent distortion of space caused by particular magnification lenses placed before the eyes of the observer. The purposes are (1) to show that, save for the induced effect, the apparent spatial distortions described in the preceding chapter can be predicted, at least qualitatively, on a geometric basis,[192] and (2) to derive the necessary formulas from which calculations can be made for the analysis of experimental data.

Since the magnifications introduced by lenses change the disparities between the images in the two eyes in an orderly fashion, a mathematical analysis of the effects is possible. Only in the case of lenses placed so that the magnification is in the vertical meridian (which causes the induced effect) does a direct analysis fail.

Suppose, as represented in Fig. 4 (p. 19), the two points F and P are seen binocularly. The separation of the two retinal images (pf) of the right eye is greater than that (pf) of the left eye. The object P is perceived farther from the observer than F through the process of stereopsis. The *geometric* disparity between the two images in the two eyes can be described in terms of the angles subtended by the two objects at the two eyes; namely, $\eta = \alpha_2 - \alpha_1$, where $\alpha_1 = $ angle $\overline{FLP}$ and $\alpha_2 = $ angle $\overline{FRP}$, taken positive as measured in a clockwise direction. For the right half of the visual field, if P is farther than F, then η is positive.

The angles α_1 and α_2 themselves (corresponding to retinal dimensions) do not provide sufficient means for the judgment of the *absolute* distance of either F or P from the eyes, but their difference does provide the stimulus for the *relative* localization (depth) of the two points. Stereopsis can be present only if there are at least two points in the binocular visual field, for

---

[*] This chapter may present some difficulties to the average reader since it is largely of mathematical character. The reader should, however, appreciate the fact that it provides the basis for quantitative studies on the apparent distortions of space caused by alterations in the relative magnification of the images of the two eyes.

otherwise no image disparity exists. Where there are many object points, a geometric disparity can be said to exist between the retinal images of *any* two, but usually the disparities are referred to the images of the point of fixation (the *Kernpunkt* of visual space).

If the image of one eye is magnified, it is clear that the separation of the retinal images of *F* and *P* for that eye is increased. This increase changes the value of η, the disparity, and correspondingly the points *F* and *P* would appear differently oriented. The essential analytic problem, therefore, is to find mathematical expressions which describe the new positions for *F* and *P*, such as would correspond to the new disparity.

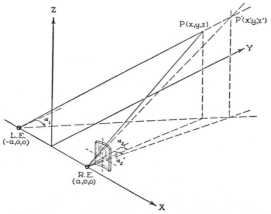

Fig. 94. The coordinate system and the geometric relationships used to study the effect of a meridional magnifying lens on the apparent positions of objects in the binocular visual field.

A MAGNIFICATION OF THE IMAGE OF ONE EYE IN THE HORIZONTAL MERIDIAN (A MERIDIONAL LENS AT AXIS 90 DEGREES)

In Fig. 94, let the "centers" of the left and right eyes (assuming coincidence of the entrance pupils with the centers of rotation) be located in a rectangular coordinate system at points $(-a, 0, 0)$ and $(a, 0, 0)$, respectively. The *XY* plane is the objective *visual plane*, *XZ* is the *frontal plane* and *YZ* is the *median plane* of the eyes. Consider a point at a very great distance on the *Y* axis, and a second point *P* at coordinates *x*, *y* and *z*. The horizontal visual angles between the points and the eyes are designated α_1 and α_2 for the left and right eyes, respectively.

Now let a meridional afocal magnification lens be placed before the right eye, with geometric axis vertical (axis 90 degrees) so that the retinal image is magnified in the horizontal meridian only. The visual angle α_2 is then enlarged to α_2' and the original geometric disparity between the two eyes is then changed and becomes $\eta' = \alpha_2' - \alpha_1$. Correspondingly, the stereoscopic stimulus is changed, as though given by a point *P'* at *x'*, *y'* and *z'*. The transformation of *x*, *y*, *z* to *x'*, *y'*, *z'* in terms of the angular magnification of the lens and the interpupillary distance $2a$ is to be found.

It is convenient to define the angular magnification of the lens by $M_a = \tan \alpha'/\tan \alpha$ (Fig. 68). Also, M_a is assumed constant for all values of α. Small changes in the effective magnification of the lens when objects are nearer the eyes will also be neglected. The lens is placed before the observer's eyes with optical axis parallel to the Y axis. However, small variations from this position do not change essentially the general characteristics of the apparent space distortion.

Since the magnification acts in the horizontal meridian only, we can write

$$\tan \alpha_1 = (x + a)/y \qquad \tan \alpha_2 = (x - a)/y$$
$$\tan \alpha_1' = (x' + a)/y' \qquad \tan \alpha_2' = (x' - a)/y'$$
$$\tan \alpha_1' = \tan \alpha_1 \qquad \text{and} \quad \tan \alpha_2' = M \tan \alpha_2$$

Eliminating the $\tan \alpha$'s from the six relations we obtain the transformation equations:

$$x' = -a[(M + 1)x - (M - 1)a]/[(M - 1)x - (M + 1)a] \qquad (1)$$
$$y' = -2ay/[(M - 1)x - (M + 1)a] \qquad (2)$$

and since $z'/z = y'/y$,

$$z' = -2az/[(M - 1)x - (M + 1)a] \qquad (3)$$

These equations relate the coordinates of any point in the x, y, z space to one in the x', y', z' space and depend only on the magnification of the lens and the interpupillary distance of the eyes. Because these transformations are linear, it follows that straight lines in one space remain straight lines in the other; conic sections in one remain conic sections in the other, and so forth.

Since the lens magnifies only in the horizontal meridian, x' is independent of y and z. Thus, all planes parallel to the median plane (the YZ plane) remain parallel in the transformation, but will be displaced in the direction of the X axis. With increasing distances on the right side of the median plane (Fig. 95), the apparent displacement to the right increases and when the critical distance $x = a(M + 1)/(M - 1)$ is reached, the apparent plane should be infinitely far to the right. Planes at increasing distances on the left side appear also displaced to the right to a position never farther from the eyes than the distance $x' = -a(M + 1)/(M - 1)$. In fact, all planes to the left go into the region between $x' = -a(M + 1)/(M - 1)$ and $x' = -a(M - 1)/(M + 1)$. The transformed planes corresponding to equally spaced objective planes on the left have $x' = -a(M + 1)/(M - 1)$ as a limit plane. Planes between $x = -a$ and $x = +a$ are slightly displaced to the left.

The inverse transformation equations

$$x = a[(M + 1)x' + (M - 1)a]/[(M - 1)x' + (M + 1)a] \qquad (4)$$
$$y = 2aMy'/[(M - 1)x' + (M + 1)a] \qquad (5)$$
$$z = 2aMz'/[(M - 1)x' + (M + 1)a] \qquad (6)$$

are useful in studying the corresponding apparent distortion of any surface or figure in space the equation of which is known.

Consider now in particular planes parallel to the frontal plane (the XZ plane), given by $y = y_0$. The corresponding "apparent" plane is given by

$$y' = [(M - 1)y_0/2aM]x' + (M + 1)y_0/2M \tag{7}$$

Thus all "apparent" planes corresponding to frontal parallel planes intersect the X axis at the point $x' = -a(M + 1)/(M - 1)$. These transformations and those discussed before, both illustrated in Fig. 95, conform closely to the actual appearances of side and front walls under the conditions assumed, providing those walls have few perspective features, and at the same time have many details which provide stimuli for stereoscopic vision. Each plane appears rotated about a vertical axis through the angle given by

$$\tan \psi = [(M - 1)/2M] [y_0/a] \tag{8}$$

Clearly ψ increases with the distance of the objective plane y_0 and decreases with the interpupillary distance $2a$.

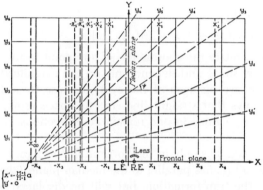

Fig. 95. Objective planes parallel to the median plane and planes parallel to the frontal plane, compared to their stereoscopic localization when the image of the right eye is magnified in the horizontal meridian.

If the optical axis of the lens is directed to a point in the median plane on a given surface, as for example in the horopter apparatus, and so forth, then the angle through which the surface through that point appears to have been rotated will be

$$\tan \psi = (M - 1)b/(M + 1)a$$

which practically differs very little from equation (8).

It remains to find the transformations affecting floors and ceilings. Here $z = z_0$, and, as previously, we find

$$z' = [(M - 1)z_0/2aM]x' + [(M + 1)z_0/2M] \tag{9}$$

Planes parallel to the visual (XY) plane become inclined. For planes above the visual plane (z_0 positive) the slope of the transformed planes is positive, that is, the plane is higher on the right than on the left. For those below the visual plane (z_0 negative) the transformed planes incline in the opposite direction, the right-hand side is lower than the left. These transformations are illustrated schematically in Fig. 96. Again all the transformed planes intersect the X axis at the point $x' = -a(M+1)/(M-1)$. Table 14 gives approximately the position of this unique point for different magnifications of the lens.

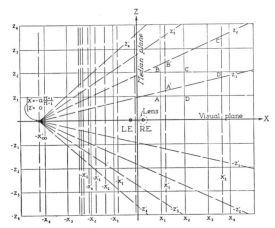

Fig. 96. Objective planes parallel to visual plane and those parallel to median plane, compared to their stereoscopic localization when the image of the right eye is magnified in the horizontal meridian.

Table 14

THE CALCULATED DISTANCE FROM THE EYES TO THE POINT OF INTERSECTION OF ALL THE APPARENT PLANES CORRESPONDING TO A SERIES OF FRONTOPARALLEL PLANES, WHEN MAGNIFICATION OF THE IMAGE OF THE RIGHT EYE IS INCREASED IN THE HORIZONTAL MERIDIAN

	INCREASED MAGNIFICATION (RIGHT EYE IMAGE)			
	1% $M = 1.01$	2% $M = 1.02$	3% $M = 1.03$	4% $M = 1.04$
x' (cm.)	−653	−328	−220	−166
	5% $M = 1.05$	6% $M = 1.06$	7% $M = 1.07$	10% $M = 1.10$
x' (cm.)	−133	−112	−96	−68

The apparent distortion of a "leaf room" when viewed with a meridional magnification lens before the right eye is as predicted on a geometric basis just outlined. The right wall appears farther to the right, the left nearer, the ceiling is inclined up to the right, the floor down to the right.

Very striking also is the fact that in the "leaf room" the leaves on the right wall appear much larger and those on the left smaller. Since the angular size of the leaves remains practically the same without and with the lens before the right eye, the leaf that appears farther away will also appear larger (Emmert's law[24]). Figure 97 illustrates the geometric relationships. From equations (2) and (3) previously given, it is clear that for a given wall parallel to the median plane, the apparent dimensions of a figure on that wall are always proportional to the real size. That is,

$$y_2' - y_1' = k(y_2 - y_1) \quad \text{and} \quad z_2' - z_1' = k(z_2 - z_1)$$

where

$$k = -2a/[(M - 1)x - (M + 1)a]$$

and there is no distortion of the figure. The natural perspective (in the sense of decrease in angular size with distance) remains undisturbed.

For the frontal wall the apparent size of details changes progressively with the distance from the center; that is, it varies with x (equation 1). See

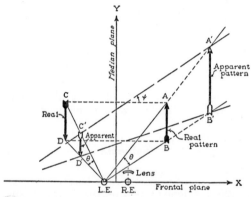

Fig. 97. The change in the apparent size of patterns on side walls observed with stereoscopic vision when the image of the right eye is magnified in the horizontal meridian.

Fig. 98. The apparent vertical extension of objects on a frontal wall will also be changed, depending not only on x, but also on the distance of the figure above or below the visual plane, that is, on z (equation 3). The general idea of this distortion of figures can be visualized in Fig. 96, by comparing any square in the rectangular pattern (A, B, C, D) with the corresponding transformed pattern (A', B', C', D').

One further aspect of this problem is the apparent rotation of a surface that is inclined with respect to the Y axis. A case in point is the large tippingboard (Fig. 92), where the observer looks down on a horizontal plane, which is thus inclined with respect to the observer's visual plane, as schematically illustrated in Fig. 99. The plane can be represented by $z = (y - b) \cot i$, where b is the observation distance to the plane and i is the angle of inclination measured from the Z (vertical) axis. Substituting the inverse transformation equations (4), (5) and (6), we have for the new surface

$$x'[(M - 1)b] - y[2Ma] + z'[2Ma \tan i] + [(M + 1)ab] = 0$$

Inspection of this equation shows that the inclination of the transformed plane is the same as before, though there is a small displacement along the Y axis because of the position of the lens. The rotation of this plane about

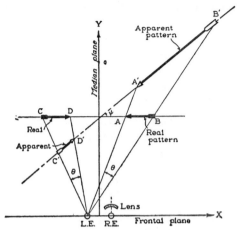

Fig. 98. The distortion of details on a frontal wall, when the image of the right eye is magnified in the horizontal meridian.

the Z axis is the same as that for any surface at the distance b, given by (8).

The degree of rotation about the axis $A \ldots A$ (Fig. 99) depends, however, on the inclination angle, i, as given by

$$\tan \psi_i = [(M - 1)/2M]\,[b/a]\cos i \tag{10}$$

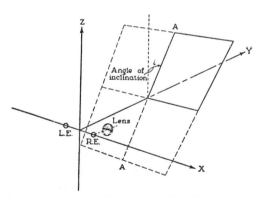

Fig. 99. A surface inclined to the frontal (XZ) plane.

Experimental measurements of the apparent rotation of inclined surfaces when the image of one eye is magnified in the horizontal meridian are in good agreement with this relationship. Therefore, this effect has often been referred to as a *geometric* effect in contradistinction to the induced effect.

If the meridional lens is placed before the left eye, the direction of all the apparent distortions resulting from stereoscopic localization is correspondingly reversed. ($1/M$ takes the place of M in the transformation formulas.)

In surroundings where empirical factors of depth perception predominate, this stereoscopic spatial distortion may be much less apparent. There are situations, moreover, in which the degree of the apparent distortion will not be as great as might be expected on the basis of a purely geometric consideration of the changes in the retinal image disparities. For example, according to equation (1) the apparent distance of the right side wall of a leaf room should be infinite for an objective distance of $x = a(M + 1)/(M - 1)$. However, the wall, though appearing much farther away, does not appear infinitely far. Thus though other factors may enter to dampen the magnitude of the stereoscopic effect or suppress it, nevertheless we conclude that the stimuli which correspond to an incorrect stereoscopic localization of space must be ever present.

A MAGNIFICATION OF THE IMAGE OF ONE EYE IN THE VERTICAL MERIDIAN (A LENS AT AXIS 180 DEGREES)

If the meridional magnification lens is placed before the right eye with axis horizontal (axis 180 degrees) so as to magnify the image in the vertical meridian only, the overall localization of objects in space is again distorted. In ordinary surroundings this distortion appears identical with that resulting from the same lens placed before the *other* eye to magnify in the *horizontal* meridian. Thus, it seems that a vertical magnification of the image of one eye *induces* a magnification of the image of the other eye in the horizontal meridian, the effects of which have just been analyzed. The induced effect, which will be discussed in Chapter 15, presents a complex process of binocular vision.

Because of the induced size effect, the magnification of the image of one eye with an "overall" magnification lens (an afocal magnifying lens with spherical surfaces) causes little or no stereoscopic distortion of space. The induced effect seemingly compensates for the geometric effect of a magnification in the horizontal meridian.

THE IMAGES OF BOTH EYES ARE MAGNIFIED IN OBLIQUE MERIDIANS

The third type of stereoscopic spatial distortion results when meridional magnifications at oblique meridians are introduced before one or both eyes. A single lens before one eye that introduces a meridional magnification at an oblique axis changes the disparities of the images both horizontally and vertically and, therefore, affects stereoscopic spatial localization as described previously. In order to remove this complication, equal meridional magnifications can be placed symmetrically before both eyes. For the maximal effect one lens is placed at axis 45 degrees, and the other at axis 135 degrees. The vertical and horizontal components of the magnifications are then equal for both eyes, but there remains a torsional (scissors) effect of the images which causes the characteristic spatial distortion experienced. The optical effect is illustrated in Fig. 100, where the image of a circular object becomes elliptic owing to the meridional magnification.

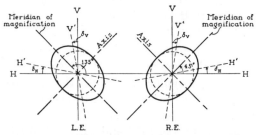

Fig. 100. The positions of the meridional magnifications at oblique axes for maximal effect (case of axes of magnifications converging up), showing the "scissors" or rotary deviations of the images of vertical and horizontal lines.

These distortions can also be predicted on the basis of geometric analysis. Consider, first, the angular displacement of the image as seen through a meridional lens magnifying in an oblique meridian (Fig. 101). The magni-

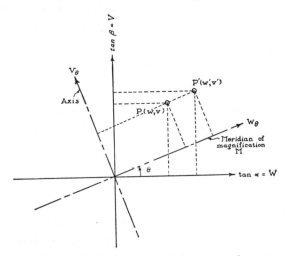

Fig. 101. Diagram for finding the displacement of the image of a point, due to a meridional magnification M at meridian θ.

fying effect takes place parallel to the meridian at θ. For any point ($w = \tan \alpha$, $v = \tan \beta$), the distances w_θ, v_θ, from the principal meridians of the lens are

$$w_\theta = w \cos \theta + v \sin \theta \qquad w = w_\theta \cos \theta - v_\theta \sin \theta$$
$$v_\theta = v \cos \theta - w \sin \theta \qquad v = w_\theta \sin \theta + v_\theta \cos \theta$$

Because of the magnification M, we have $w_\theta' = M w_\theta$, and $v_\theta' = v_\theta$, and therefore the coordinates of the image point P' (w', v'), corresponding to P (w, v), are

$$w' = Aw + Bv \tag{11}$$
$$v' = Bw + Cv \tag{12}$$

where

$$A = \tfrac{1}{2}[(M + 1) + (M - 1)\cos 2\theta]$$
$$B = \tfrac{1}{2}[(M - 1)\sin 2\theta]$$
$$C = \tfrac{1}{2}[(M + 1) - (M - 1)\cos 2\theta]$$

Refer again to Fig. 94, remembering that now there are two lenses, one before the right eye with magnification M in the meridian θ, the other before the left eye with magnification M in the meridian $(180° - \theta)$. Using subscripts 1 and 2 for the left and right eyes, respectively, we have $A_1 = A_2 = A$, $B_1 = -B_2 = -B$, and $C_1 = C_2 = C$, and substituting point coordinates for the w's and v's in (11) and (12), we obtain

$$(x' + a)/y' = A(x + a)/y - Bz/y$$
$$(x' - a)/y' = A(x - a)/y + Bz/y \tag{13}$$

$$z_1'/y' = -B(x + a)/y + Cz/y$$
$$z_2'/y' = B(x - a)/y + Cz/y \tag{14}$$

In order to get a unique z', we put $z' = \tfrac{1}{2}(z_1' + z_2')$, an assumption that is justified because B is small. For small absolute values of x the expression represents a good approximation, and for all points on the plane $x = 0$, it is exact. Then, solving for x', y' and z', we find

$$x' = Aax/(Aa - Bz) \tag{15}$$
$$y' = ay/(Aa - Bz) \tag{16}$$
$$z' = a(Cz - Ba)/(Aa - Bz) \tag{17}$$

Both x' and y' depend on z, and thus the apparent displacement of any point changes with its position above or below the visual plane. On the other hand, z' is independent of x and y, indicating that planes parallel to the visual plane, though displaced, remain parallel in the transformation. This prediction conforms to the appearance of the floor and ceiling as experienced by observers wearing the lenses described previously. According to (17), as z becomes very large, z' approaches the value $-aC/B$. The transformed planes that correspond to equally spaced object planes approach the plane $z' = -aC/B$ as a limit. Figures 102 and 103 illustrate this transformation.

The transformation of planes parallel to the median plane $(x = x_0)$ and to the frontal plane $(y = y_0)$ can be determined by eliminating z from (15) and (17), and, again, from (16) and (17). We find

$$z' = [a(AC - B^2)/ABx]x' - [Ca/B] \tag{18}$$

and

$$z' = [a(AC - B^2)/By]y' - [Ca/B] \tag{19}$$

The transformed planes corresponding to $x = x_0$ are parallel to the Y axis, but are increasingly inclined from the vertical as x_0 increases. This result conforms to the general appearance experienced by observers; side walls appear sloping away at the top, nearer at the bottom. The transformation is schematically illustrated in Fig. 102. All transformed planes pass through the point at $z = -a(C/B)$ of the Z axis.

The transformed planes corresponding to frontoparallel planes, $y = y_0$, are parallel to the X axis but are also inclined with top farther away. The angle of inclination measured from the vertical increases with increasing y_0. Again, this result describes, at least qualitatively, the appearance of a rear wall as experienced by an observer wearing the lenses described pre-

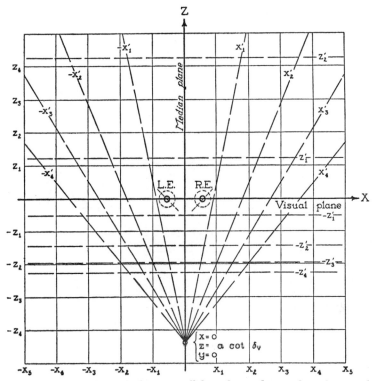

Fig. 102. The transformation of planes parallel to the median and to the visual planes related to meridional magnifications of the images of both eyes at oblique meridians.

viously. Again, all transformed planes pass through the point $z = -a(C/B)$ of the Z axis. The transformation is illustrated in Fig. 103.

It can easily be shown that the ratio $B/C = \tan \delta_v$ where δ_v is the rotary deviation (declination) of the images of verticals caused by the lens (see δ_v in Fig. 100). Similarly $B/A = \tan \delta_h$, where δ_h is the rotary deviation of the image of the horizontal lines. Thus the unique point in these transformations is related to the interpupillary distance and to the vertical declination angle* (Fig. 104).

---

* In this connection it may be of interest to point out Helmholtz's deduction (*Physiological Optics*, the Optical Society of America, 1925, Vol. III, p. 349) of the position of the horopter surface that exists under the assumption that the meridians V′ for both eyes (Fig. 104) are corresponding retinal meridians.

If the meridians of magnification are reversed, $\theta > 90$ degrees, the direction of the distortion described previously will be reversed.

The predictions derived from this geometric analysis are in striking agreement with the actual appearances of surfaces when observed through meridional magnifying lenses.

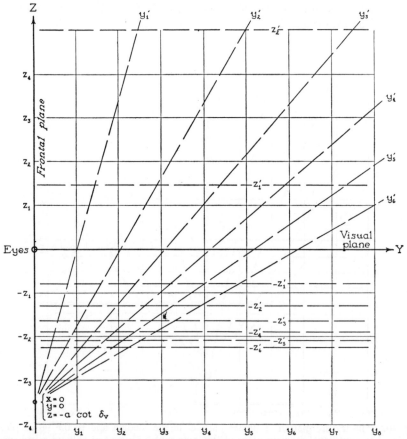

Fig. 103. The transformation of planes parallel to the frontoparallel and to the visual planes related to meridional magnifications of the images of the two eyes at oblique meridians.

If the observer changes the position of his head, looks down or to the right or to the left, the apparent distortions change slightly, though the overall appearance of surfaces remains essentially as predicted.

THE IMAGES OF THE TWO EYES ARE MAGNIFIED UNSYMMETRICALLY IN ONE MERIDIAN

A flat ophthalmic prism placed before the eye introduces an angular magnification that increases toward the apex of the prism (see p. 130). For practical purposes the magnification in the base-apex meridian (apex to the right) can be described by

$$M = M^0 + h \tan \alpha$$

where α, as before, is the visual angle; M_0 is a constant magnification and h is the gradient coefficient of magnification, both depending on the prism power, the base curve and other factors. A nonuniform meridional magnification without prismatic deviation can be had in the "asymmetric distortion lens" (p. 132).

If a pair of prisms or a pair of the prism combination lenses is placed before the eyes, with the bases of the flat prisms toward the nose (base-in) or toward the temples (base-out), the disparity of the retinal images of objects in space is changed, and consequently stereoscopic space perception is affected.

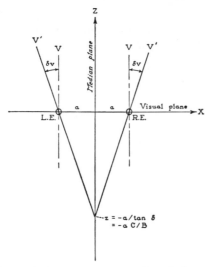

Fig. 104. Relationship between the point $z = -aC/B$, and the vertical declination angles of the two eyes.

A combination lens before the left eye (base-in) changes the visual angles according to

$$\tan \alpha_1' = \tan \alpha_1 (M_0 - h \tan \alpha_1)$$

and one before the right eye (base-in) according to

$$\tan \alpha_2' = \tan \alpha_2 (M_0 + h \tan \alpha_2)$$

Since the constant magnification M_0 is effective equally to both eyes, we replace it, for our purpose, by unity. Introducing point coordinates, we obtain the relations

$$(x' + a)/y' = (x + a)/y - h(x + a)^2/y^2$$
$$(x' - a)/y' = (x - a)/y + h(x - a)^2/y^2$$

from which we find the transformation equations

$$x' = ax[y - 2ah]/[ay - h(x^2 + a^2)]$$
$$y' = ay^2/[ay - h(x^2 + a^2)]$$
$$z' = ayz/[ay - h(x^2 + a^2)]$$

We note that, according to this transformation, plane surfaces appear convex toward the observer. A front wall, $y = y_0$, appears cylindrically convex for $x^2 < ay_0/h$. The cross section is approximately a parabola symmetrical to $x = 0$. A side wall, $x = x_0$, $x_0 > a$, appears also cylindrically convex; for $y >> 2ah$, the cross section is approximately a hyperbola with $x = x_0$ and $y = 2ah$, as asymptotes. The apparent convexity of floors and ceilings, $z = z_0$, is more complex.

These predictions are qualitatively borne out by actual experience with these lenses. If the lenses are placed with bases toward the temples (base-out), the apparent distortions are reversed, that is, the plane surfaces appear concave. This brief description may suffice here, for the effects of prisms are complex, not only because of additional optical distortions that are present, but also because of certain psychologic factors which, varying with the configurations and details present, affect the spatial localization.

CHAPTER 15

The Induced Effect

INTRODUCTION

A T THIS POINT it should be clear that the spatial distortions discussed in the preceding chapters, due to an increased magnification of the retinal image of one eye in the *horizontal* meridian (a meridional lens at axis 90 degrees), or to meridional magnifications of both eyes at symmetrically oblique axes, are geometric in origin and are a stereoscopic response to the horizontal disparities of the images between the two eyes. This distortion, with certain limitations, has actually been predicted from geometric considerations.

However, when the image of one eye is magnified in the *vertical* meridian, for example, by a meridional lens with axis horizontal or at 180 degrees, we should expect no spatial distortion because the changed image disparities are entirely vertical, and vertical disparities do not give rise to a stereoscopic-like depth experience.[231] The fact that a marked distortion does occur, which appears exactly like the spatial distortion produced by a meridional lens that magnifies in the horizontal meridian only, is a startling and extraordinary phenomenon. When one observes the leaf room with (say) a 3 per cent meridional afocal lens placed at axis 180 degrees before the right eye, the entire room appears distorted in every particular as though the lens had been placed before the left eye at axis 90 degrees, so as to magnify the image of that eye in the horizontal meridian. The magnification in the vertical meridian *induces* an *effect*, as though the lens had been put before the other eye with magnifying effect horizontal. This phenomenon explains why an overall magnification lens causes little or no distortion (under ordinary circumstances) because the induced effect offsets the geometric effect of the lens.

The leaf room cannot provide the information as to whether a given apparent distortion is due to a difference in the magnifications of the images of the two eyes in the horizontal or the vertical meridians—due to the geometric or the induced effects.

Historically, Lippincott[151] had reported a spatial distortion due to an ophthalmic cylinder placed before one eye at axis 180 degrees, as Green did later. Friedenwald[80] and Lippincott both noticed that the amount of distortion of object figures when observed with a cylinder at axis 180 degrees before one eye was not always as great as that with the cylinder at axis 90 degrees, and they were aware of some subtle distinction between the two space effects, besides their being merely in directions opposite to each other. Lippincott[153] later was pressed to explain the phenomenon in terms of "perceptual" images. At the Dartmouth Eye Institute the phenomenon was encountered when the effect of lenses on binocular spatial perception was being studied on the Ames horizontal tilting board (Fig. 92). The significance of the findings was not, however, immediately appreciated.

The fundamental facts about the effect may be listed as follows:

(1) When the effect occurs at all, the entire binocular visual field is involved. It is not a separate function of the individual vertical disparities of the images of each point in space.

(2) At least two vertically separated points or contours must be present in the field of view.

(3) The effect occurs within a finite range of vertical magnifications, a fact that specifically differentiates it from the geometric effects.

(4) The magnitude of the effect varies with
   a. the amount of detail in the visual field,
   b. horizontal disparities between the images of the vertically separated contours,
   c. individuals in several different respects.

This chapter will be devoted to a systematic and quantitative description of the effect. The evidence for the foregoing characteristics will be summarized.

Quantitative studies of the induced effect can be simply made on the tilting plane apparatus,[180] as described previously (p. 153). An observer, whose head is held in position by a chin cup and adjustable forehead rests, fixates the center of a test plane at a visual distance of 40 cm., in symmetrical convergence, and with the observer's visual plane horizontal: The support for the test plane is free to rotate about a vertical axis through its center. A protractor, engraved in half degrees, and an indicator permit an assistant to read the actual rotated position of the plane from the objective frontoparallel plane, to an estimated 0.1 degree. The test plane consists of a sheet of plate glass 30 by 30 by 0.3 cm. Suitable details and figures of different types are drawn on this glass with India ink or black paint. The observer sees these details silhouetted against a large sheet of white cardboard that is uniformly illuminated and mounted for a background at some distance behind the test plane. A screen of white cardboard, with a suitable aperture placed before the eyes, so restricts the visual field to the plane that the edges cannot be seen even at extreme rotations. This screen is usually illuminated to the same uniform brightness as the background. The observer can adjust the position of the test plane by means of a cord or rod, which itself cannot provide tactile clues as to the position of the plane.

To measure the apparent rotation of the binocular visual field, caused by a meridional lens before one eye, the observer adjusts the position of the plane until it appears "normal" in the sense of its being perpendicular to the subjective visual direction of the center of the plane—the apparent frontoparallel position. The actual rotation is obviously in a direction opposite to the corresponding apparent skewness of a fixed surface. During the experiment a number of settings of the plane are made, from different starting positions, and a mean of the readings is obtained.

THE BASIC INDUCED EFFECT CURVES

With the test plane covered by a large number of scattered ink dots, a maximal differential response to induced effect is obtained. In Table 15 are given the data[180] of four observers, and these data are shown graphically in Fig. 105. Data for lenses placed at axis 90 degrees (geometric effect) as well

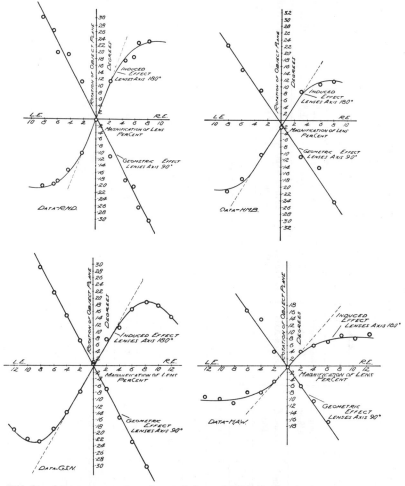

Fig. 105. Graphic representation of typical data of Table 15 for the geometric and induced size effects. The observation distance was 40 cm.

as at axis 180 degrees (induced effect) before one eye are given for comparison. These data are typical of those obtained on several hundred subjects. In the graph the per cent magnification is plotted on the abscissa, right eye positive, and the rotational position of the plane in degrees is plotted on the ordinate taken positive counterclockwise, right side farther from, left side nearer the observer.

The important characteristics of the induced effect evident from these

Table 15

DATA FOR FOUR OBSERVERS, SHOWING THE GEOMETRIC AND INDUCED EFFECTS*

	OBSERVER							
MAGNIFICATION OF SIZE LENS USED, PER CENT	H.A.W.		H.M.B.		G.S.N.		R.H.D.	
	Geometric Effect Lenses Axis 90°	Induced Effect Lenses Axis 180°	Geometric Effect Lenses Axis 90°	Induced Effect Lenses Axis 180°	Geometric Effect Lenses Axis 90°	Induced Effect Lenses Axis 180°	Geometric Effect Lenses Axis 90°	Induced Effect Lenses Axis 180°
BEFORE RIGHT EYE								
12.5		8.8 (0.8)				14.3 (0.8)		
10.3		8.1 (0.2)				17.7 (0.4)		
8.2		9.0 (0.2)	−24.2 (0.6)	11.6 (0.9)	−30.0 (0.7)	18.8 (0.5)	−30.3 (0.6)	23.1 (0.3)
6.6							−26.1 (0.3)	23.0 (0.8)
6.1	−16.7 (1.1)	7.1 (0.4)	−14.0 (0.6)	10.8 (0.8)	−22.6 (1.4)	16.6 (0.6)	−20.2 (0.9)	18.8 (0.3)
4.5							−18.3 (0.1)	17.5 (0.4)
4.0	−10.5 (1.3)	6.0 (0.5)			−15.4 (0.3)	11.1 (0.9)		
3.0			−10.9 (0.2)	8.5 (0.8)				
2.0	−6.1 (0.3)	4.3 (0.3)			−7.0 (0.4)	7.7 (0.3)	−11.2 (0.2)	11.3 (0.3)
No Lenses	−0.5 (0.4)	−0.5 (0.4)	−2.3 (0.5)	−2.3 (0.5)	0.4 (0.3)	1.0 (0.2)	−0.2 (0.3)	−0.2 (0.3)

BEFORE LEFT EYE								
2.0	4.2 (0.4)	−4.8 (0.6)			7.5 (0.4)	−7.7 (0.3)	11.1 (0.8)	−11.2 (0.3)
3.0			8.9 (0.4)	−10.4 (0.6)				
4.0	13.8 (0.3)	−7.9 (1.4)			15.0 (0.7)	−13.9 (0.7)		
4.5							19.1 (0.6)	−15.1 (0.1)
6.1	16.4 (0.2)	−7.9 (0.8)	14.9 (0.9)	−17.5 (0.9)	21.7 (1.0)	−18.8 (0.6)	19.8 (0.3)	−18.5 (0.4)
6.6							26.5 (0.8)	−19.5 (1.0)
8.2		−11.0 (1.0)	22.2 (0.9)	−21.1 (0.5)	29.2 (0.4)	−22.6 (1.0)	30.4 (0.1)	−20.0 (1.0)
10.3		−9.8 (1.2)				−21.7 (2.7)		
12.5		−9.2 (1.2)				−18.9 (1.9)		
Maximal Differential Response 0/%	−2.84	2.03	−2.87	2.75	3.72	3.36	−3.86	3.90

* The data are the degrees of rotation of the plane about a vertical axis from an objective frontal position. The observation distance was 40 cm. The data in parentheses are the mean deviations of settings.

data and from general experience associated with obtaining the data are as follows.

The points representing the data fall on a sigmoid-like curve, showing very definite maximal rotations for particular magnifications when the lens is before the right eye and before the left eye. This is in contrast to the geometric effect, wherein no such maximal effect occurs irrespective of the magnification introduced. In general, the sigmoid curve is symmetrical on the two sides of the graph, but the center of symmetry of the curve will not necessarily coincide with the origin of the graph. Such a displacement may indicate a basic difference in magnification of the images of the eyes or a disturbed subjective spatial frame of reference. So far as possible, the symmetrical curve that best fits all the data points is always that drawn on the graph.

The differential response—namely, the degrees rotation of the plane caused by a change in vertical magnification of the image of one eye by 1 per cent —obviously changes on the induced curve, but is greatest at the center of symmetry. For test surfaces with many details to stimulate fusion and stereopsis, the differential response at this point, I, may be as great as that of the geometric effect, G. Almost never is it greater, but very often it is found smaller.

The mean variations in settings of the test plane given in Table 15 (the numbers in parentheses) are representative of those usually found. Undoubtedly the less experienced is the observer in making critical visual judgments, the larger is the variation. From the table the mean variation is about ±0.5 degree, which is representative. Only occasionally is the variation greater than 1.5 degrees. Since a 1 per cent difference in vertical magnification causes the plane to be rotated about 3 degrees, for the observation distance of 40 cm., this mean deviation corresponds to a sensitivity of about ±0.2 per cent difference in magnification. In general the variations in the settings become greater (the sensitivity less) near the points of maximal effect. There, also, the observer finds that the plane is more difficult subjectively to adjust because of an increased feeling of uncertainty.

The general results just described for an observation distance of 40 cm. are also found for other observation distances.[180] At 3 meters, the degree of rotation of the plane is much greater, and seemingly the settings are more influenced by extraneous factors, and greater concentration on the part of the observer is required.

With the tilting plane the induced effect seems to occur immediately when the lens is introduced before one eye. However, a number of seconds usually elapse before a setting of the plane can be made. Very often some subjects would not experience the effect at once, and a number of seconds would pass before a full effect could be appreciated. Even Lippincott[151] and Friedenwald[80] reported this slower development of the apparent distortion of objects found with some subjects, and the former expressed the belief that this could be ascribed to a poorer or defective efficiency of binocular vision. Empirical factors seem more effective in masking the induced effect than the geometric effect. Unless the lens is worn continuously before one eye for a long time (Chapter 21) no demonstrable aftereffect is found when the lens is removed.

The sigmoid shape of the induced effect curve is not due to cumulative effects or fatigue, for the same curve is usually found irrespective of the order in which the points on the curve are obtained. Furthermore, the repeatability of the curve for the same observer, even after a lapse of time, is good. While the experimental methods, the previous training and even the physical condition of the observer may affect the magnitude of the response, the curves found for a given observer who has normal binocular vision are fundamentally the same.

THE NULL METHOD

There was a possibility that the sigmoid curve and the existence of a maximal rotation with increased vertical magnification of the image in one eye could be due to inhibiting empirical factors arising from the details on the test plane, especially in the rotated position, even though such did not occur with the geometric effect. The "null" method of studying the effect, however, eliminates this possibility. The test plane remains at all times more or less objectively frontoparallel, for, instead of rotating the plane so that it will appear normal, the apparent skewness is offset by employing the geometric effect; namely, by introducing before the proper eye a meridional magnification in the horizontal meridian (at axis 90 degrees). A lens at axis 180 degrees placed before the right eye would cause the plane to appear skew with the right side nearer; to offset this we can introduce a meridional magnification in the right eye at axis 90 degrees to cause the right side to move back until the skewness disappears. The adjustable magnification unit (p. 127) is convenient for this purpose. The accuracy of the setting of this unit in an experiment can be easily checked, because, if correct, an adjustment of the rotational position of the test plane should result in a "zero" reading. Usually several adjustments of the magnification unit will be necessary, and the final value will be interpolated from the readings of the rotational position of the test plane, for a zero reading.

Data obtained by this method are shown graphically in Fig. 106, in which the magnification of the lens placed at axis 180 degrees is plotted on the abscissa and the corresponding magnification introduced at axis 90 degrees necessary to make the test plane appear normal is plotted on the ordinate, both in per cent. This curve is typical of that for the same observer obtained by the rotated plane method. It is evident that in this experiment the induced effect and the geometric effect are of equal magnitude, for the slope of the curve at the center of symmetry is very nearly unity (inclined 45 degrees).

THE INVOLVEMENT OF THE ENTIRE BINOCULAR VISUAL FIELD

Unlike the stereoscopic response to horizontally disparate images in the two eyes, in which the sensation of depth is a function of and confined only to that disparity, the induced effect involves the entire binocular visual processes at the same time. The apparent orientations of *all* objects in the binocular visual field seem to be affected as a whole.

This fact is well illustrated by experiments with the horopter apparatus (p. 20 and following), with which the observer adjusts the position of the rods until all appear to lie in a frontoparallel plane, while fixation is maintained on the central rod. A meridional lens with axis 180 degrees placed before the right eye will increase the magnification of the image in that eye in the vertical meridian, but this will have no effect on the apparent positions of the rods. An effect would not, of course, be expected, for the rods are perfectly smooth with no details on them; consequently any degree of magnification in the vertical meridian cannot affect their images. If, how-

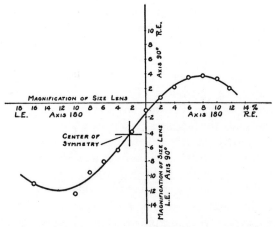

Fig. 106. The induced effect curve determined by a "null" method; that is, the apparent rotation of the test plane caused by a vertical image magnification is offset by the effect of a horizontal magnification.

ever, two small separated objects, such as small beads, are attached to the fixation rod, then with the same lens it is found that the orientation of *all* the other rods in the visual field is affected, for they will appear to lie on a surface that is slightly skewed about the fixation rod, those on the right side appearing nearer than those on the left side. When these rods are then adjusted so as to appear to lie on the frontoparallel plane, they will be found to lie actually on a skew curve, the right side being farther away from the observer, the left side nearer.

In the quantitative experiment, the horopter apparatus was reduced to four lanes, 4 and 8 degrees on each side of the central or fixation rod, and the observations were conducted at an observation distance of 40 cm. Two small beads consisting of lead shot with holes drilled through them were slipped over the fixation rod and adjusted for a separation of 2 cm. These beads constituted the only separated stimuli for fusion in the vertical meridian in the entire binocular visual field. Now for each of a series of meridional afocal magnification lenses in fixed steps of magnification placed at axis 180 degrees before one eye or the other, the rods were adjusted for the apparent frontoparallel plane and the records were made as described on p. 24 and following. The data were analyzed according to the method outlined and the amount of skewness or rotation in degrees about the fixation point was computed.* Figure 107 illustrates graphically the results obtained by two observers. In these the per cent vertical magnification is plotted on the abscissa, right eye as positive, and on the ordinate is plotted the corresponding value for rotation of the curve determined by the rods. The curves drawn are the symmetrical curves that best fit all the points. The important fact, of course, is that the apparent positions of *all* the rods in the visual

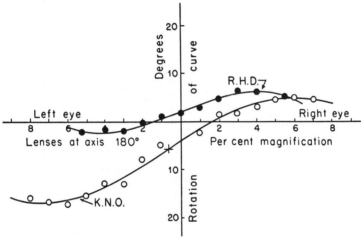

Fig. 107. The equivalent angle of rotation of the curve of the rods of the horopter apparatus when adjusted for the apparent frontoparallel plane. These data illustrate the induced effect when the only vertically separated contours in the entire binocular visual field are two beads on the central rod. Data are shown for two subjects.

field are influenced by the lens when there are only two separated contours for fusion in the vertical meridian.

With only the two beads on the central rod as vertical fusion stimuli, the induced effect is usually not great, and for some few subjects may be scarcely observable. If beads are attached to all five horopter rods, the effect is markedly increased. Care must be taken to arrange the beads on the rods so that they will have different separations and be at different levels; otherwise an inhibiting empirical factor of form may be introduced.

RESTRICTED FUSION STIMULI

The experiment with the horopter apparatus just described shows that the induced effect will occur when as few as two vertically separated fusion

* The rotation, ψ, had to be computed from the values of R_0 found from the analytic graph by $\tan \psi = (R_0 - 1)b/(R_0 + 1)a$, where, as before, b is the observation distance and a is one half of the interpupillary separation (p. 162).

stimuli are present in the binocular visual field. This being so, it is important to learn how the effect depends on the separation of these stimuli, that is, on the peripheral angle of the retinas upon which the images of these stimuli fall.

It is simpler to study the phenomenon by using the tilting field instead of the horopter apparatus, because the degree of rotation of the plane can be read directly. The essential problem is to simplify the details on the test plane (Fig. 108). In doing this several considerations should be taken into account. There must be details to provide horizontal stimuli by which the orientation of the plane about the vertical axis can be discriminated stereoscopically. These details themselves must not, however, be sufficient to cause the induced effect. A single row of irregularly spaced small ink dots, 0.5 to 0.75 mm. in diameter, is placed horizontally through the center of the plane. A vertical line or thread is also fastened in the axis of rotation of the plane to assist fixation and fusion in the horizontal meridian. If the plane is

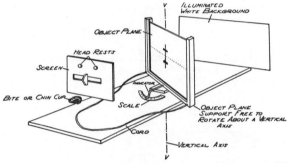

Fig. 108. Perspective drawing of the tilting plane with one type of simplified pattern used to study the induced effect with limited contours.

left entirely clear except for this row of dots and the vertical line, no induced effect should be demonstrated. With larger dots, however, even as much as 3 mm. in diameter (0.5 degree visual angle), or if the row of dots is not precisely in the visual plane, a small effect may be found.

The following types of stimulus contours can be used. (1) At a given distance above and below the row, two small black paper rectangles, with long dimension horizontal, can be attached to the glass and centered with the vertical line. These rectangles furnish the separated contours, whose images fall on particular regions of the retinas and which provide the stimuli necessary for the effect (see Fig. 108). (2) Small wooden hemispheres (1 cm. in diameter) painted black may also be used, attached to both sides of the glass. These have the advantage that their angular shape to the eyes does not change as the plane is turned. (3) Even simpler is to eliminate the glass plate and substitute for the row of dots a small white thread with a number of narrow ink rings spaced at irregular intervals of about 1 cm., stretched horizontally across the frame. A second thread is fastened vertically to coincide with the axis of rotation of the frame. Above and below the horizontal thread, identical strips of heavy black cardboard or small spheres are supported in the plane of the intersecting threads by a suitable framework independent of the rotatable frame. The inner edges of the strips, placed at equal distances above and below the horizontal thread, provide the desired separated contours. The outer ends of the strips and the supports lie outside the field of vision. These contours do not change with the rotation of the test thread. (4) The effect can also occur if one of these strips is removed, because the edge of the other and the horizontal row of dots constitute the necessary separated contours.

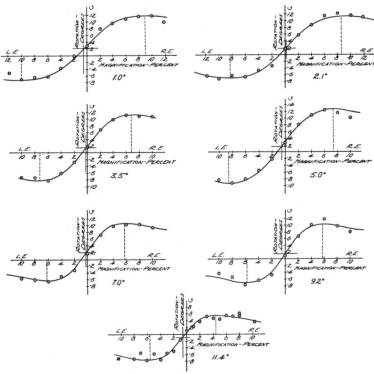

Fig. 109. Data (R.H.D.) showing the induced effect curves for different vertical distances of a single contour above and below the visual plane.

With any one of these simplified test patterns, the characteristic sigmoid curve is obtained. Inexperienced observers, it is true, may not always respond readily to so simple a pattern. The response to the effect by experienced observers is, however, only slightly less with the simple pattern than with the more complex.

Figure 109 illustrates typical data obtained by one observer for a series of different separations of the contours. These separations are expressed as the visual angles in degrees. The results of several observers[181] with these simple separated contours can be summarized as follows:

(1) The differential response (the slope of the curve at the center of

symmetry), in degrees rotation caused by 1 per cent change in the magnification of the image of one eye in the vertical meridian, is the *same for all separations of the contours* of the same pattern. The single contour of the strip with the horizontal row of dots showed lower values. The differential response even with the two contours was less than that for a test plane full of dots.

(2) The average magnification at which the maximal rotation of the test plane occurred, measured from the center of symmetry, decreased by approximately a third with increase in visual angle to the contours. This is to say, the larger the visual angle to the contours, the lower were the values of magnification corresponding to the maximal rotation. These values were considerably different among observers and with different patterns on the plane.

(3) The average maximal rotation of the test plane, however, decreased only slightly with increase in visual angle for the same subject but its magnitude varied considerably with the pattern and between observers. It was lowest for the single contour above the row of dots.

COMMENT

Let us consider for a moment the factors involved in these data and their meaning. A meridional magnification lens placed before one eye at axis 180 degrees increases the sizes of the retinal images in that eye in the vertical meridian. With two vertically separated contours as in these experiments, the separation of the retinal images in one eye is thus greater than that of the other. There is an angular difference in the height in the retinal images of one of those contours above the visual plane and this difference constitutes a *vertical* disparity between the images of the two eyes (Fig. 110). Thus, if the angular distance of the contour above the visual plane is 1 degree, and the meridional lens increases the image 4 per cent, then the disparity between the images in the two eyes would be 4 per cent of 1 degree, or 0.04 degree, or 2.4 minutes of arc. For a visual angle of 10 degrees the disparity would be 24 minutes of arc.

Now the stimulus and the concomitant innervations that give rise to the induced effect must originate in the cerebral recognition of these disparities, in the same sense that stereoscopic depth perception results from a recognition of horizontal disparities. The magnitude of the vertical disparity alone, however, does not determine the magnitude of the effect. The fact that the differential response, 1 degree per 1 per cent, is found to be the same for all visual angles to the stimuli shows that the magnitude of the response depends upon the ratio of the disparity to the visual angle, which in turn is identical to the per cent magnification introduced by the lens.

The similarity between the fusional movements caused by a single peripheral stimulus (Chapter 9) and the phenomenon being discussed should be pointed out. In the case of the induced effect, fusional movements cannot occur in response to the vertical disparity of the images, because the images

of the other contours would then become disparate and stop those movements. In the peripheral fusion experiments, nothing prevented such movements and, accordingly, they took place up to certain limits of disparity. A
sigmoid-like curve showing actual movement in response to the vertical disparity resulted.

We could, therefore, build a case for the hypothesis that the induced
effect arises as a result of the stimuli for vertical fusional movements—movements that cannot actually occur. The magnitude of the stimulus for the
fusional movement would obviously depend on the disparity of the image,
and we could account for the fact that the differential response of the induced effect could be constant for all visual angles. Such a hypothesis is con-

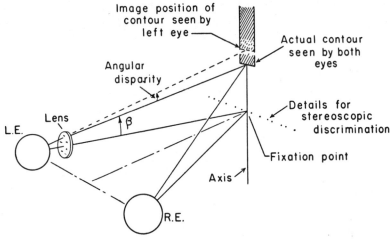

Fig. 110. The vertical disparity introduced between the images of the two eyes of
vertically separated contours, when the image of one eye is magnified in the vertical
meridian.

sistent with that already suggested for the origin of stereoscopic depth
perception;[77] namely, the stimuli for horizontal fusional movements that cannot or do not occur.

THE RELATION TO PANUM'S FUSIONAL AREAS

The vertical disparities introduced by the lens at the point of maximal
effect can be likened to Panum's areas of fusion, and considerable interest
is attached to that fact. It would not be unreasonable to expect that the
dimensions of these vertical disparities and those of Panum's areas would
be the same and that the fusion of the vertically disparate images would be
a factor in the development of the induced effect. However, the data from
these experiments with restricted stimuli as well as the observer's personal
experience seem to bear out the fact that the disparities at the maximal induced effect are actually *larger* than Panum's areas in the vertical meridian.
Figure 111 shows the calculated sizes of the vertical disparities between

the images for the average magnification at which the maximal effect occurs, and also the estimated vertical sizes of Panum's areas. It is questionable whether the difference between the two contours (rectangles) and the single contour are statistically significant. For visual angles of up to about 2 degrees, Panum's areas are probably about 6 to 8 minutes of arc. Thus, Panum's areas and those corresponding to the maximal induced effect are of the same order near the macula. No data exist for the vertical extent of Panum's fusional areas in the periphery. The approximate values (Chapter 7) for Panum's area in the horizontal meridian are plotted on the graph for comparison, although these probably are larger than those in the vertical meridian. In the experiment while data for the induced effect curve with the restricted contours are being obtained, the observer is frequently

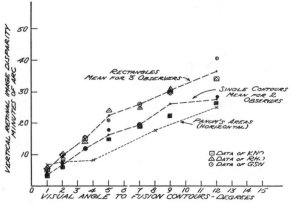

Fig. 111. The vertical disparity between the retinal images of the two eyes that exists at the maximal induced effect and its change with increasing visual angle. For comparison the approximate dimensions of Panum's fusional areas are also shown.

conscious of a doubling of those contours as the point of maximal response is reached and passed.

THE CONTINUED RESPONSE BEYOND THE MAXIMUM

Although there are differences between individual observers, in general the sigmoid curve that describes the induced effect slowly descends after the maximal response has been reached. This is illustrated by the curves in Fig. 112, where magnification changes of more than 20 per cent were used. The slow descent of these curves is evidence that there is a continuing stimulus for the effect even though it becomes weaker with larger and larger vertical disparities. In this part of the curve, the images of the contours, except those near the macula, will be double, because the images lie far outside of Panum's fusional areas.

It has been found that these curves can be described by the equation

$$y = Axe^{-B|x|}$$

where y is the rotation of the test plane, x is the vertical magnification introduced (which is proportional to the vertical disparities introduced), $|x|$ being the absolute value independent of sign, and A and B are constants. Thus, for small values of x, y is almost directly proportional to x, but as x increases, the magnitude of the second part of the equation becomes more important, and when $x = A/B$, a maximal value of y is obtained. One could consider from this point of view that two processes are active here, an excitation process that is directly *proportional* to the vertical disparity and an

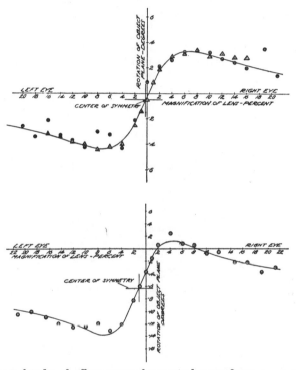

Fig. 112. Typical induced effect curves for vertical magnifications up to 20 per cent. The fusion in the vertical meridian for these data is restricted to two separated contours. The observation distance was 40 cm.

inhibitory or resistance process that increases *exponentially* with the vertical disparity. The curves drawn to the data on the graphs are the result of fitting this equation to the data. Other expressions also can be made to fit the data, for example, $y = Ax/(1 + Bx^2)$. While these express the same types of component processes, perhaps no special importance should be attached at this time to the actual form of the equation. The fact that the effect seems finally to decrease exponentially with the disparity has implication, of course, on our concepts concerning the neurologic connections between the corresponding retinal areas of the two eyes and their spatial representation in the brain.

THE INFLUENCE OF HORIZONTAL DISPARITIES ON THE SEPARATED VERTICAL CONTOURS

The differential response of the induced effect as measured on a tilting plane, the surface of which can be inclined to the vertical, is found to be less than that when the plane is vertical.[182] This difference must be attributed to the horizontal disparities between the images of details on the plane as the latter is inclined. The problem of the induced effect when the images of the contours are disparate is thus of importance.

The apparatus consists of a haploscope used jointly with a tilting test plane, as shown schematically in Fig. 113. The haploscope consists of two arms which can turn about vertical axes that pass through the entrance pupils of the two eyes when the head of an observer is correctly positioned. On these two arms before the eyes, half-silvered mirrors are so mounted that suitable patterns on targets farther out on the arms can be seen by reflection, appearing when the images are fused as though they were a single pattern in front of the observer. A test plane at an observation distance of 40 cm. in front of the

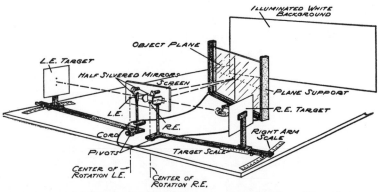

Fig. 113. Perspective sketch of the haploscope combined with a tilting plane apparatus used to study changes in the induced effect when horizontal disparities are introduced in the images of fusable patterns.

instrument is also seen through the half-silvered mirrors. This plane can be rotated about a vertical axis and its rotational position as controlled by the observer can be recorded from a suitable protractor scale.

The pattern on the plane consists of a horizontal row of irregularly spaced small dots through the center of the plane. By means of these dots the rotational position of the plane can be discriminated stereoscopically. The horizontal row of dots is seen against a uniformly illuminated white background. A vertical line drawn or a thread stuck on the plane so as to coincide with the axis of rotation assists in holding the convergence of the eyes.

The three types of haploscope target patterns were used.[182] The first consisted of two identical black disks, 8 mm. in diameter, drawn on white cardboard 3.5 cm. above and below the center of the target; the second, of two vertical black wedge-pointed strips, which are also equally separated from the center of the targets, and the third, of five horizontal white disks (4 cm. apart) on a black background the same distance above and below the center of the target. In the third case the contrast scheme was reversed, and a black background was suspended beyond the test dots. In each case the pattern subtended a vertical visual angle of about 5 degrees from the row of dots. Identical patterns which were photographic prints were used on each target of the haploscope.

When the instrument is in adjustment for zero horizontal disparity, the images of the patterns on the two targets are seen stereoscopically to coincide with the test plane in space. The arrangement is then essentially that used in the experiments described previously.

With this adjustment of the apparatus, when a meridional afocal magnification lens is placed before one eye to increase the magnification of the image in the vertical meridian, the expected induced effect takes place; that is, the test plane appears skew. The observer adjusts the plane so that the horizontal row of dots appears normal; the actual rotational position is the magnitude of the effect. With a sequence of meridional lenses of increasing magnification, the data for a typical S-shaped curve for the effect are obtained.*

Now, a horizontal disparity is introduced between the images of the patterns and the plane of the row of dots by turning each of the haploscope arms

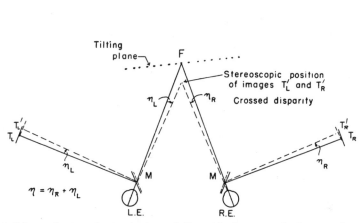

Fig. 114. Scheme for introducing horizontal disparities between the images of patterns in the haploscope relative to those of the tilting plane.

through a small angle (Fig. 114). If the arms are turned *outward* (the ends of the arms toward the observer), the fused images of the pattern contours appear stereoscopically to recede behind the test plane in uncrossed (homonymous) disparity; if turned *inward* (the ends away from the observer), the fused images of the patterns appear to approach the observer in crossed (heteronymous) disparity.

The induced effect curves, or S-curves as they may be called, were obtained for each of a number of different horizontal disparities introduced in the images of the target pattern. It was found that the differential sensitivity decreased with the horizontal disparity, and yet the effect was measurable even when the horizontal disparities were so large that the observer was aware of double images of the pattern.

In Fig. 115 are illustrated the data for one observer, when the strip-wedge

* Precisely the same effect can be had by changing slightly the distance of one of the haploscope targets, instead of using the lenses, for the angular size of the pattern is changed, and vertical disparities are introduced between the images of the two eyes.

type of target was used. In order to include all the curves in one figure, the abscissal units are left unnumbered, each division, however, corresponding to a 2 per cent difference in the magnification of the images in the vertical meridian as introduced by the lenses. The part of the curves lying to the

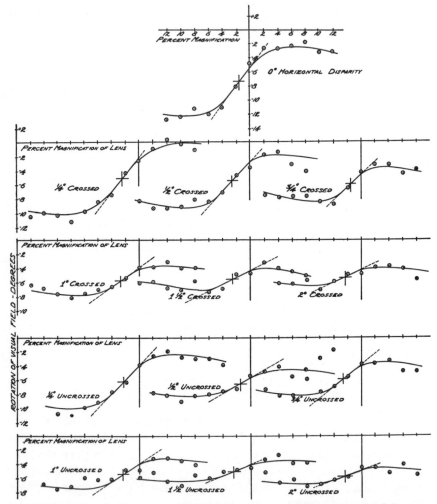

Fig. 115. The induced effect curves (K.N.O.) for a series of different horizontal disparities of the fusion contours.

right of the ordinate axis represents data taken when the right image is increased; that on the left, when the left image is increased. The differential response, which is the important feature of the data and is indicated by the slopes of the curves at the centers of symmetry, decreases markedly as the horizontal disparity increases. The curves show, on the other hand, scarcely any change in the average difference in the magnification of the images for which the maximal rotations occur.

If we plot the differential sensitivity of these curves as ordinates against the angular horizontal disparity as the abscissa, crossed to the right and uncrossed to the left, we obtain a sharply peaked bell-like figure, which shows the rather rapid decrease in the response as the horizontal disparity between the images of the contour increases. This curve appears to be symmetrical on the two sides, showing that the decrease in response is the same

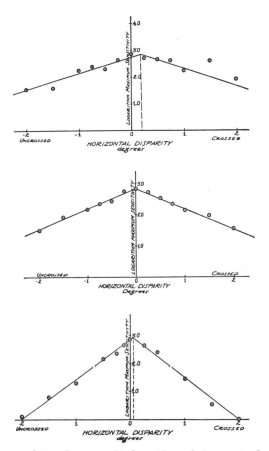

Fig. 116. The linear relation between the logarithm of the maximal sensitivity of the induced effect and the horizontal disparity of the fusion contours.

for either crossed or uncrossed disparity. The particular shape of these curves suggests that the differential response, I, might be described by an inverse exponential function of the type

$$I = I_0 e^{-c|(\eta + \sigma)|}$$

where I_0 is the maximal differential response when the functional horizontal angular disparity $(\eta + \sigma)$ is zero, where also $|(\eta + \sigma)|$ is the absolute value of the functional horizontal angular disparity; η is the (geometric) disparity as adjusted on the haploscope, σ is the angular value of the fixation disparity, and c is a constant. The disparity η will be taken positive or negative, according to whether it is crossed or uncrossed. It appears in the equation as the absolute value, a device for obtaining a symmetrical curve of the first power. The relationship can be written

$$\log I = \log I_0 - c|(\eta + \sigma)|$$

and this is a linear equation. If we take the logarithms of the differential sensitivities of the data and plot these as ordinates against the disparity, η, on the abscissa, we can test the degree to which the differential response decreases with the logarithm of the disparity.

The data of three observers so treated are shown in Fig. 116. It is clear that these data are adequately described by this relationship. Thus, one could state that on the basis of these data the interaction between vertically disparate images giving rise to the induced effect decreases logarithmically with the horizontal disparity introduced between those images.* Data[182] also show that this relationship is independent of the vertical visual angle to the contours.

One should note that in one of the graphs and to a less extent in a second the maximal differential response is obtained when the targets in the haploscope are adjusted to a small crossed disparity of about 0.1 degree or 6 minutes of arc. This angle is, of course, the fixation disparity of the eyes of the observer for this visual distance, and this is consistent with measurements made in other ways. This fact is important, for it definitely shows that maximal induced effect occurs when the physiologic or functional horizontal disparity of the images is zero.

INCLINED TILTING PLANES

In the preceding chapters it was shown that the apparent skewness of an inclined plane due to an increased magnification of the image of one eye in the *horizontal* meridian (geometric effect) was independent of the inclination if measured about a vertical axis, but that it decreased with the inclination if measured about an axis in the inclined plane. The differential response in the induced effect, on the other hand, decreases with the inclination measured about either axis, but that measured about the inclined axis shows a greater decrease. We might expect this decrease on the basis that the images of all points on the inclined plane, except those actually in the visual plane of the observer, will be horizontally disparate. The problem is not easy to solve analytically, but empirically the differential response is approximately proportional to the cosine of the angle of inclination when measured about a vertical axis, and to the cosine squared of that angle when measured about the inclined axis.

---

* Attention should be called to the importance of these data, because they imply a neurologic organization of corresponding retinal areas of the two eyes in the horizontal meridian far outside those indicated by the size of Panum's areas, here to an angular size of 2 arc degrees and greater! The functional response to disparities within these dimensions, however, appears to decrease logarithmically.

The fact that the differential response to meridional magnification lenses placed axis horizontal (axis 180 degrees) of subjects viewing the large tilting plane[4] (Fig. 91) was about one half of that of the response to meridional magnification lenses placed axis vertical (axis 90 degrees) must be attributed to this phenomenon. The angle of inclination of that plane to the normal to the visual plane of the observer is about 60 degrees.

THE SIMULTANEOUS GEOMETRIC AND INDUCED EFFECTS

It has been amply demonstrated that the two effects, the geometric meridional effect (lenses at axis 90 degrees) and the induced effect (meridional lenses at axis 180 degrees), can act independently and yet simultaneously.

A meridional magnification lens has its chief magnifying property in one meridian and none in the meridian at right angles (the axis). When placed

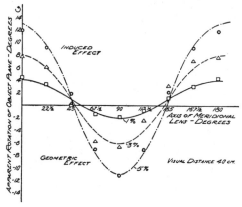

Fig. 117. Typical data (H.F.) showing the magnitude of the rotation of a tilting plane about a vertical axis, caused by a meridional magnification lens which is adjusted to different angular positions before the right eye.

before one eye with axis 90 degrees, the principal magnifying effect is in the horizontal meridian, none in the vertical. If the lens is now placed before one eye with axis at an oblique angle, there will be components of the principal magnification in the horizontal and vertical meridians, the amount depending on the angle at which the axis is set (Appendix, p. 305). At 45 degrees, the two components are equal, that is, the magnification in the horizontal is equal to that in the vertical. When one uses the tilting plane which has many details, the geometric response and the induced effect response are substantially equal though opposite in direction, so that the meridional lens at axis 45 degrees or 135 degrees before one eye will not cause an apparent skewness of the test plane about a vertical axis. (It will, of course, cause an apparent inclination about a horizontal axis due to the small rotary deviations between the images of the two eyes.)

A typical set of data is illustrated graphically in Fig. 117 and shows the usual cosine type of curve. When the magnifying effect of the lens is in the horizontal meridian (axis 90 degrees), the apparent rotation is entirely geometric; when it is in the vertical meridian (axis 180 degrees), the apparent rotation is due solely to the induced effect. At the oblique meridians of 45 degrees and 135 degrees, the two effects more or less offset each other, since the magnification components of the lens in the vertical and horizontal meridians are equal. At all other oblique meridians, one effect or the other dominates.

In surroundings where there are many stimuli for stereoscopic vision, the magnitude of the induced effect is equal but opposite to that caused by the

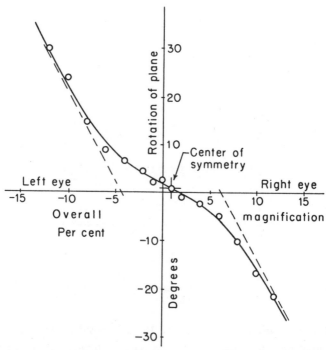

Fig. 118. Typical results of the rotation of the tilting plane, when overall afocal magnification lenses are used. The test was at 40 cm., and the contours on the plane were few in number and restricted to vertical angles of about 5 degrees. Data of D.S.

geometric effect for the same difference in magnification. An overall magnification lens (one which magnifies equally in all meridians) of not too high magnification before one eye would, therefore, have little or no effect on the apparent orientation of objects in space. However, because of the fact that, as the difference in magnification increases, the induced effect finally reaches a maximum and then decreases, it would be expected that for overall lenses of magnifications of more than 5 to 7 per cent, the geometric effect would be evident. Such is shown to be the case with the tilting plane.

In Fig. 118 are illustrated the typical data of the rotation of the plane necessary to appear normal when each of a series of overall afocal magnification lenses was used. The test plane in this particular experiment had a restricted number of details, so that the differential response of the induced effect never was as great as that of the geometric, and hence a small geometric effect appears even for small magnifications. For larger values, the rotation of the plane necessary to appear normal gradually approaches the purely geometric effect.

THE DIFFERENCES BETWEEN SUBJECTS

The induced effect S-curves have been obtained on more than 200 subjects, many of whom were patients. The curves vary between individuals in several aspects; namely, the differential response, the maximal degree of rotation, the magnification difference for the maximal effect, and the displacement of the center of symmetry from the origin of the graph. Examples of

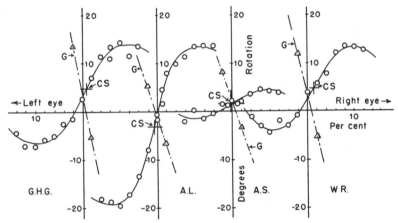

Fig. 119. Selected cases of curves showing variations in the S-curve induced effect obtained with different subjects.

these differences are illustrated in Fig. 119. These data were obtained with a vertical tilting plane at 40 cm. observation distance, and the details on the plane consisted of a scattered horizontal row of ink dots through the center, and above and below the center a small cluster of ink dots subtending an average visual angle of 5 degrees. The degree of the geometric effect, G, is also shown, and this seems fairly constant unless the subject has no stereoscopic vision at all.

Some subjects show great differences between the two effects, others very small ones. Those with the greater differences have more difficulty in adjusting the plane. While there are not statistics available to prove the point, general observation of such cases suggests that the binocular vision is poorly developed and often rather large refractive errors are found. Subjects with whom the induced effect is found smaller than the geometric effect usually see a distortion of the leaf room when an overall magnification lens is placed before one eye.

The displacement of the center of symmetry of the curve from the center of the graph varies with observers. This may be indicative of the initial difference in magnification of the images of the two eyes normally existent. The horizontal displacement would be related to the error in the vertical meridian (axis 180 degrees), while the vertical displacement could be related to the error in magnification in the horizontal meridian (axis 90 degrees) and also to ocular dominance. This problem becomes quite complicated and has not been satisfactorily worked out.

The reproducibility of these S-curves is on the whole quite satisfactory.

THEORIES OF THE INDUCED EFFECT

The induced effect has wide implications in our general theory of space perception and of stereoscopic vision. One would first seek the origin in physiologic processes because of the following facts. The phenomenon has a specific threshold of sensitivity in spatial orientation of the same order as that from stereoscopic stimuli; it varies with the degree of the stimulus in an orderly and symmetrical manner, and it has definite limits of stimulus magnitudes within which it occurs.

One might suggest that the introduction of an increased magnification of the image of one eye in the vertical meridian would cause some type of compensatory physiologic process within the binocular systems to offset this difference. Such a compensation might conceivably be due to changes of some kind in the dioptric system, such as an axial displacement of the crystalline lens, or it might be due to actual anatomic changes, both of which logically would be in the nature of an overall magnification. The overall compensation for a vertical difference would leave a residual magnification difference between the images of the two eyes in the horizontal meridian, of the right magnitude and in the right direction to account for the effect. Moreover, one would expect a definite range within which such compensatory processes could occur. Under this hypothesis, then, an actual magnification difference in the images of the two eyes in the horizontal meridian could be accounted for.

Experiment, however, does not verify such expectations. For example, with the horopter apparatus, the nonius (p. 36) method, by which the primary subjective visual directions are equated, can be used to determine the longitudinal horopter. With the fixation rod free of details, the normal positions of the 4 degree and 8 degree rods are obtained at which each appears in the same subjective visual direction. A number of small beads separated about 1 cm. are then slipped over the fixation rod. These beads furnish the necessary vertically separated contours for the induced effect. With a meridional afocal magnification lens at axis horizontal, 180 degrees, before one eye, the rods are again adjusted according to the nonius method. No significant differences in the positions of those rods with or without the lens are evident (Table 16). Had the effect been due to a true change in the relative magnifications of the images of the two eyes, the positions of the rods should have been found to lie on a skew curve as they were with the apparent frontoparallel plane criterion. Other experiments with the eikonic target (p. 244) give the same result. We must conclude then that the phenomenon is *psychologic in origin, though depending on specific physiologic stimuli, and is essentially described as a subjective rotational change in a frame of reference for the entire binocular visual field.*

The implications of this fact are of great importance in our concept of stereoscopic depth perception. Consider for a moment the experiment with the horopter apparatus in which the rods were adjusted for the apparent frontoparallel plane. With the beads on the fixation rod and a meridional

Table 16

DATA WHICH SHOW THAT IN THE PRESENCE OF THE INDUCED EFFECT NO CHANGE
OCCURS IN THE SETTINGS OF THE RODS FOR THE LONGITUDINAL
HOROPTER AS DETERMINED BY THE NONIUS METHOD*

VERTICAL MAGNIFI-CATION INTRODUCED	LEFT HALF VISUAL FIELD		RIGHT HALF VISUAL FIELD	
Lane	−8 degrees	−4 degrees	4 degrees	8 degrees
2% L. E.	−9.7 (1.6)	−3.1 (1.0)	−1.8 (0.9)	−10.1 (2.1)
Normal	−9.8 (1.7)	−4.6 (1.3)	−3.1 (1.3)	−8.8 (1.5)
2% R. E.	−9.4 (1.6)	−3.7 (1.0)	−1.9 (0.8)	−8.5 (3.0)
4% R. E.	−10.5 (3.3)	−4.5 (1.4)	−1.5 (1.3)	−5.4 (1.3)
5% R. E.	−10.1 (1.9)	−4.8 (1.2)	−1.9 (1.9)	−8.4 (1.8)
5% L. E.	−12.1 (1.7)	−6.1 (0.9)	−2.9 (0.9)	−4.5 (2.3)

* Data (K. N. O.) measured from objective frontoparallel plane in millimeters. A negative sign implies that points were in front of this plane. Figures in parentheses are the mean variation in settings.

afocal lens at axis 180 degrees before one eye, the other rods are set to appear normal and in a plane. When so adjusted they are found to lie on a skew curve, a curve rotated about the point of fixation. Since no true magnification between the ocular system has been introduced into the horizontal meridian, then actually the *images of those rods must be horizontally disparate though they appear in the frontoparallel plane.*

This fact might appear to be an actual denial of the Hering criterion for the determination of the longitudinal horopter; namely, that rods set so that they appear in a frontoparallel plane to include the fixation rod will determine the longitudinal horopter. We already have seen that this was not strictly true because of fixation disparity, but in that case we assumed that the concept of frontoparallel plane was transferred from pairs of corresponding points to pairs of equally disparate retinal elements.

However, the Hering criterion is not entirely vitiated by these deductions, for the shape of the skewed curve (the H parameter) seems to be essentially that found when the induced effect was not present. Furthermore, Hering's criterion for the longitudinal horopter was based on the concept of corresponding longitudinal sections of the two retinas, and would not involve the fusional or directional effects of details in the vertical meridians. Thus only smooth threads or rods would be used in the apparatus.

Nevertheless, it is clear that our subjective spatial sense of what constitutes the "normal" and "equidistant" is influenced by the presence of separated contours in the vertical direction in the binocular field, for depending on these is the particular subjective orientation of the stereoscopic egocentric frame of reference. This is the striking fact to be observed in the apparent distortion of the leaf room when a meridional afocal lens at axis 180 degrees is placed before one eye, for the horizontal disparities between the images in the two eyes have not been changed. Actually, then, a regular pattern of horizontally disparate images is psychically correlated with a particular skewed frame of reference. It must also be remembered in this that the fundamental basis of stereoscopic depth perception arising from the disparities between the images in the two eyes of points in space has not been altered. The stereoscopic activity and discrimination of depth difference between objects at different distances are the same as before. Only the psychic frame of reference for an absolute space perception has been changed by the presence of the induced effect. Except in artificial cases this effect does not occur under normal conditions for symmetrical convergence.

One of the explanations of this phenomenon involves the concept of "perceptual images." Lippincott[153] based his explanation of the apparent distortion of objects in the binocular visual field due to weak ophthalmic cylinders at axis 180 degrees before one eye on such a hypothesis. In observing a square, with the lens at axis 90 degrees, before the right eye, the square seen by that eye would be rectangular—larger in the horizontal than in the vertical dimension. By "stereoscopic" vision the two "perceptual" images would give the impression of a rotated and distorted figure. Likewise with the lens at axis 180 degrees, the vertical dimension of the rectangle perceived by the right eye would be the larger. But according to this concept the brain combines these two figures as wholes, not according to their absolute retinal image sizes but rather their relative shapes, and in this case the horizontal dimension of the left image is greater than that of the right; hence the direction of the distortion would be reversed.

Such explanations are also in line with the thinking of some of those interested in Gestalt psychology. Linksz has proposed a similar explanation for the induced effect. The concept that stereoscopic perception of space depends on the combination of the perceived forms of figures seen by the two eyes has been expressed before, for example, by Lau.[143] He claims to have experienced stereoscopic depth in the haploscope from figures whose stimuli for the stereoscopic depth were pure illusions and which did not actually introduce disparities between the retinal images. Most experimenters have failed to verify these experiments, however.

Although there may be, perhaps, a basis for such explanations for familiar figures or objects in the field of view, it cannot account for the *skew rotation* of the entire visual space about the fixation point, when only *one* pair of vertically separated contours exists in the binocular field of view.

An entirely consistent theory for the induced effect lies in those phenomena of space perception associated with the asymmetric convergence of the eyes (Chapter 17). For objects in the median plane of the observer with the eyes in symmetrical convergence, the retinal images of the two eyes are equal in the vertical dimension, but when one observes the same object in asymmetric convergence to the right (say) at a near visual distance, the vertical extent of the image in the right eye is larger than that of the corresponding image in the left eye, because the distance of the object to the right eye is less than that to the left. Now *if* our stereoscopic spatial localization is concerned with egocentric localization, that is, the discrimination of the distance of objects from ourselves, then it is important that those discriminations be made relative to a *normal* surface to the direction in which the eyes are fixating. This necessitates a rotation of the binocular visual field about the point of fixation. The difference in sizes of the images in the two eyes in the vertical meridian provides the physiologic cue for such a rotation, and the induced effect follows.

CHAPTER 16

Asymmetric Convergence

INTRODUCTION

WHEN THE EYES turn to observe a near object in asymmetric convergence, differences in the sizes of the images on the retinas of the two eyes would be expected because the distance of the object from one eye will be longer than that from the other (Fig. 120). The difference will obviously be greater the nearer the object and the greater the degree of lateral turning of the eyes.

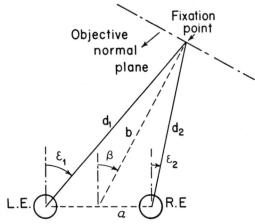

Fig. 120. The geometric relationships when the eyes are converged asymmetrically on a near object.

One can compute the magnitude of this difference from the geometry. The ratio, R, of the size of the image of the right eye to that of the left ($R{:}L$) from inspection of the figure will be $R = d_1/d_2 = \cos \epsilon_2/\cos \epsilon_1$, where ϵ_1 and ϵ_2 are the angles of turning from the primary position, and d_1 and d_2 are the object distances, of the left and right eyes, respectively. This relationship is *correct only for the vertical meridian*, because in the horizontal meridian the geometric difference in image size depends also on the orientation of the face of the object, in the sense of a rotational position about a vertical axis at the fixation point. If the face of the object is normal to the direction of the fixation point, that is, if it coincides with the objective normal plane, then the geometric difference in size between the two images will be quite accurately the same in all meridians. Table 17 gives the magnitude of the difference in size of images in per cent for various degrees of asymmetric convergence.

That such differences actually exist was first pointed out by Desaguliers in 1717, and later shown by Wheatstone, in the following simple experiment. If one observes a small object, a coin, for example, in asymmetric convergence at near vision, and lets the eyes overconverge or underconverge slightly so that the object is observed in double vision, one can easily verify the fact that the image seen by the nearer eye appears the larger. One would conclude that under normal visual conditions monocular images of slightly different form and size are somehow combined into a single binocular image. With a small object such as the coin, this is easily understood because the

Table 17

THEORETICAL DIFFERENCES BETWEEN THE MAGNIFICATIONS OF THE RETINAL IMAGES WITH THE EYES IN ASYMMETRIC CONVERGENCE, IN PER CENT*

VISUAL DISTANCE	DEGREE OF ASYMMETRIC CONVERGENCE			
	10°	20°	30°	40°
6 meters	0.2	0.3	0.4	0.6
75 cm.	1.5	3.0	4.4	5.7
40 cm.	2.8	5.6	8.4	10.9
33 cm.	3.3	6.9	10.2	13.4
20 cm.	5.4	11.4	17.3	22.9

* Computation for an interpupillary distance of 65 mm.

differences in the sizes of the images will usually be well within Panum's retinal areas of fusion. No difficulties are said to be experienced with this type of observation.

More important than this problem of fusion when the eyes are converged asymmetrically at near vision, however, is the problem that arises in an attempt to understand the binocular stereoscopic spatial localization. Without there being a compensatory change in the relative magnification of the images in the two eyes, or a compensatory psychologic change in our perceptual frame of reference, our binocular stereoscopic vision will lead to an incorrect egocentric spatial localization.

Consider Fig. 121, in which the eyes are first converged symmetrically and fixated on a point F in the median plane. The sensation of farness or nearness through stereoscopic vision is referred to the horopter surface which normally is tangent to the Vieth-Müller circle at F. Stereoscopic depth perception depends on the disparity between the images of points in space reckoned from that surface. If, now, the eyes change their positions to fixate

a point F' in asymmetric convergence (say) to the right, at the same observation distance, then those same disparities of the images would be referred to a surface still tangent to the Vieth-Müller circle at the fixation point, as shown by the line T'. Such a surface, however, is not normal
to the visual direction of the point of fixation, and points on that surface on
the right side of the fixation point would actually be too *near*, those on the
left side, too far away. To obtain a normal egocentric spatial localization,
spatial objects must be referred to a surface that is normal to the direction
of gaze, as suggested by the line N'.

This necessary reorientation in the visual localization of objects in space
by stereoscopic vision is equivalent to the effect of a change in the relative

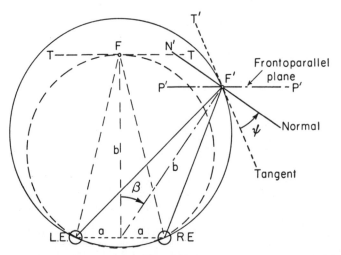

Fig. 121. Scheme for illustrating the problem of egocentric stereoscopic spatial localization
when the eyes are converged asymmetrically.

magnification of the images in the two eyes, for the essential spatial change
is a rotation of the binocular field about the point of fixation (through the
angle ψ). For asymmetric convergence to the right, the image of the left
eye would have to be increased (relative to that of the right) in the horizontal meridian.

The needed reorientation would occur automatically if the magnification
of the image of the eye that turns nasally were increased so as to compensate for the difference in distance of the fixation point from the two eyes.

While studying the efficacy of certain targets in the haploscope as a
means for measuring the relative sizes of the images in the two eyes, Ames
about 1931 found that when the arms of the haploscope were rotated so as
to cause his eyes to turn in to an asymmetric convergent position, he observed an apparent change in the sizes of those targets. This apparent
change in relative image size was in the direction which would have corrected the difference in the geometric sizes of the images, had the eyes been

observing under actual conditions an object with the same degree of asymmetric convergence. Following this lead, a rather extensive study of this phenomenon was made.[113, 183, 184]

THE EXPERIMENTS WITH THE HAPLOSCOPE

The head of the observer is carefully adjusted in the haploscope so that the centers of rotation of the eyes are directly above the pivot points of the two arms (Fig. 122). On these arms, half-silvered mirrors are mounted so that the reflected images of appropriate targets farther out on the arms are seen binocularly by the observer as a single target in front. When the two eyes of the observer are so adjusted accurately the two targets will always remain the same distance from the eyes, regardless of the angles through which the arms and the eyes are turned. The condition of asymmetric convergence can be obtained by turning the arms in the same direction.

Under these experimental conditions any change which might occur between the relative sizes of the images of the two eyes with lateral gaze will

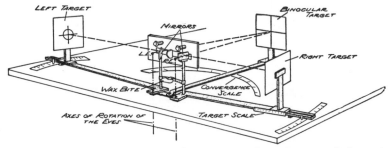

Fig. 122. Schematic drawing of the haploscope as used to observe and determine the apparent change in sizes of the images when the eyes are asymmetrically converged.

then be susceptible to observation and even measurement. With appropriate power lenses before the eyes and with a corresponding change in the convergence of the arms, the images of the targets can be projected optically to any desired observation distance. The angular size of each target can be changed either by moving it a small distance along the arm, or better, by using appropriate afocal magnification lenses before the eyes. The efficacy of the instrument, of course, depends on the choice of suitable target patterns that will make a sensitive test. Only the three types shown in Fig. 123 need be described.

The Circle and Square Patterns. The simplest target consists of a square before one eye and a circle before the other, drawn with India ink on heavy drawing paper. The diameter of the circle is the same as the length of a side of the square (3 cm. for the observation distance of 33 cm.). Fusion is maintained either by means of crossed lines at the centers of the targets or by a single pair of crossed lines on a third target mounted in front of the subject and viewed through the half-silvered mirrors. The circle will appear tangent to the sides of the square if the observer has neither an initial difference in the sizes of the images nor a fixation disparity. A fixation disparity will cause the circle to appear displaced slightly relative to the square. The sizes of the circle and square can be easily compared, however, in spite of this displacement.

The arms of the haploscope are first set so that the eyes are symmetrically converged, and the targets are adjusted until the circle and the square appear the same size. The arms are then turned so that the eyes are converged asymmetrically, and the observer then compares the apparent size of the square with that of the circle. At near vision, with ordinary observation where the eyes are allowed to rove freely over the targets, nearly all observers have reported that the target before the eye that turns nasally appears larger than the target before the other eye. Thus, as represented

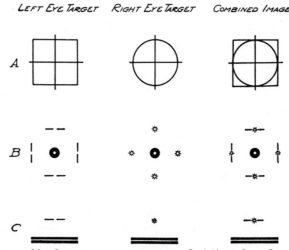

Fig. 123. Types of haploscopic target patterns used: (A) circle and square with central cross for fusion; (B) eikonic pattern, the stars representing points of light (original pattern used by Ames), and (C) central fixation peripheral fusion pattern.

in Fig. 124, when the square is seen by the left eye and the circle by the right, as the arms are turned so that the eyes converge asymmetrically to the right, the circle appears inside the square. Especially striking is this difference in the vertical meridian, but in the horizontal it is very often less evident, though a few reported that they experienced the same change in the horizontal as in the vertical meridian. Most observers reported difficulty in making judgments in the horizontal, which they attributed usually to an unsteady fixation disparity.

When appropriate power lenses are placed before the eyes, so that the targets are optically at 6 meters, and the convergence is correspondingly corrected, it is found on turning the eyes to converge asymmetrically that no change occurs in the apparent sizes of the targets.

The magnitude of the difference can be readily determined, either by the amount that one of the targets must be displaced along the arm toward or away from the eye* or by the selection of a particular afocal magnification lens which, placed before one eye, equalizes the apparent sizes of the patterns. By either technic a larger change was usually found in the vertical than in the horizontal meridian, though several observers obtained the same change in both meridians. This apparent change in the relative apparent sizes of the targets is in that direction which would compensate for the difference in distances which would normally occur in an asymmetric convergence of the eyes.

Different results are found, however, depending on whether the eyes were allowed to rove freely over the targets or a constant fixation was maintained at the centers. In the latter case the apparent sizes can be compared only by indirect or peripheral vision, which is a more difficult task. Actual data[183]

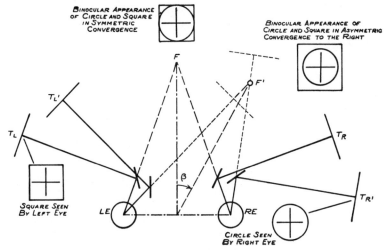

Fig. 124. Representation of the apparent change experienced in the relative sizes of the circle and the square target patterns in the haploscope when the eyes are turned to converge asymmetrically.

show, moreover, almost *no* change in the apparent sizes of the circle and square in either the vertical or horizontal meridian when central fixation is maintained, as the eyes are converged asymmetrically.

The Eikonic Targets. To obtain more accurate data, target patterns as shown in *B* (Fig. 123) were substituted for the circle and square. In the center of each were identical rings, the images of which were for holding fusion. On the right target, small points of light were arranged in the vertical and horizontal meridians at visual angles of 4 degrees from the center. On the left target, pairs of small broken lines were drawn, the gaps arranged so as to match the pattern of the lights for the right target. An observer with neither an initial difference in size of the images nor a fixation dis-

* This method is permissible, because the changes are too small (at 40 cm., 4 mm. displacement corresponds to 1 per cent) to blur the image of one eye or upset the state of accommodation.

parity, in symmetric convergence, sees the lights within the gaps of the broken lines. If, however, the right image is made larger than the left, the lights appear outside the gaps. Fixation disparity causes an equal displacement of the lights to the same side of their corresponding lines. Judgments of the relative positions of the lights with the lines involve eye movements, for the observer must actually look from one pair of lines and lights to the other in the same meridian. Reliance is placed on the fusion of the central rings to maintain the pointing of the eyes during these ocular excursions (Chapter 9).

With these target patterns the same phenomenon occurs when the arms of the haploscope are turned to converge the eyes asymmetrically. The magnitude of the apparent difference in size can be measured by using the adjustable magnification units (p. 127) before the eyes. These are adjusted so as to increase the magnification of the image of the eye that appears smaller, until the lights appear in the line gaps or are equally displaced in the same direction from them.

The data taken with these targets show small mean variations and are, in general, consistent. Typical results for observation distances from 20 cm. to 5 meters are shown graphically in Fig. 125. The same phenomenon as already described is found, especially in the vertical meridian. For near observation distances a change appears in the relative sizes of the images, as though the image of the eye which turns nasally were enlarged. This apparent change in size with lateral gaze becomes greater the nearer the targets are to the eyes. The narrow lines on the graph for the vertical meridian indicate the theoretical change in magnification that would be necessary to compensate, under natural conditions of observation, for the difference in the sizes of the retinal images due to the difference in distance of the object from the two eyes. The data show remarkable agreement with these theoretical lines. In the horizontal meridian, on the other hand, these particular data (which are representative) show only a slight change in the direction of a compensation.

Data cannot be taken with constant central fixation, using the eikonic targets, since the lights and lines are too small for their relative positions to be discriminated in peripheral vision.

The particular eikonic targets used in this experiment were made so that the state of accommodation of each eye could also be determined. Point light sources were projected by means of suitable lens systems through openings in the center of each of the targets. These points of light could be moved along the arms of the haploscope, and thus along the visual axes of the eyes. They could therefore be adjusted by the observer for the sharpest focus. The position of a point image for the sharpest focus would be conjugate to the retina, and the reciprocal of that distance (in meters) from the eye would be the measure of state of accommodation (in diopters).[8] These data showed that within 0.15 diopter there was little or no change in the state of accommodation of the two eyes when they were turned to asymmetric convergence, nor was there any evidence of a different accommodation of the two eyes.

Before ending this discussion it should be pointed out that the changes in the apparent sizes of the targets in the haploscope occur with overconvergence or underconvergence of the arms of the haploscope, and the magnitude of that change is of the order of the difference in distance from the two eyes of the equivalent intersection point of the targets, irrespective of

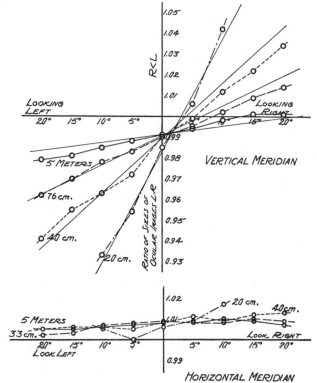

Fig. 125. Data taken on the haploscope with free fixation using eikonic targets. The ratio of the magnifications of the images of the two eyes when a lens had to be introduced in order to equalize the apparent sizes of the targets is plotted against the angular degree of asymmetric convergence.

the distance of the targets. Again these results are found only with free fixation and then principally in the vertical meridian.

Peripheral Fusion Pattern. The measurements made with the eikonic target patterns just described necessitated small ocular movements of about 4 degrees when judgments of the displacements of the lights relative to the lines were made. The fact that different results were obtained when the circle and square patterns were observed with and without eye excursions suggests that the apparent compensatory change in the sizes of the ocular images with asymmetric convergence might be some phenomenon associated with these differential eye movements.

In order to obtain data without such movements, target patterns as illustrated in C (Fig. 123) were used. These consist of two identical horizontal bands placed at equal distances above or below the centers of the targets, to serve as peripheral stimuli for fusion. A small dot was placed at the center of one target and a short horizontal broken line at the center of the other target. The observer fixates the centers of these targets binocularly during the experiment. To control the convergence of the eyes, narrow vertical lines of unequal length were drawn across the bands on each target. With the haploscope set for symmetric convergence, the targets were carefully adjusted by the observer so that the dots appeared to lie in the gap of the line. Reliance was placed on the fusion of the two black lines in the periphery to hold the directions of the eyes.

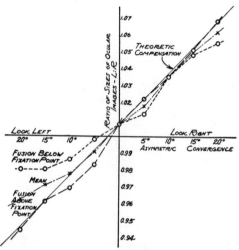

Fig. 126. Data obtained by one observer on the haploscope with peripheral target patterns (C in Fig. 123). The observation distance was 33 cm.

If a difference in size was introduced between the images in the eyes in the vertical meridian, the observer saw the dot displaced vertically from the gap. The magnitude of this displacement could be determined by the distance that the target with the dot had to be moved along the haploscope arm or by using suitable afocal magnification lenses before the eyes, which would cause the dot to reappear in the center of the gap. In order to test the efficacy of these targets, various afocal magnification lenses were placed in front of one eye and corresponding displacements of the dot were measured by movements of a target. To offset any vertical fixation disparity and inequality in the targets, measurements were first obtained with the fusion lines below and then with the fusion lines above the fixation device (which assumes that the fixation disparity is not influenced by the position of the patterns). The results showed that the observer responded accurately to these targets. Accordingly, they were considered suitable to be used with the eyes in asymmetric convergence.

The data[183] obtained by one observer are illustrated in Fig. 126. Again, the theoretical change for a complete compensation of the relative sizes of the images is shown. The measurements with these targets which involve no patent large voluntary eye movements clearly indicate a compensatory change in the sizes of the images in the vertical meridian when the eyes are turned in to asymmetric convergence.

It was found difficult to use these target patterns to measure the phenomenon in the horizontal meridian because of the unsteady fixation disparity and probably also because of a greater tendency to make voluntary eye movements. At any rate, no consistent data were obtained.

After-Image Tests. Granting some type of compensatory change in the relative magnifications of the images of the two eyes in asymmetric convergence, after-image tests ought to be instructive as to whether that process might be due to changes in the optical characteristics of the eyes.

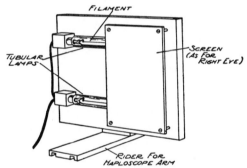

Fig. 127. Schematic drawing of the type of target used on the haploscope for inducing after-images.

Glowing filaments for inducing the after-images were mounted on the targets of the haploscope and properly screened. The type of target is illustrated schematically in Fig. 127, where two tubular lamps with single line filaments were mounted in a horizontal position, one above and the other below the center of each target. These were separated so as to subtend a vertical visual angle of 10 degrees at an observation distance of 33 cm. Suitable screens were mounted before the two targets so that each eye saw the opposite halves of corresponding filaments. To hold binocular fixation during the exposure, a target with horizontal and vertical crossed lines was set up on the arm in front of the haploscope to be seen by the observer through half-silvered mirrors.

The after-images induced in the two eyes by the filaments constituted nonius (vernier) lines, to be observed in peripheral vision. If the targets were adjusted accurately, an observer without a difference in the magnification of the images should see the after-image lines co-linear. If a difference in magnification were introduced, the separation of the lines as seen by one eye should be greater than that seen by the other. At the outset the observers reported great difficulty in judging the apparent separations between the right and left halves of the after-images, owing mostly to their short duration and instability. Trial and error showed that usually a 4 per cent difference in the sizes of the images could be recognized; therefore, the difference found in previous experiments with the eyes converged asymmetrically 15 to 20 degrees should be discernible.

The experiments, with various modifications, were conducted over a period of several weeks, but on the whole the results were variable and unreliable. So difficult were the judgments that even a trend was not evident. The results were consistent with the general impression of most observers that data which demanded peripheral judgments of image size from fixed stimuli were usually unsatisfactory and unreliable.

Herzau[113] (in Tschermak's laboratory) similarly exposed luminous patterns of various designs (circle and square, and so forth) in symmetrical and asymmetric convergence. He reported that their instrument permitted them to observe differences in the sizes of the after-images as seen by the two eyes. In every case, however, they found no change in the relative sizes of the after-images in the transition from a symmetrical to an asymmetric convergence of the eyes.

THE NONHAPLOSCOPIC EIKONIC TARGET

Obviously, the haploscope apparatus in which the targets always remain the same distance from the two eyes does not duplicate the actual conditions under which the eyes are ordinarily used when turned for an asymmetric convergence. Positive results with its use would indicate that the phenomenon was associated with proprioceptive-like influences of the external muscles of the eyes, or sensory components of the innervations to those muscles, but certainly not the result of direct stimulus, for there was none. To duplicate natural conditions, an apparatus was devised which would permit a target to be placed laterally with the eyes asymmetrically converged and also a measurement of the difference in the apparent sizes of the images.

A transparency, a negative photographic plate of a pattern consisting of lines, arrows and a circle, as shown in Fig. 128, and illuminated from behind, was used. Pieces of polarizing film were attached to the plate behind the arrows, so that the light passing through the even-numbered ones was polarized in one plane, while that passing through the odd-numbered arrows was polarized in a plane at right angles to that of the even-numbered ones. The light from the circle and lines was not polarized. The plate was mounted vertically on an arm which would turn about a vertical axis through the midpoint of the centers of rotation of the eyes. The plate then remained normal to this central arm. Polaroid plates were also mounted before each of the two eyes with the planes of polarization at right angles to each other but agreeing with those of the two sets of arrows. The observer would see the circle and lines binocularly but could see only the even-numbered arrows with one eye and the odd-numbered opposing arrows with the other eye.

If the magnifications of the images in the two eyes were equal, the opposing arrows would be directly opposite each other, that is, at the same distance from the center of the target, but if the image of one eye was larger than that of the other eye, the corresponding arrows seen by that eye would appear farther from the center than would the opposing arrows seen by the other eye. By means of suitable magnification lenses placed before one eye or the other, the apparent difference in the magnification of the images could be equalized and a measure of the difference could be obtained. If no difference could be measured when the target was turned for asymmetric convergence of the eyes, then a full compensation must have occurred between the magnifications of the images. Otherwise, a difference in the apparent size of the target would have been evident because of the difference in distance of the target from the two eyes.

The data were taken in two ways: first, with free fixation, that is, the eyes were allowed to rove at will, in which case the relative positions of the

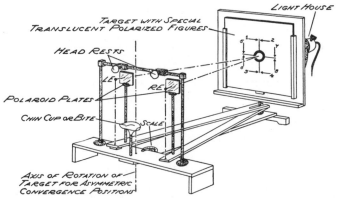

Fig. 128. Schematic drawing of apparatus using an eikonic target and Polaroid for determining the relative sizes of the images of the two eyes when they are asymmetrically converged.

opposing arrows were observed directly; and second, with the fixation of the eyes maintained steadily at the center of the target, in which case the arrows were observed in indirect vision, without ocular movements. Measurements by the latter method were again found somewhat difficult to make, because of the decreased perceptibility. The results obtained by one observer are illustrated in Fig. 129. With a 20 degree convergence to the right and with free fixation, the computed geometric difference shows that the right image is larger than the left by 7 per cent. But to equalize the apparent sizes of the images, the magnification of the left eye was increased only 0.8 per cent in the vertical meridian, and 1 per cent in the horizontal. Thus, associated with the asymmetric convergence there seemed to be a functional change in the relative magnifications of the images of the two eyes, as though the image of the left eye had been effectively increased 6.2 per cent in the vertical meridian and 6 per cent in the horizontal.

A marked difference results again, depending on whether or not eye movements have occurred in the process of making discriminatory judgments.

With free fixation, nearly a complete compensation is indicated in both the horizontal and the vertical meridian. With constant central fixation, on the other hand, the data show only a slight trend in that direction.

THE LONGITUDINAL HOROPTER WHEN THE EYES ARE ASYMMETRICALLY CONVERGED

A study of the longitudinal horopter when the eyes are fixed upon the center rod in an asymmetric convergence also contributes data on this problem.

The horopter determined by a subjective plane criterion leads to some difficulty when the eyes are converged asymmetrically. Herzau[110] concluded

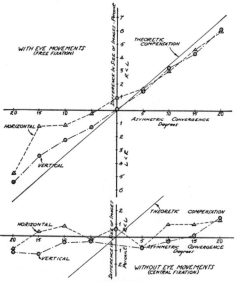

Fig. 129. Data obtained by K.N.O. with Polaroid type targets for an observation distance of 33 cm., showing the differences obtained with and without free eye movements.

that he obtained different results depending upon the particular method which he used to obtain asymmetric convergence. In the first, the head support and wax bite were mounted on a rider which could be moved along a track in the objective frontal plane. By this method, the head would be displaced laterally with respect to the fixation rod of the horopter apparatus; in every case the objective frontoparallel plane remains parallel. In the second method, the headrest, although centered with regard to the apparatus, would be rotated through a given angle about a vertical axis at the mid-point of the interocular separation. The head in this case was actually turned and in order for the eyes to fixate the center rod they were asymmetrically converged. Herzau was confused between the criterion of the apparent frontoparallel plane and that of the apparent "normal" plane—that plane normal to the subjective visual direction of the rod being fixated.

In Fig. 121, the objective frontoparallel plane and the objective normal plane are suggested by P' . . . P' and N', respectively.

Subsequent experiments[11, 113] repeated under more controlled conditions have shown that in both cases Herzau used the criterion of the apparently

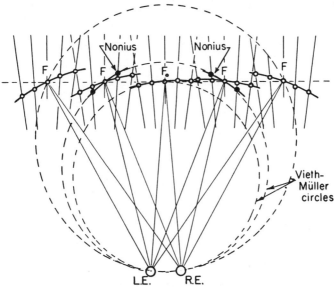

Fig. 130. The apparent normal plane and the nonius horopter settings with the eyes asymmetrically converged by head displacement. Data of W.H.

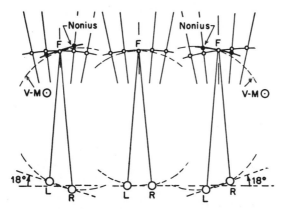

Fig. 131. The apparent normal plane and the nonius longitudinal horopter settings with the eyes converged asymmetrically by rotation of the head. Data of W.H.

normal plane. Data were obtained by both the methods. Typical results are illustrated in Fig. 130, when the head was displaced, for an observation distance of 40 cm. Figure 131 similarly shows the data for the same observer when the head was turned.

The criterion of equal subjective visual directions, the nonius method, was also used in these two methods of obtaining data,[11] for this method is independent of the stereoscopic spatial localization and is therefore the only reliable method with which to establish the position of the longitudinal horopter. The results are shown also in Figs. 130 and 131. The striking fact about the data obtained by this method is that the points on the horopter curve lie close to the Vieth-Müller circle at the fixation point. This indicates that there has been *no* significant change in the effective functional patterns of corresponding points in the horizontal meridian when the eyes turn in to an asymmetric convergent position, and therefore no physiologic compensatory change between the images of the two eyes.

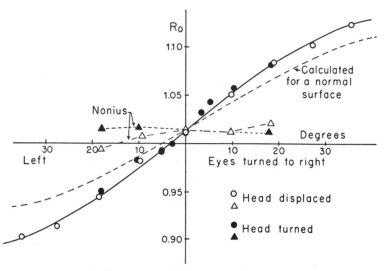

Fig. 132. The calculated values of R_0 for the data illustrated in Figs. 130 and 131, showing the equivalence of the data obtained by head displacement and head turning, and also the approximate constancy of the nonius horopter data.

Inspection of the data obtained by the two subjective spatial criteria shows that in general the curves approach the actual objective normal plane. We can study these data quantitatively by the mathematical device described in Chapter 3, whereby the value R_0, on the one hand, describes the degree to which a given curve is rotated about the point of fixation from the tangential position to the Vieth-Müller circle, and on the other hand, defines the *equivalent* of the rotation in terms of the ratio of the functional magnifications of the images of the two eyes in the horizontal meridian. The values of R_0 calculated for all these data for one observer (W.H.) are illustrated graphically in Fig. 132. The fact that the data obtained from the two methods appear to lie on the same curve* proves that the same subjective criterion was being used in both methods. The values of R_0 calculated corresponding to the position of the objective normal plane for the various

* These data have been plotted together, in spite of the small increase in observation distance introduced when the head is displaced to obtain the asymmetric convergence.

asymmetric convergences are also shown on this graph, after being displaced upward to coincide with the experimental value of R_0 for symmetrical convergence. A comparison of the data with the computed values suggests that the observer overestimated the degree of asymmetric convergence slightly (perhaps owing to the influence of the esophoria of the observer?).

These results show unmistakably that the subjective criterion of the apparent normal plane utilizes an entirely different set of retinal elements in the two eyes in asymmetric convergence from that utilized for symmetrical convergence. Furthermore, those used in asymmetric convergence are not corresponding retinal elements.* From one point of view, the complex of retinal disparities corresponding to the apparent normal plane with the eyes in asymmetric convergence would be only a little more complicated than that for the apparent frontoparallel plane with the eyes in symmetrical convergence, where the retinal elements involved must all have the same difference in disparity across the visual field due to the fixation disparity. The only question that arises in these experiments when the eyes are in asymmetric convergence, however, is upon what clue does the pattern of disparities depend? Must it be a proprioceptive sense of the extraocular muscles, or the sensory component of the innervations going to those muscles? Certainly no other clues on the horopter wires or in the apparatus exist.†

The data obtained by determining the longitudinal horopter with the eyes asymmetrically converged show no evidence of a compensatory change in the relative magnifications of the images of the two eyes. Unfortunately no data were obtained on the horopter apparatus with beads on the central wire, for fusion in the vertical meridian. However, no significant difference from the results without their use is expected.

THE INDUCED EFFECT WITH THE EYES CONVERGED ASYMMETRICALLY

The induced effect S-curve suggests that there is a compensatory change in the relative magnifications of the images of the two eyes when the eyes turn from a symmetrical to an asymmetric convergence. The evidence for this will be clear from the following experimental data.

The difference in the magnification of the retinal images when the eyes are asymmetrically converged may be considered an overall difference, especially if the face of the object observed is normal (or nearly so) to the line joining the interpupillary midpoint and the point of fixation. An overall magnification is equivalent to two equal meridional magnifications the principal meridians of which are vertical (axis 180 degrees) and horizontal (axis 90 degrees). The apparent rotation of the test plane caused by the

* One subject found the setting of the apparent frontoparallel plane difficult because of a tendency for the images of the outer rods to appear double. This fact indicates that the images were quite disparate, outside Panum's areas.

† There may be some influence of the aperture which restricts the field of view of the eyes to the rods only. In both cases it was maintained parallel to the objective frontal plane.

lens, the axis of which is 180 degrees before one eye, will be due to the induced effect, while that of the lens the axis of which is 90 degrees will be due to the geometric effect.

Since the S-curve itself is a phenomenon of the difference in the magnifications of the images in the vertical meridian, it should be clear that if an overall magnification lens is kept before one eye a constant difference will be added to those differences used to obtain the curve. Thus the curve should be displaced along the horizontal axis of the graph. The maximal

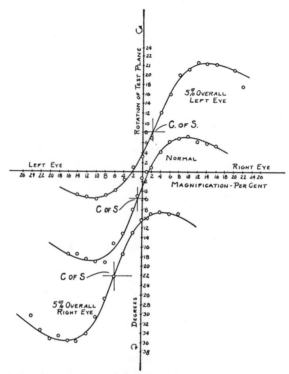

Fig. 133. Typical induced effect S-curve showing the displacement caused by an overall magnifying lens maintained before the right or the left eye.

rotations would remain the same; only those vertical differences in the magnifications of the images at which these maxima occur should be displaced.

In a similar manner the S-curve should be displaced along the vertical direction of the graph owing to the magnification of the images introduced in the horizontal meridian.

The displacement of the normal S-curve, due to an afocal overall magnification lens before one eye, will be a combination of the horizontal and vertical displacements, the magnitudes depending on the relative differential response of the eyes to the two effects. With the simple pattern used in the experiments to be described, the differential response of the induced effect is generally about one-half as great as that of the geometric effect, and therefore a vertical displacement of the curve on the graph might also be expected. With the overall lens before one eye, there should always be a horizontal displacement of the curve on the graph, because of the vertical component of the overall magnification.

Data were obtained by several observers for the induced effect S-curve with the eyes in symmetrical convergence, first, without and then with a 3 or a 5 per cent overall magnification lens placed before the right eye and then before the left. The results of one observer are illustrated graphically in Fig. 133. A regular displacement of the curve occurs when an overall magnification lens is kept before one eye throughout the experiment. When the lens is before the right eye, the curve is displaced to the left of the normal curve; when the lens is before the left eye, the displacement is to the right. These displacements are in the directions that might be anticipated, though the magnitudes are generally less than those that might be expected.

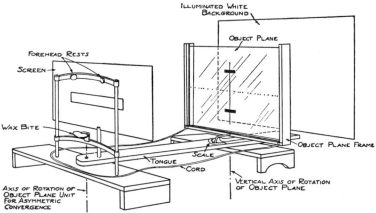

Fig. 134. Schematic drawing of the apparatus used for studying the induced effect with the eyes in an asymmetric convergence.

These data have shown that an overall magnification of the image of one eye causes a lateral displacement of the induced effect S-curve on the graph. It now remains to be seen if the magnification difference introduced between the images of the two eyes, when they are converged asymmetrically, does or does not cause the corresponding type of displacement.

The apparatus used, which is illustrated schematically in Fig. 134, is essentially the same as that described previously except that the entire tilting plane, background and other parts of the apparatus are mounted as a unit on a tongue which can be turned about a vertical axis through the midpoint of the centers of rotation of the eyes. When this tongue is turned to a lateral position, the eyes will converge asymmetrically when they are looking directly at the plane. The head of an observer is held in position by a wax bite and suitable forehead rests. The observer fixates the tilting plane through a slit aperture in a screen. Suitable lens holders (not indicated in the figure) are so mounted before the eyes that their axes coincide with the visual axes of the eyes in all positions of asymmetric convergence. A protractor, with a suitable indicator below the frame of the test plane, shows the angular position of the plane as measured from the normal position.

In the center of the tilting plane, a horizontal row of small dots, irregularly spaced, was drawn to provide the stimuli by which the observer could ascertain stereoscopically the rotational position of the plane. A vertical black thread to control the convergence of the eyes was stretched through the center and axis of the plane. Above and below the center, at a distance of 3.5 cm., small black rectangles, 1.5 by 0.15 cm., were drawn in a horizontal position. These rectangles provided the necessary separated fusion contours in the vertical meridian, without which the induced effect does not occur when a difference is introduced in the sizes of the images of the eyes in the vertical meridian. A modification of this fusion pattern is the substitution of small black hemispheres for the rectangles. The hemispheres have the advantage that they do not change shape when the plane is rotated.

In making a setting of the tilting plane, the observer is instructed to adjust its rotational position so that it appears "normal," that is, at right angles to the subjective visual direction of the central point of the tilting plane. For symmetrical convergence, this amounts to setting the plane for an apparent frontoparallel position. In asymmetric convergence, it is merely a "normal" setting. Objectively, the true normal position would correspond to a zero scale reading on this apparatus. For the purposes of this experiment, however, the particular criterion used in the setting of the plane is not important as long as it is the same for all the adjustments in all sets of data. A different criterion for each set would result merely in a displacement along the vertical axis of the graph. The same criterion, however, must be used throughout the series of data.

The usual procedure is followed to determine the data for the S-curve. The observer makes a number of independent settings of the plane for each of a sequence of meridional afocal magnification lenses placed at axis 180 degrees before one eye, up to and including 12.5 per cent magnification. The corresponding rotational positions of the test plane were recorded by an assistant. The averages of the settings for each of the various lenses were then plotted as before. S-curves were then obtained with the eyes in symmetrical and then asymmetric convergence.

The data[184] of one observer for asymmetric convergences of 10 and 20 degrees to the right and to the left of the median plane are illustrated graphically in Fig. 135.

At the observation distance of 40 cm. and for an average interpupillary distance (65 mm.), the difference in the relative magnification of the retinal images for an asymmetric convergence of 10 degrees would be about 2.8 per cent, and for 20 degrees it would be about 5.6 per cent. Hence, a measurable horizontal displacement of the S-curve from that taken in symmetrical convergence would be expected. For example, when the eyes are turned in asymmetric convergence to the right, a larger image in the right eye would be expected, and the S-curve should be displaced to the left relative to the curve obtained in symmetrical convergence. In view of the experiments with the overall lenses, appreciable displacements would certainly be anticipated. The curve in each graph indicated by the broken line is the expected position of the induced effect curve according to the full geometric difference in the magnifications of the retinal images due to the difference in the distance of the object plane from the two eyes.

However, no regular displacement of the S-curves themselves of this kind is evident. In fact, the actual curves present excellent evidence that there is no regular horizontal displacement of the curves as the eyes converge asymmetrically. Thus, one must conclude that there has been an *equivalent* compensatory change in the relative magnifications of the images of the two eyes in the vertical meridian, which offsets the difference in magnification due to difference in distance.

Consistent vertical displacements of the S-curves were also found for all observers. When the eyes turn to the right to observe a near object, the curves found are displaced downward; when the eyes turn to the left the curves found are displaced upward. The magnitude of these displacements

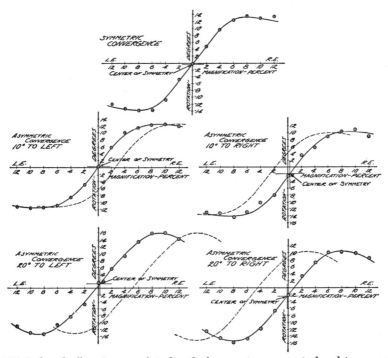

Fig. 135. Induced effect S-curves found with the eyes in symmetrical and in asymmetric convergence. The observation distance was 40 cm.

is different for the several observers. The direction of these displacements is such as to suggest that the tilting plane tends to be adjusted toward the position tangent to the Vieth-Müller circle. However, this cannot be used as evidence for or against a change in the relative magnifications of the images in the eyes, for we are confronted with the problem of the meaning of the subjective criterion of the "normal."

SUMMARY

The results of the several experiments described in this chapter present inconsistent evidence that a functional change can occur in the relative magnifications of the images in the two eyes, when the eyes are converged asymmetrically.

The experiments described might be summarized as follows:

Experiment	Results
1. Haploscope	
A. Circle and square	Striking appearance of a compensatory change in the magnifications of the images with *free fixation*, particularly in the vertical meridian; but much less and even no apparent change with steady fixation at center, and especially in the horizontal meridian.
B. Eikonic target	Excellent quantitative results, apparently showing a full compensatory change in the magnifications of the images for all visual distances, especially in vertical meridians, and very much less in the horizontal meridians for most subjects. These movements necessitated eye movements. Judgments with peripheral vision were not possible because the details were too small for peripheral discrimination.
C. Peripheral fusion pattern	A central steady fixation method with peripheral fusion, the results from which showed a compensatory change in the magnifications of the images in the *vertical* meridian. The test could not be used for measurements in the horizontal meridian.
D. After-image tests	Most tests performed proved too variable to give reliable data. Those performed in Tschermak's laboratory showed no evidence of a change of the relative magnifications of the images of the two eyes.
2. Nonhaploscopic test	Full compensatory change in the magnifications of the images was indicated with *free fixation*, but only a slight change, if any, was indicated with central fixation and peripheral judgments.
3. The horopter apparatus	The nonius method of obtaining the longitudinal horopter showed no compensatory effect in the relative magnifications of the images in the two eyes in the horizontal meridian.

4. Induced effect S-curves .... Nearly a full compensatory change in the magnifications of the images of the two eyes in asymmetric convergence in the vertical meridian. No evidence was available for changes in the horizontal meridian.*

From the various experiments with the haploscope in which the angular sizes of the test patterns subtended by the two eyes remained the same, a compensatory change in the magnification of the images is apparently associated with the turning of the eyes in an asymmetric convergent position, especially when eye movements are involved in the discrimination. No optical stimuli for such changes arise from the patterns themselves. This fact is of importance in studying the nature of the phenomenon and it certainly suggests a myosensory influence of the ocular muscles.

Only in the experiments with the polarized targets and the induced effect would there be unequal angular sizes of the patterns to act as stimuli for innervations for a compensatory change in the relative magnifications of the images. The other experiments involve conditioned reflexes associated with some type of myosensory influences of the muscles of the eyes.

In two rather abstruse papers Schubert[217, 259] discussed the phenomenon of the apparent change in the sizes of the circle and square in the haploscope. He attempted to explain it on the basis of a "special involvement of the receptor and motor apparatus of the two eyes," and declared that the haploscope introduces unnatural conditions, in which the images of targets in the two are "projected" at different distances and therefore their apparent sizes are judged accordingly. This explanation, at the moment, is not convincing nor easily understood.

The significant fact in the experiments described in this chapter would seem to be that the compensatory-like phenomenon occurs with judgments made when eye movements were involved, and does not occur when such movements are absent or small. The peripheral fusion target on the haploscope (Fig. 123C) and the induced effect S-curves are the exceptions. In the first, even small eye movements may be involved, and in the second, since the nature of the induced effect is not clear, it may not constitute a tool for use in such a study. The apparent change in the size of the targets when eye movements are involved could be due to some myosensory influence that originates from the different tonic states of the external muscles of the eyes when the eyes are converged asymmetrically as compared to when they are converged symmetrically. This might be more true in the vertical meridian, for in the horizontal the eyes are more accustomed to unequal changes resulting from voluntary eye movements.

* Another way in which the problem can be attacked is by determining the changes in the limits of the regions of single binocular vision. In the vertical meridian this can be done on the haploscope, and in the horizontal meridian it can be accomplished best on the horopter apparatus.

CHAPTER 17

A Theory of the Induced Effect

IN THE PREVIOUS chapter it was pointed out that when the eyes change their positions from one of symmetrical convergence to one of asymmetric convergence in observing a near object there is a problem presented of how egocentric stereoscopic spatial localization can be maintained.

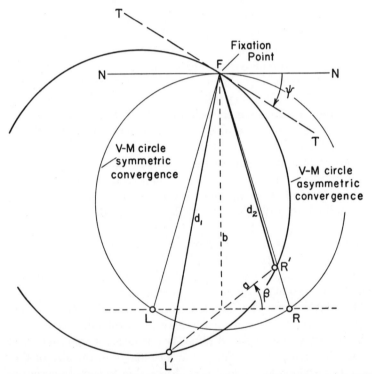

Fig. 136. Diagram used in discussion of a theory of the induced effect.

When the eyes are symmetrically converged (Fig. 136) the stereoscopic discrimination of whether an object is farther or nearer than the point of fixation F will depend on the disparity between the images in the two eyes and the discrimination will be referred to some surface tangent to the Vieth-Müller circle, here indicated by $N \ldots N$. Now if the head is turned (for example) about the midpoint of the interocular base line, the Vieth-Müller circle passes through the point of fixation at a skewed direction relative to

$N \ldots N$. This result is due entirely to the geometry involved, wherein the distance of the point of fixation from each of the two eyes is now different. If our subjective stereoscopic localization of "farther" or "nearer" depends upon the same patterns of image disparity as in symmetrical convergence, then the stereoscopic discrimination will be relative to some surface still tangent to the Vieth-Müller circle at the fixation point in this skew position, here indicated by $T \ldots T$. But then objects in space will be incorrectly localized with respect to the observer's body (egocentric localization), for those on the right side of the fixation point will be perceived too far away, those on the left too near. For egocentric stereoscopic localization to be maintained, a change must occur in the binocular visual processes equivalent to a change in the relative magnifications of the images of the two eyes in the horizontal meridian, which compensates for the difference in distance of the fixation point.

Since the evidence as presented in the previous chapter generally denies the existence of any physiologic compensatory change, we are forced to fall back upon a hypothesis of a psychical change which results in a reorientation of the frame of reference for stereoscopic localization, partially in the sense of a rotation of the entire binocular perceptual space about the fixation point.

This phenomenon, which basically must arise from the vertical disparities of images in the two eyes, which in turn are caused by the difference in distance of the point of fixation from the two eyes, provides a basis for an explanation for the induced effect. When one increases the magnification of the image of the right eye in the vertical meridian by a suitable lens, an apparent distortion of space occurs in the sense that objects at the right of the fixation point appear nearer, those on the left farther—a clockwise rotation of the field. Thus the stereoscopic reference surface must have been rotated counterclockwise. This is the direction in which the reference surface must also be rotated when the eyes are asymmetrically converged to the right, if egocentric stereoscopic localization is to be maintained. This rotation of the subjective binocular visual field is not a pure rotation alone, but is the principal aspect consistent with an increase in the magnification of the image of the left eye in the horizontal meridian.

We can compare the two phenomena quantitatively by the following. Referring again to Fig. 136, the distances of the point of fixation from the left and the right eye, respectively, will be $d_1 = \sqrt{b^2 + a^2 + 2ab \sin \beta}$ and $d_2 = \sqrt{b^2 + a^2 - 2ab \sin \beta}$, where, as before, b is the observation distance, $2a$ is the interpupillary distance, and β is the angle through which the head has been turned. An object at the fixation point having details in the vertical meridian will have images in the two eyes of different size. In fact, the ratio R of these sizes (ratio of the magnification of the right image to that of the left image) will be the inverse ratio of the two distances d_1 and d_2; namely, $R^2 = (1 + g \sin \beta)/(1 - g \sin \beta)$, in which $g = 2ab/(b^2 + a^2)$.

Now we can make the hypothesis that the induced effect, in which the image of one eye is magnified in the vertical meridian, corresponds to the geometric situation in which the eyes are converged asymmetrically, and the result in both cases is a change in the egocentric stereoscopic spatial localization. The increase in magnification of the image caused by a given meridional lens determines the value of R, and for a given observation distance b, and interpupillary separation $2a$, the corresponding value of β can be found from

$$\sin \beta = (R^2 - 1)/(R^2 + 1)g \qquad (1)$$

obtained by solving the preceding equation for $\sin \beta$. We then find ψ, the angle through which the Vieth-Müller circle has been turned at the fixation point. The rotation of the stereoscopic frame of reference will be equal to this angle but opposite in direction.

The Vieth-Müller circle will be that circle which passes through the pupils of the two eyes and the point of fixation; namely, the points in the coordinate system $(-a \cos \beta, -a \sin \beta)$, $(a \cos \beta, a \sin \beta)$ and $(0, b)$. This circle will be represented by

$$x^2 + (A \tan \beta)x + y^2 - Ay - a^2 = 0 \qquad (2)$$

in which $A = (b^2 - a^2)/b$. The slope of the tangent line to this circle, which is equal to the derivative dy/dx, at the fixation point F $(0, b)$ will be

$$\tan \psi = -(b^2 - a^2) \tan \beta/(b^2 + a^2) \qquad (3)$$

When b may be considered large with respect to a, the angle ψ is substantially equal to β. By means of the formulas (1) and (3), we can find the relationship between R and ψ, these quantities being the two involved in the induced effect. R is determined by the magnification of the lens introduced and ψ is the angle through which the tilting plane has to be turned when it appears frontoparallel. Figure 137 illustrates calculated values for several observation distances and an average interpupillary distance of 64 mm.

The change in ψ corresponding to a small change in R, which is equivalent to the differential response of the induced effect S-curve at the center of symmetry, can be obtained from the figure or computed from the expression

$$I = -(b^2 - a^2)/2ab$$

This is found by differentiating equations (1) and (3) with respect to R, and evaluating them when $R = 1$ and $\psi = \beta = 0$. If b is large compared to a, this reduces to $I = -b/2a$. To put the result in degrees rotation per 1 per cent change in magnification, this quantity must be multiplied by the factor $180/100\,\pi$.

Now experiment has shown that for a binocular visual field that contains many details, the differential response of the induced effect is usually equal to the geometric effect, or to that phenomenon in which a spatial distortion is caused by increasing the magnification of the image of one eye in the *horizontal* meridian only. Moreover an overall magnifying lens placed before one eye does not cause any apparent distortion of space, because the two effects seem to offset each other exactly. The "null" method (p. 179) also showed the two effects to be equal in magnitude. The corresponding expression for the differential response for the geometric effect (obtained by differentiating the relation $\tan \psi = (R -)b/(R + 1)a$ [p. 162], with respect to R, and evaluating at the point $R = 1$) is

$$G = b/2a$$

Thus, upon the hypothesis just made, the magnitude of the theoretical differential responses of the two effects, I and G, are substantially equal

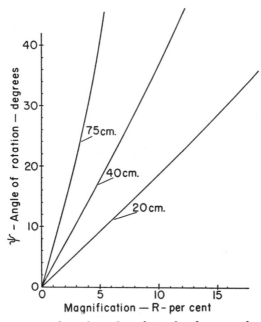

Fig. 137. Curves computed to show the relationship between the ratio (R) of the magnifications of the images of the two eyes and the equivalent angle of rotation (ψ) of the stereoscopic space, were that ratio due to an asymmetric convergence of the eyes.

but opposite in direction. Thus this hypothesis for an explanation of the induced effect has quantitative agreement with the experimental facts. In comparing many of the actual data obtained on the tilting plane, we must reckon with the amount of detail on the plane, and the presence of empirical factors which may dampen the magnitude of the two effects (p. 155).

Householder[122] similarly studied this problem but from the point of view of the subjective localization of the median plane when the eyes are asymmetrically converged. The angular deviation of this plane from the normal median plane was taken as the same as the rotation of the binocular visual field about the point of fixation. While he assumed that the asymmetric convergence corresponded to a displacement of the head parallel to the objective frontoparallel plane, instead of a rotation of the head as was done in our studies, his values for the degree of rotation of the field also agreed fairly well with experimental results. From his geometric construction he also predicted the breakdown of the effect for higher values of R; these values are, however, too high. In this connection it should be pointed out that no observer has ever reported that magnifying the image of one eye in the vertical meridian gave him a sensation of his eyes being asymmetrically converged.

According to the hypothesis outlined here, the induced effect is the psychical response of the binocular visual processes to stimuli that consist of vertical disparities between the images of the two eyes. These disparities normally occur only when the eyes are asymmetrically converged on a near object, and the response makes possible an egocentric stereoscopic spatial localization. This response would not necessarily involve a proprioceptive sense arising from, or sensory component of, innervations to the extrinsic muscles of the eyes. We must attribute the maximal induced effect to limits in the physiologic visual processes probably associated with fusion, and to the neurologic organization of corresponding areas of the two retinas. Asymmetric convergences over 20 to 25 degrees are rarely sustained in normal vision.

There is some evidence that under special experimental conditions a varying induced effect across the visual field occurs. For example, by means of optical arrangements in a combination haploscope and horopter apparatus, the vertical size of the image in the right eye can be made progressively larger than that of the left eye to the right of the fixation point, and progressively smaller than that of the left eye to the left of the fixation point. Such stimuli change the curvature of the apparent frontoparallel plane as determined by setting the horopter rods.

CHAPTER 18

The Sensitivity of the Eyes in the Discrimination of Differences in the Relative Magnifications of Their Images

---

INTRODUCTION

IN THE CHAPTERS just preceding we were concerned with the effects produced by changing the relative magnifications of the images of the two eyes, particularly the effects on binocular spatial localization. A question which usually arises in this connection is how sensitive are the binocular visual processes to differences in magnification of the images in the two eyes. This chapter will be devoted to a consideration of this question.

VISUAL ACUITY

The discrimination of differences in magnification of the images of the two eyes will be essentially a discrimination of differences in retinal dimensions. If an individual with normal eyes in symmetrical convergence observes a circle in the frontoparallel plane, the sizes of the functional images in the two eyes will be identical. If the image in one eye is now magnified by placing before it an appropriate lens, the retinal image will be made larger, and it will, therefore, fall on retinal elements located more peripherally than the image in the other eye. A discrimination of the difference in size of the images will depend on the binocular appreciation of the difference in retinal dimensions equal to the difference in the sizes of the images in the two eyes.

The actual magnitude of the difference will be proportional to the size of the circle and to the change of magnification. The difference in retinal dimension will be twice as great if the circle is twice as large for the same change of magnification. For example, suppose the eyes are fixating the center of a number of concentric circles, the radii of which subtend at the eyes visual angles of 5 degrees, 10 degrees, 15 degrees, and so forth. Before the right eye is placed a 2 per cent afocal overall magnification lens. The angular sizes of the radii of the retinal images of the right eye will be 2 per cent larger than those of the left eye. Multiplying the radii by the magnification 1.02, we find their effective image sizes to be 5.10 degrees, 10.20 degrees, 15.30 degrees, and so forth. The retinal distances to be dis-

Table 18

Relative Visual Acuities of Central and Peripheral Parts
of the Visual Field

PERIPHERAL ANGLE, DEGREES	WERTHEIM	FICK	LUDVIGH
0	1/1	1/1	1/1
2	—	—	1/2.3
5	1/3	1/4	1/3.8
10	1/5	3/20	1/6.6
15	1/7	1/10	—
20	1/9	1/12	—

criminated are then 0.10 degree at 5 degrees, 0.20 degree at 10 degrees, 0.30 degree at 15 degrees, and so forth.

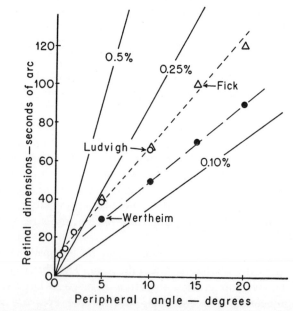

Fig. 138. Thresholds of visual acuity (visual angle of resolution) for various peripheral angles, together with the retinal dimensions corresponding to differences in the magnification of the dioptric image on the retina for the same peripheral angles.

The capacity of the binocular visual apparatus to appreciate these differences will depend on the visual acuity or more specifically on the resolving

power of the two eyes in the retinal regions concerned. Since the approximate visual acuities of the eyes for various peripheral parts of the retinas
have repeatedly been reported in the literature, we can predict from them
on theoretical grounds what can be expected for the sensitivity of the eyes
to differences in the relative magnifications of the images.[9]

The comparative visual acuities relative to that at the fovea from the data
reported by Wertheim, by Fick and by Ludvigh are given in Table 18. The
ability to discriminate retinal distances between images is, of course, much

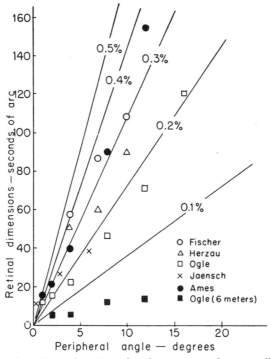

Fig. 139. Mean deviations of settings for the apparent frontoparallel plane on the
horopter apparatus, and retinal dimensions corresponding to changes in magnification of
the image on the retina.

greater than that suggested by the visual acuity alone. A voluminous amount
of data can be found in the literature for the thresholds of foveal discrimination. For an average value we can take 10 seconds of arc as the threshold
of such discrimination, though even this may be lower for certain types of
test objects, the contours of which bring into play many contiguous retinal
elements.[244] We can then ascertain the corresponding discriminations at
various peripheral angles of the eye, by dividing 10 seconds of arc by the
relative acuities given in Table 18. The results of doing so are shown graphically in Fig. 138. The difference in retinal dimensions corresponding to magnifications of the image of 0.1 per cent, 0.25 per cent and 0.5 per cent are
shown in the lighter solid lines. Where these lines are above the data, the

difference due to a change in magnification should be discernible. Thus, from inspection of this chart we should expect that a change to 0.25 per cent and less could be sensed.

STEREOSCOPIC ACUITY

In the horizontal meridian the differences in dimensions on the retinas of the two eyes provide the stimuli for stereoscopic vision, so that the visual capacity to discriminate a difference in the magnification of the images of the two eyes is also its capacity for differentiating stereoscopic depth. We can thus compare the retinal dimensions obtained from the mean variation of the settings for the apparent frontoparallel plane on the horopter apparatus, with those corresponding to differences in magnification for the various peripheral angles. Such a comparison is shown in Fig. 139, where the data have been taken from papers by Fischer,[71] Herzau,[110] Frübose and Jaensch, and Ames, Ogle and Gliddon.[11] For the most part these values pertain to data obtained for a visual distance of from 33 to 40 cm., and these are usually higher than those obtained for more distant vision. One set of data for distant vision is shown. From an inspection of these data on the graph it is clear that even for the least sensitive observer a 0.35 difference in magnification between images of the two eyes would be discernible.

"AUGENMASS" STUDIES

The capacity of the eyes to recognize differences in length and size has often been studied[118] and reported under the term "Augenmass." A particular interest in those studies was to ascertain whether Weber's law held for such judgments, that is, whether the least perceptible difference in the comparison of lengths or distances is a constant fraction of those lengths. While it is questionable whether Weber's law can be applied to such measurements on theoretical grounds, it is true that the majority of the studies are in fair agreement that the mean variation of settings in the equating of lengths or areas is proportional to the lengths involved, provided those lengths are not too small or too large. This fact is of interest to us, for the ratio of the threshold of length discrimination to the length of the lines is comparable to a per cent magnification. Free eye movements and binocular vision were permitted in most experiments reported. Typical results from the literature are shown in Table 19, the values being the percentage mean variation of setting to the lengths. These results are likely to vary greatly with different experiments, and especially in the same experiment depending on the conditions such as separation of the lines and location in the visual field, length of exposure, and so forth. Such data as these do not measure the capacity of one eye to compare size against that seen by the other. However, they do indicate a basic capacity of the eyes to compare sizes.

EXPERIMENTAL STUDIES

Gross Uniocular Comparisons. There are several ways in which the gross size of an object as seen by one eye can be compared with that seen by the other. None is very accurate or reliable, because unavoidable factors exist which tend to interfere with judgments. The least reliable method is to place a large square on the wall in front of an observer, and then by covering one eye after the other to ask for estimates to which eye the square appears larger. Afocal magnification lenses can be used before one eye or the other to introduce actually a difference in the effective size. Much depends on the rapidity with which one eye is uncovered and the other is covered, and the presence of vertical and horizontal phorias. The average observer may be able to detect a 4 per cent image magnification difference, and sometimes experienced observers may be able to detect even less.

Table 19

TYPICAL RESULTS FROM "AUGENMASS" EXPERIMENTS

AUTHOR	EXPERIMENT	MEAN VARIATION, PER CENT
Volkmann[107]	Comparison of spaces between three vertical lines	0.93 — 1.13
Fechner	Line segments	1.60
Kundt	Bisecting horizontal lines	0.31 — 0.66
Chodin	Comparison of horizontal lines Comparison of vertical lines	0.89 — 2.56 1.66 — 3.12
Fischer[74]	Equating arms of a cross Bisection of vertical line Bisection of horizontal line	0.94 — 1.56 0.55 — 0.83 0.58 — 0.90
Merkel	Comparison of adjacent horizontal lines	0.55 — 0.74
Hofmann	Comparison of lengths of two vertical lines, each 20 degrees from a constant fixation point	3.5 — 7.8
Leeser	Comparison of areas (105 mm. on diagonals at 80 cm. distance)	3.4 — 4.3
Veniar	Least perceptible distortion of squares	1.4

When a 6^Δ prism is placed base-up before one eye, and another base-down before the other, the same square on the wall will be seen double, one image being above the other. A more direct comparison of the squares is then possible, and trained observers may detect 2 per cent differences in overall magnification.

One often runs into difficulties not foreseen when attempting to make more accurate estimations of the capacity to differentiate gross differences of size. For example, identical target patterns, such as postage stamps, can be used on the haploscope that has the half-silvered mirrors (Fig. 140). Suitable power lenses placed on the arms just outside the mirrors cause the images of the stamps to be optically the same distance as the wall across the room, upon which the stamps will appear. Details such as a pair of crossed lines can be put on the blank wall, the images of which provide fusion stimuli. The targets on the haploscope are then adjusted until the stamp images are in opposite quadrants of the crossed lines. Screens with suitable apertures are essential to exclude the images of extraneous details in the room.

If one magnifies the image of one eye by an overall afocal magnification lens, or just by displacing the target slightly toward the eye, it will be found that instead of the stamp appearing larger it appears *nearer* with no *apparent* increase in size. This effect is, of course, a particular aspect of the psychologic size-constancy phenomenon, although this is the first evidence that the phenomenon can take place in one eye *independently* of the

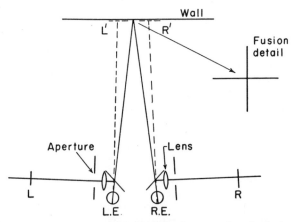

Fig. 140. Haploscope arrangement with half-silvered mirrors by which the apparent sizes of identical targets seen separately by each eye can be compared.

other. Least perceptible changes in the apparent distance of the two stamps are of the order of 0.5 per cent magnification. A *meridional* magnifying lens inserted near the power lens seemingly produces essentially the same effect, but to a less marked degree. The experiment is unsuitable for measuring the capacity of the eyes to recognize gross differences in the sizes of the images of the two eyes.

Eikonic Targets. A suitable target can be made for use on the haploscope if all the similar details are seen by both eyes, and their retinal images therefore fuse, while the dissimilar test details needed for comparison are seen by each eye separately. Such a target, as originally developed by Ames, is illustrated in Fig. 141.[10]

At the center of each target is an identical figure, a broad line circle, that subtends a visual angle of about 1½ arc degrees. At about 4 degrees from the center of each target, above, below, and right and left, the test figures are located. For the target seen by the left eye, these consist of short narrow lines with a central gap. For the target seen by the right eye these are point light sources, produced by miniature lamps behind small holes drilled in the target plate.

When observed binocularly in the haploscope, the images of the central circle fuse, and ideally the point lights will be seen in the gaps of the lines. If the magnification of the image of one eye is greater than that of the other, the distance between the points of light will be slightly different from that between the lines in the same meridian. This difference is discerned by the observer's actually looking at the light and lines and comparing their relative positions above the center with those below (or right with those left). The fusion of the images of the central figure is relied upon to control the pointing of the eyes. If a difference in magnification is present, the distance from this center to the lights of one eye will be different from the corresponding distance from the center to the lines of the other; so that in looking toward a given light and line, one eye may accurately fixate the light, but then the other eye will actually point slightly to one side or the other of the corresponding lines. If a fixation disparity is present, as might be ex-

Left   Right

Fig. 141. Direct comparison eikonic target designed (by Ames) for use on the haploscope.

pected in the horizontal meridian, the lights on both the right and left sides will appear displaced in the same direction. The difference in the displacement of the images of the lights on the two sides can be readily recognized, however, if a magnification difference of the images is also present.

In studies made with this target and with the adjustable magnification units it has been shown that if the visual acuity in both eyes is normal or better, an observer can usually detect differences in magnification of 0.25 per cent and often even smaller. Especially is this true in the vertical meridian, where a fixation disparity is less likely to interfere with accurate judgments. Nearly all subjects with normal visual acuity, irrespective of previous experience in making judgments, can discriminate 0.5 per cent difference in magnification, and usually less in the vertical meridian. Only subjects who exhibit a highly variable fixation disparity, whose fusional processes are poorly developed or whose visual acuity is low, will have lower sensitivities.

Similar targets can also be designed so as to place the test meridians obliquely, but experience has shown that these generally prove unreliable, primarily because of the influence of fixation disparity.

Stereoscopic Discrimination. In the horizontal meridian, differences in retinal dimensions due to differences in the images of two points in space constitute a disparity between those images. The change in the horizontal disparities introduced by a magnification lens before one eye causes a false spatial orientation of the positions of objects as experienced in binocular vision. The stereoscopic sensitivity of the eyes to such changes in magnification will depend upon the stereoscopic acuity in the retinal regions involved.

The essential difference between this stereoscopic test and that with the eikonic target previously described will be clear from a study of Fig. 142. Let points P and Q correspond to the gaps and lights of the eikonic target, and to two points in the same relative location in the objective frontoparallel

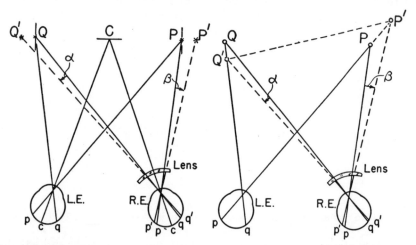

Fig. 142. Relationship between the direct comparison (eikonic target) and stereoscopic methods of determining the sensitivity of the eyes to differences in magnification of their images.

plane for the stereoscopic test. The images of P and Q will be at the retinal points p and q in the two eyes. If, now, one magnifies the image in the horizontal meridian of the right eye, say, by a suitable lens, the images of P and Q in the right eye will be displaced to retinal positions p' and q', respectively.

In the case of the eikonic target, the central detail at C is sufficient to maintain the fusion during the coordinated movements of the two eyes. The left eye sees the lines and the right the points of light. The test depends on the subject's simultaneous uniocular discrimination of the retinal distances pp' and qq', represented by angles α and β, and therefore depends on the elemental function of the retinas, the discrimination of relative visual directions. Actually, this discrimination also depends on the degree to which the accuracy of fusion is maintained.

In the stereoscopic test, where both eyes see the points P and Q simultaneously, these points will be seen in the stereoscopic depth corresponding to spatial positions P' and Q'. This test depends on the discrimination of the same retinal dimensional difference as does the other test, corresponding to the angles α and β.

The Leaf Room. Studies with many subjects in the leaf room (p. 144 and following) show that individuals with normal visual acuity in both eyes usually recognize a meridional magnification change of 0.25 per cent and in some cases even less. By skillfully asking the unexperienced subject certain questions about the appearance of various features of the room, the examiner can easily learn whether the subject is truly recognizing the apparent distortion associated with the particular lens used. Subjects also usually recognize the spatial distortion caused by meridional magnifying lenses of 0.25 per cent placed symmetrically at oblique axes before the two eyes.

Often individuals for whom no stereopsis could be demonstrated by conventional methods (hand stereoscopes, and so forth) responded readily to meridional magnification lenses while observing the leaf room. This method therefore constitutes a much more critical and functional test than other methods.

Tilting Planes. The mean variations of settings in the tilting plane experiments, as described on p. 153 and following, are measures of the stereoscopic sensitivity to differences in magnification of the images of the two eyes. With complex patterns on the plane these mean deviations are of the order of 0.5 degree[180] for an observation distance of 40 cm. Since the differential response—the amount of apparent rotation caused by a 1 per cent difference in magnification—is about 3.2 degrees per 1 per cent, these mean deviations represent a sensitivity of 0.16 per cent in magnification difference.

Vertical Plumb Lines. The most precise measurements under controlled and optimal conditions have been made with a single pair of plumb lines.[193] The experimental setup is illustrated in Fig. 143.

A pair of plumb lines, of smooth green-colored cords, were suspended in the frontoparallel plane and placed symmetrically with respect to the median plane of the observer, at a distance of 2.4 meters. The cords were hung from a 2 meter stick from wires and thus their separation could be changed. These plumb lines were seen against a background of stretched black velvet cloth. Between the cords and the eyes was placed a suitable screen with an aperture which restricted the view to the cords and prevented their ends and the scale from being seen. The cords were illuminated by four Lumiline lamps on the back of the screen and appeared vividly delineated against the background without shadows. The entire apparatus was enclosed by black sateen cloth, but the general illumination of the room was supplied by a 15 watt lamp.

The head of the subject was held before an optical test system by forehead and temple buttons and by a wax bite. This arrangement eliminated head movements and the possibility of depth discrimination from parallax movements.

To determine the stereoscopic sensitivity, the disparities between the images of the two eyes were changed by adjustable magnification units placed before the eyes. By means of special indicators these units could be set and the magnification could be measured in steps of 0.05 per cent with a maximal error of 0.02 per cent, having been accurately calibrated on a special testing instrument.[191] A shutter before the right eye interrupted binocular vision when the lens unit was adjusted.

The stereoscopic thresholds were measured by the method of constant stimuli,[100] a method which will be clear from the following discussion.

If one magnifies the image of the right eye in the horizontal meridian, and thus changes the disparities between the retinal images of the two plumb lines, the right line will appear farther away than will the left. If the magnification of the image is decreased, the right cord will appear nearer than the left. The least change in magnification which can be recognized in the apparent displacement of the two cords would be a measure of the threshold, and, therefore, of the sensitivity. Such a minimal change,

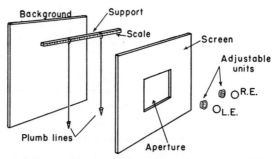

Fig. 143. Scheme of the apparatus used to determine the sensitivity of the eyes to differences in the magnification of their images by the stereoscopic method.

however, will not always be recognized; and, again, occasionally even a smaller change might be perceived. The problem becomes a statistical one. In what percentage of times will certain given changes in magnification be recognized in an apparent displacement of the two cords?

A few preliminary trials usually established the approximate limits in change of magnification for which the right cord first appeared just farther away and then just nearer than the left. This range was then broken into five equally spaced changes in magnification, and each of these changes was presented to the subject forty times in a random order. Thus, a series of 200 judgments of random changes in magnification was obtained. With each presentation the subject was asked to state whether he saw the right cord "farther" or "nearer" than the left, though occasionally a "can't tell" or a doubtful response was allowable. The number of doubtful responses was small, and for each stimulus these were distributed in the "nearer" and the "farther" category in proportion to the number of judgments in those categories. In any given experiment if the judgments were found difficult to make, one-minute rest periods were permitted after each twenty-five judgments, to reduce the possible effect of fatigue. The shutter was lowered immediately after a response from the subject. No limit was placed on the time required by the subject to make a judgment, though on the average this varied between two and eight seconds. During this period the subject was also free to use ocular movements in making the judgment if he so desired. He was cautioned, however, to use the same criterion for judgments throughout the experiment.

The data in any one experiment consisted of the number, and therefore the percentage, of the judgments for each magnification setting in which the right cord was judged to be "nearer" or "farther" than the left cord. Typical data are illustrated in Fig. 144, the curves being the well-known psychometric curve.

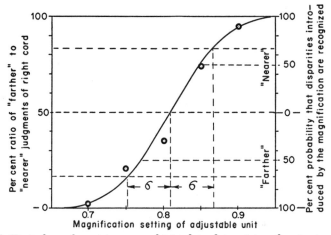

Fig. 144. Typical psychometric curve obtained in determining the stereoscopic sensitivity for a pair of separated plumb lines to changes in the magnification of the image of the right eye in the horizontal meridian.

That magnification for which 50 per cent of the judgments were reported "farther" and 50 per cent "nearer" is the most probable magnification for which the two lines appeared at the same distance. At this magnification the judgments were made by pure guesswork, and the distribution of responses found was due solely to chance. At the extremes of the curve, there is nearly 100 per cent certainty that the apparent displacements of the cords due to the change in magnification from the 50-50 per cent point would be seen. Between these limits the proportion of judgments varies from near certainty to pure chance. From this curve the threshold of stereoscopic sensitivity can be found directly, the value depending on what percentage of certainty one chooses to consider as the threshold.

The entire psychometric curve for a given set of data can be described quantitatively by a single constant,* σ, the so-called "standard deviation." This quantity is therefore generally accepted as a measure of the accuracy

* The curve is the integral of the probability function, expressed by the equation $y = [1/\sigma \sqrt{2\pi}] \exp(-x^2/2\sigma^2)$.

of any series of responses. Roughly, it is only slightly smaller than the average deviation of a series of settings if the subject were to adjust the magnification units himself. The smaller is σ, the steeper is the central part of the curve and the smaller is the threshold value. A small σ would represent a high sensitivity; a large σ, a low sensitivity. A change in magnification of 0.6745 σ would be recognized 50 per cent of the time, and a change of σ would be recognized correctly about 68 per cent of the time. The standard deviation, σ, is a useful measure of the threshold.

For a given set of data, the most probable value of σ and the value of that magnification at the center (the median) of the curve are found by

Table 20

STEREOSCOPIC THRESHOLDS OF THE EYES FOR A DIFFERENCE IN THE APPARENT
DISTANCE OF TWO PLUMB LINES AT DIFFERENT SEPARATIONS[*]

SEPARATION OF PLUMB LINES	STANDARD DEVIATIONS, PER CENT CHANGE IN MAGNIFICATION		
	V.J.E.	N.W.	K.N.O.
5 cm. (1.2°)	0.118	0.124 0.105 0.081	0.128
15 cm. (3.6°)	0.079	0.078	—
25 cm. (6.0°)	0.051 0.063	0.053	0.080
50 cm. (11.9°)	0.061	0.051 0.052 0.054	0.059
65 cm. (15.2°)	0.069	0.057	

[*] The observation distance was 2.4 meters. The stereoscopic thresholds in seconds of arc can be obtained from the product $S \times \Delta M \times 36$, where S is the angular separation of the lines in degrees and ΔM is the per cent change in magnification threshold.

the method of least squares, after attaching weights to the data according to the Müller-Urban process.[257]

Three subjects whose visual acuities with uncorrected vision were a little greater than normal obtained data. Two of these had had considerable experience in making stereoscopic judgments of depth; the other had had no previous experience. Table 20 summarizes the results obtained for various separations of the plumb lines, in which the angular separations of the cords and the standard deviation of the data in per cent change in the relative magnifications of the images of the two eyes are given. There is general consistency in the results of the three observers, except for N.W. in the larger separations of the cords. One can conclude that for average separations of the lines the standard deviation which is taken as the threshold of response to differences in magnification of the images of the two eyes under these ideal conditions is close to 0.06 per cent.

Since eye movements were permitted during the judgments, it is clear that except for very small separations of the cords, the images of one of the cords will always fall on the more peripheral parts of the retinas of both eyes, whether the eyes are fixating one of the cords or a point between the two cords. In the last analysis this test is a test for stereoscopic acuity, and the results probably cannot exceed the visual acuity for the same type of test objects. For the separation of the cords subtending visual angles of 8 to 15 arc degrees, the thresholds are essentially constant and maximal, the value of σ averaging about 0.055 per cent magnification change. For the average separation of 10 degrees, σ corresponds to an angular disparity between the images of the two eyes of about 19 seconds of arc. This probably does not represent the stereoscopic acuity for a peripheral angle of 10 degrees, but for some intermediate value because of the influence of the eye movements.

An Oblique Cross. A configuration consisting of smooth cords stretched between the corners of a square frame to form an oblique cross with point of intersection in the median plane (see space eikonometer, p. 247) provides a useful test for detecting differences in the relative meridional magnifications of the images of the two eyes. It has the unique property of appearing to rotate about a vertical axis in one direction when a horizontal difference in magnification (axis 90 degrees) is introduced and in the opposite direction when a vertical difference in magnification is introduced (Appendix II).

Such a cross was set up in the apparatus (Fig. 143) to replace the two plumb lines. Using the same method of constant stimuli, the threshold of discrimination of differences in meridional magnification between the two eyes was determined by the same three observers.[193] The standard deviation, as a measure of the threshold, for the three observers was found to be between 0.10 per cent and 0.13 per cent difference in meridional magnification. There was some evidence that introducing vertical plumb lines in front of the cross, into the field of view, also lowered the threshold (σ) slightly.

Part IV

THE EXPERIMENTAL AND THEORETICAL BASES
FOR ANISEIKONIA

CHAPTER 19

The Instruments for Measuring Differences
in the Magnifications of the Images
of the Two Eyes

INTRODUCTION

INSTRUMENTS with which the difference in the magnification of the images
of the two eyes can be measured, especially as devised for clinical use,
have been called "eikonometers,"* a word meaning literally "to measure
image" (*eikon* = image; *meter* = to measure). Only the two types found
most practical and accurate will be described here.

It must be borne in mind that these two instruments represent the culmina-
tion of a number of years of research and development. Many different
methods were tried, and many instruments were devised. All these were
evaluted both in the laboratory and clinically, from the point of view of their
accuracy, pertinent data, convenience and reliability. Into the development
of the two instruments described here has gone a great amount of thought
and labor and in this Ames played the chief role, especially in the basic
designs. Many of the devices that were tried have since been described in
the literature by others.†

In general there are only three methods by which differences in the relative magnifications of the images of the two eyes can be measured: (1) that
depending upon a direct visual comparison of the sizes of suitable target
patterns as seen by each of the two eyes; (2) that depending upon the determination of fusional movements induced by rotary prisms until certain
details appear double—that is, of fusional widths (Allen); (3) that depending upon the subject's stereoscopic spatial localization.

---

* Several of the early instruments were called "ophthalmo-eikonometers," because in
addition to their being eikonometers, they incorporated also the means by which the
refractive errors of the two eyes could be determined by the stigmatoscopic method.[8]

† For examples, see Barker, Allen, Field (see also Lancaster[139] for comments on Field's
paper), de Gramont,[96] Fuog, Brecher,[29] Miles[167] and Elvin. In several of these papers
the instrument is suggested as a "screening test." However, experience has shown that
an instrument precise enough for screening must be essentially as accurate as that needed
for actual careful measurements. Hence all the same problems are involved in either case.

The first two of these methods necessitate solving the problem of keeping separate the targets seen by each of the two eyes. The following have been used: the stereoscope or haploscope, parallax arrangements,[10, 50] flicker (alternating vision of each eye corresponding to presentation of different patterns[70]), red-green anaglyphs and Polaroid. The stereoscope is found not sufficiently accurate and the haploscope is too cumbersome outside of the laboratory.

Polaroid film has provided an ideal method. The target pattern may be a transparency or an image projected upon an aluminum-surfaced screen (a metallic surface prevents depolarization of the reflected light). In either case the details of the target are light figures seen upon a black background.

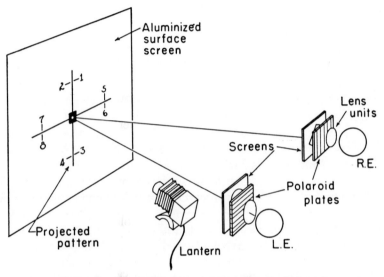

Fig. 145. Scheme of the eikonometer for distant vision with which the relative sizes of the images in the two eyes can be compared directly.

THE DIRECT COMPARISON EIKONOMETER

The essential features of an instrument based on this method are shown in Fig. 145. The subject views a special target pattern projected on a front screen through Polaroid plates and suitable apertures.

The target pattern consists of vertical and horizontal lines intersecting at a circular disk configuration, the images of which in the two eyes stimulate and maintain fusion, thus coordinating the eye movements. At angular distances of 4 degrees from the center, two pairs of numbered opposing arrows are located in the vertical and horizontal meridians. By means of Polaroid film, the light coming from the odd-numbered arrows and numbers is polarized in one meridian; that from the even-numbered arrows and numbers is polarized in the meridian at right angles. Correspondingly oriented Polaroid plates interposed before the two eyes permit the observer to see the odd-numbered arrows with one eye only, and the even-numbered arrows with the other eye only. The light from the central configuration is left unpolarized, to be seen by both eyes. The light from the extreme ends of the lines is also polarized so as to prevent fusion stimuli from the ends of the lines. Fusion stimuli from objects or contours surrounding the target in the peripheral field of view are eliminated by the screens with unlike apertures (a circle and a square) before the eyes.

The procedure is to ask the subject to compare the apparent distances between opposing arrows in each meridian. If there is no difference in the sizes of the images of the two eyes (and no fixation disparity) the observer will see opposing arrows directly opposite each other, aligned: that is, corresponding opposing arrows will appear the same distance from the center of the target. If a fixation disparity is present (and it usually will be in the horizontal meridian), the arrows seen by one eye will appear equally displaced in the same direction compared with the corresponding opposing arrows.

If there is a difference in magnification between the images of the two eyes, the images of this target will be of unequal size, and the arrows seen by the eye having the larger image will appear farther from the center of the target than the corresponding arrows seen by the other eye. Usually the displacements of the arrows due to a fixation disparity do not prevent a comparison of the relative distances between corresponding arrows seen by the two eyes. Only when the disparity is large and unsteady (as often occurs) will difficulty be encountered. By means of suitable lenses before the eyes, the sizes of the images in the two eyes can be equalized and thus the difference can be measured.

To ensure the required accuracy the headrest is sturdy and yet very flexible, so as to hold and maintain the subject's head and the eyes in a fixed position relative to the test lenses (Fig. 146). The arrangement of test lenses consists of (1) cells for holding whatever refractive lenses are needed, and (2) mounts for the adjustable magnification units. Corneal aligning devices are attached to the test lens supports in order that the eyes can be located at the specified distance from the test lenses. The eyes are aligned with respect to the test lenses by means of centering lenses (which are blank lenses with heavily etched cross lines) inserted temporarily before each eye in one of the cells of the instrument. The operator adjusts the instrument until the centers of the crossed lines are aligned with the centers of the pupils of the two eyes. Before each eye are two adjustable magnification units, one providing changes in overall magnification, the other in meridional magnification. The axis of the latter can be placed at either axis 90 degrees (vertical) or axis 180 degrees (horizontal). Provision has been made so that the tests can be made at both distant and near vision. In the latter case the entire test arrangement can be lowered and tilted as though rotated about the interocular axis to the reading position (20 degrees), the convergence and interpupillary adjustments of the test lenses being made automatically.

In the actual measurement of the difference in the sizes of the images of the two eyes, the method of limits is used in which one determines the limits of magnification change introduced by the lens units within which the subject reports equality of the two images. The midpoints of these limits are taken to indicate the actual differences. One half of the range between these limits (expressed as ± per cent) is a measure of the sensitivity of the subject or at least identifies the precision of the measurement. The procedure is to ask for reports from the subject for different settings of the adjustable magnification units.

When the subject looks from the center of the target to a given pair of opposing arrows, the images of the target center in the eyes will fall on more peripheral parts of the retinas. We must rely on the fusional processes to control the pointing of the eyes in keeping those images nearest correspond-

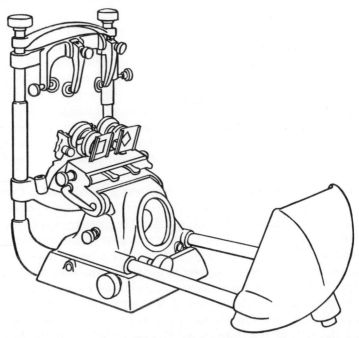

Fig. 146. The direct comparison eikonometer, showing the details of the headrest and test lens arrangement.

ing retinal points in these peripheral areas. This procedure has been shown to be valid experimentally, and is confirmed by the high sensitivity to changes in magnification with this target (p. 233). It must be clear, however, that if a difference in the sizes of the images exists, then when one turns the eyes from the center to look at a pair of opposing arrows, one eye must actually point beyond its arrow, that is, one eye turns slightly too far. Thus if one eye accurately fixes its arrow, the image of the opposing arrow seen by the other eye will be slightly displaced from its fixation point and hence one sees the difference in position of the two arrows.

When a fixation disparity is present, we must assume that the stimuli for fusion hold on the "edges" of Panum's areas, or at least a constant distance from corresponding retinal points. A difference in the sizes of the images of the two eyes will appear because the apparent displacement of opposing arrows will be greater on one side of the center than on the other side. In many subjects, however, the fixation disparity may be so unsteady that these measurements are unreliable.* An unsymmetric magnification between the images of the two eyes of the type discussed in connection with the curvature of the horopter (Chapters 3 and 4) also causes a small apparent displacement of the arrows in the horizontal meridian as seen by the two eyes that cannot be distinguished from the displacement due to a fixation disparity when the eyes are underconverged.

The direct comparison eikonometer has its limitations in that measurements can be made only in the horizontal and vertical meridians. Targets have been prepared for measurements in oblique meridians, but these have proved unreliable mainly because of the disturbing effect of the fixation disparity, especially that in the horizontal meridian.

Repeatability tests[199] indicate that for the horizontal and vertical meridians this method of measurement is reliable at distant vision. In the horizontal meridian at near vision it is less reliable, and considerable judgment is necessary to evaluate the measurements obtained.

THE SPACE EIKONOMETER

The space eikonometer depends on binocular stereoscopic spatial localization.[5] As the name would imply, the instrument measures the difference in magnification between the images of the two eyes on the basis of the apparent spatial orientation of selected types of test objects. Figure 142 illustrates the equivalent relationships between the displacement of monocularly seen detail as in the direct comparison eikonometer and the change in image disparity which should be recognized as a change in stereoscopic depth.

The design of such an instrument necessitates suitable test elements, so that by their apparent orientation separately or in combination we can measure the amount and characteristics of the differences in magnification of the images in the eyes. All empirical clues to spatial localization must, so far as possible, be eliminated, for these would tend to mask or interfere with a "pure" binocular stereoscopic spatial localization. Hence, the simplest of contours are necessary, all adequately screened from other objects in the room.

The Theory. Since the stereoscopic vision is a function of the disparities between the images in the two eyes in the horizontal meridian, the difference in magnification between the images would be more easily measured in that than in another meridian. The experiments with the horopter

---

* In this respect it must be pointed out that for some subjects, especially when tested at near vision where the fixation disparity is likely to be large and much more unsteady, an apparent large image size difference with poor sensitivity will be found. In addition a strange phenomenon may occasionally also be encountered, for if the Polaroid plates before the eyes are interchanged, the apparent image size difference may also be found reversed in direction. Attempts to unravel this "reversal phenomenon" have so far been unproductive.

apparatus, in which the stimuli are smooth vertical threads or wires and in which an apparent rotation about the fixation point occurs with a difference in magnification, constitute the obvious method (Fig. 79). For simplification only two long plumb lines set in the frontoparallel plane can be used satisfactorily, as illustrated in Fig. 143 (p. 236). If a difference in magnification of the images of the two eyes exists in the horizontal meridian, then one line will appear nearer than the other. By introducing the lens of proper magnification before one eye, the two cords can be made to appear at the same distance.

Now a pair of lines intersecting at right angles set in an oblique position in the frontoparallel plane of the observer proves unique, in that a magnification of the image of one eye in the *horizontal* meridian only causes it to appear as though turned about a vertical axis in one direction (the same as in the geometric effect), and a magnification of the image in the *vertical*

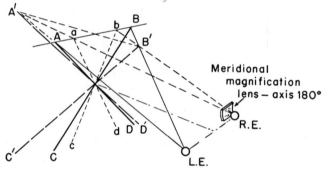

Fig. 147. Schematic illustration of the effect of magnifying the image of the right eye in the vertical meridian upon the stereoscopic localization of an oblique cross in space.

meridian only causes it to appear as though turned about the same vertical axis but in the opposite direction (Fig. 147). This phenomenon is entirely explained on the basis of horizontal disparities, and is itself a *geometric* effect.[*][189] In this figure, *ABCD* shows equidistant points on the oblique cross in the frontoparallel plane. When a meridional magnification lens is placed at axis 180 degrees before the right eye so as to magnify the retinal image in the vertical meridian only, that image is stretched in the vertical meridian, and hence to the *right* eye the cross appears as though it were the shape *a b c d*. Consider the horizontal disparities at *any* level through the cross—say the level *AB*. Then the left eye has images according to points *A* and *B*, while the right eye has images corresponding to the points *a* and *b*. The differences constitute disparities between the images of the two eyes—(*A–a*) *uncrossed disparity*, (*B–b*) *crossed disparity*. Stereoscopically then points *A* and *B* would appear as though at points *A'* and *B'* in space. Since this relationship obtains for any level through the cross

[*] This effect must be clearly distinguished from the induced effect described in Chapter 15. Here the phenomenon is purely geometric only because the lines of the cross are smooth and without details.

except at the point of intersection, the entire cross must appear as though rotated about a vertical axis with the right side nearer to, the left farther from, the observer. This is exactly the direction opposite to that had the lens been placed before the *right* eye at axis 90 degrees so as to magnify the image of that eye in the horizontal meridian only. The analytic theory of the apparent rotation of the cross is given in Appendix II.

Thus it should be clear that by using the plumb lines and the oblique cross in the same field of view, we have a means for differentiating between the horizontal and the vertical differences in magnification of the images of the two eyes making use of stereoscopic space localization. This was not possible with the leaf room or the tilting planes. Figure 148 shows how these configurations are set up to provide the chief test elements of the space eikonometer.

First the horizontal difference in magnification is determined by using the plumb lines as test objects. This difference is corrected by a suitable meridional magnification lens at axis 90 degrees before one eye. Attention is then given to the oblique cross; the degree to which it appears turned is due to a vertical difference in magnification. This is then corrected by a suitable lens at axis 180 degrees. The magnifications of the two lenses then are the horizontal and vertical corrections of the difference between the magnifications of the images of the two eyes.

These two measurements do not, however, tell the whole story, because the meridional difference in magnification between the images of the two eyes may be neither entirely horizontal nor entirely vertical, but the major part of the difference may be in some oblique meridian. The corrections found by the foregoing procedure are only the horizontal and vertical components of the meridional difference at an oblique axis together with any overall difference that may be present.

A meridional difference at an oblique axis, however, also introduces a small rotary deviation of the images of vertical lines in space (Fig. 61), which in the space eikonometer through cyclofusional movements of the eyes (Chap. 10) makes the oblique cross appear inclined in space—top away from or top toward the observer, in addition to the rotation about a vertical axis. By a suitable lens device even this effect can be corrected, and from the value obtained the complete measurement of the difference in magnification can be determined.

Description. A more detailed description of the space eikonometer[5] for distant vision follows. Reference to Fig. 148 should be made.

The essential parts of the space eikonometer are (1) a system of selected test elements; (2) suitable magnifying units, by which the magnification of the images in the two eyes can be changed optically, and (3) a headrest and suitable cells for holding ophthalmic lenses.

The test elements consist of (a) an oblique cross made up of two smooth-stretched cords at right angles to each other, and (b) two pairs of smooth vertical plumb cords, suspended two in front and two behind the cross.

The oblique cross, stretched from the corners of a 5 foot (152 cm.) square frame, is set up vertically at a distance of 3 meters from the subject's eyes. The plane of the cross is carefully erected at right angles to the subject's objective median and visual (horizontal) planes. In the plane of the cross, and through its center, a plumb line is also suspended.

Two of the vertical plumb cords are suspended 60 cm. in front of, and two 60 cm. behind, the cross. The cords in front of the cross are separated about 50 cm., and they thus subtend a visual angle of approximately 12 degrees to the observer. The cords are equidistant from the subject's objective median plane, and the plane of each set of cords is parallel with his frontal plane. Suitable screens with apertures restrict the subject's

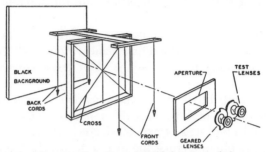

Fig. 148. Perspective drawing showing essential features of the space eikonometer.

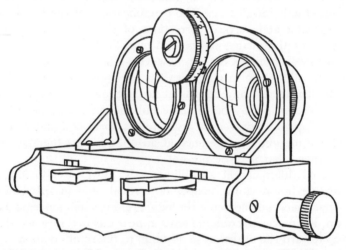

Fig. 149. The declination device used on the space eikonometer. Also shown is the location of the adjustable magnification units and cells for holding lenses.

binocular field of view entirely to the test elements and also prevent him from seeing the ends of the cords. In order to aid in their identification, the cords of the cross are red; the vertical cords in front are green, and the central cord through the cross and the two rear vertical cords are white. The test elements are illuminated by four Lumiline lamps so placed as not to produce any shadows on a uniformly black velvet cloth background against which they are seen.

The test lenses consist of adjustable magnification units before each eye and a special "declination unit." The latter, previously called the geared lens unit, consists of a pair of matched meridional afocal magnification lenses that are geared to rotate equally but in opposite directions. The headrest and chin cup support the subject's head so that the eyes can be adjusted to a steady position before the lenses and the system of test elements.

The test lenses consist of a meridional adjustable magnification unit before each eye; at axis 90 degrees before the right eye and at axis 180 degrees before the left. By means of 3 per cent afocal meridional magnification lenses placed also before each eye, axis 180 degrees before the right eye and axis 90 degrees before the left eye, the two adjustable units will indicate no difference in magnification between the two eyes, in the middle of the range of each unit. Thus, turning the ring on the unit in one direction will increase the relative magnification of the image of that eye, while a rotation in the opposite direction effectively decreases the relative magnification of the image in that eye. This arrangement simplifies the instrument and still gives wide flexibility.

Mounted directly in front of the adjustable units is the "declination device," which provides the means for determining the declination error that will exist if the meridional part of the difference in magnification of the images of the two eyes lies in an oblique meridian. Figure 149 is a drawing of the declination device. This consists of a pair of matched meridional size (afocal magnifying) lenses (2 per cent or 3 per cent) mounted in geared rings. The dimensions of the rings are such that their teeth mesh and the separation of the lenses corresponds to the average interpupillary distance. The two lenses can then rotate in opposite directions when activated by a pinion wheel. A drum is attached to the shaft of the pinion, with a scale calibrated to read directly the declination change introduced, in tenths of a degree. The "zero" position is taken when the axes of the two lenses are parallel and vertical. Stops prevent the lenses from being rotated more than 45 degrees each way from the vertical meridian.

The vertical components as well as the horizontal components of the magnifications of these lenses, irrespective of their rotation, will be equal, so that no resultant image magnification difference in these meridians will be introduced as they are rotated (see Fig. 100).

While the geared meridional magnification lenses used for correcting the declination error do not change the vertical-horizontal relationship of the image magnifications of the two eyes, they always introduce meridional image differences at the 45 degree and 135 degree meridians, the magnitude of which depends upon the degree of rotation of the two lenses. Thus, in the present space eikonometer, the magnification of the geared lenses will not affect the apparent transverse orientation of the cross itself.

The total declination angle, δ, introduced by the geared lenses will be given by

$$\delta = 0.57 \, m \, \sin 2\rho$$

where ρ is the actual angle through which the lenses have been rotated and m is the per cent magnification of the lenses. (Appendix I, p. 307.) If this rotation is such that the axes of the two lenses converge upward, δ is taken positive; if the axes converge downward, δ is taken negative. A rotation of the lenses so that δ is positive (axes converge up) causes the plane of the cross to appear inclined with top nearer the observer.

The headrest is essentially the same as that described for the direct comparison eikonometer (p. 245), and this again provides the means for holding the head so that the eyes will be centered with respect to the test lenses, and at the proper distance from trial case refractive lenses when these are used in the cells provided nearest the eyes.

Procedure. If a difference exists in the magnification of the images in the two eyes, or is introduced by lenses, in the horizontal meridian only, one of each pair of the vertical cords will appear nearer the subject than does the other. Also, the oblique cross will appear rotated about a vertical axis. The nearer cord and the nearer side of the cross will be on the side of the eye having the smaller ocular image. By increasing the magnification of the image in this eye in the horizontal meridian by means of the adjustable unit before the right eye, the cords and the two sides of the cross can be made to appear equidistant from the observer.

If a difference in the magnification of the images exists, or is introduced by lenses, only in the vertical meridian, the cross alone will appear rotated about a vertical axis (the vertical cords will be unaffected), the farther side being on the side of the eye having the smaller image. By magnifying the image in that eye in the vertical meridian by the adjustable unit before the left eye, the two sides of the cross can be made to appear the same distance from the subject, that is, frontoparallel. Thus, the presence and magnitude of a horizontal and a vertical image size difference can be detected and measured by the difference in the apparent rotation of the vertical plumb lines and the cross. When both a horizontal and a vertical image magnification difference exist, the horizontal difference must be corrected first.

If a meridional image magnification difference is present at an oblique axis, so that for vertical lines there is a resulting declination error between the images of the two eyes, then the plane of the cross appears inclined (as though rotated about a horizontal axis through the center of the cross). If the upper part appears inclined away from the observer, the axes of the geared lenses of the declination device must be rotated so as to converge upward toward the forehead of the subject in order to correct that inclination. The measured declination error, δ, will then be positive. If the upper part of the cross appears inclined toward the subject, the axes of the lenses must be rotated so as to converge downward in order to correct that inclination. The measured declination error, δ, will then be negative. By rotating the geared lenses by the proper amount and in the proper direction, the apparent inclination of the plane of the cross can be varied until it and the central vertical cord, through the center of the cross, appear in the same plane. The degree of rotation of the geared lenses measures the vertical declination error.

Controlled experiments[193] show that the sensitivity (σ) of the subject with high visual acuity to changes in the declination, as observed by changes in the inclination of the cross, is of the order of 0.1 degree or less.

The data are obtained in the same manner as are the data with the standard eikonometer, namely, by questioning the subject regarding the apparent positions of the test elements as the examiner makes different adjustments of the test units. Here, too, the method of limits within which the test elements appear correctly oriented is applied to obtain the final result. An estimate of the stereoscopic sensitivities of the patient to the three parts of the test is given by one half of the range within which he reports the vertical cords and the cross to be properly oriented.

Having found the magnification necessary to equalize the relative magnifications of the images in the two eyes m_H and m_V for the horizontal and vertical meridians, respectively, and having found the declination error, δ, necessary to eliminate the effect of any oblique meridional difference, we can find the resultant correction by calculation or from tables (Appendix I).

The Apparent Distortions of the Cross. Frequently an observer will report that the intersecting lines of the cross do not appear to lie in the same plane, and as a result he has some difficulty in trying to describe the apparent orientation of the cross. As a rule, these distortions are of only two types: (1) the plane of the two upper lines relative to the plane of the two lower lines appears twisted about a vertical axis, or sometimes the lines appear entirely separated in space, and (2) all the lines, including the central vertical line, appear to curve toward or away from the observer, in the same sense as would a concave or a convex surface.

The apparent twisting of the upper half relative to the lower half of the cross or the separation of the two lines of the cross can be attributed to a vertical phoria (more accurately, a vertical fixation disparity). An apparent counterclockwise twist of the upper half relative to the lower half would accompany a right hyperphoria, or would be seen if a prism were placed before the right eye base-up. This, except for a possible confusion just at the center of the cross, can be explained by the geometry of the configuration. For large hyperphorias the two diagonal lines of the cross actually separate in space, and it is then necessary to introduce prisms to correct the hyperphoria before the cross becomes fused at the center.

It is advisable, therefore, to introduce prisms to correct the distortion of the cross before proceeding in the examination with the space eikonometer. The magnitude of the hyperphoria, as measured by usual means, is, on the other hand, not an a priori indication that a distortion or a separation of the lines of the cross will occur.

The other type of distortion, namely, an apparently concave or convex shape of the cross configuration, can be explained only on the basis of an unsymmetric inequality of the images in the two eyes. This distortion can be simulated or corrected by placing flat prisms base-out or base-in, as needed, before the eyes. Quite frequently, the prisms necessary to correct this distortion will be in a direction opposite to that needed to correct the horizontal phorias present. This distortion, however, usually does not prevent accurate judgments being made of the orientation of the cross.

In either case, accurate measurements can be obtained if the subject describes the apparent orientation of the cross in terms of the orientation of its plane of symmetry.

There is evidence that occasionally an apparent transverse rotation of the cross affects the apparent positions of the front and rear vertical lines (a contrast effect), and to a lesser extent, vice versa. The effect varies with individuals and is not always constant with the same observer. If the cross appears rotated with the right side nearer to the observer than the left side there is a tendency for the left of the two front lines to appear slightly nearer. The maximal effect is less than 0.12 per cent horizontal image size difference for each 1 per cent vertical image size difference introduced. Although this effect is small, it suggests that the most reliable data obtained from the space eikonometer can be obtained by correcting by successive approximations, first, the horizontal (axis 90 degrees) image size difference; second, the vertical (axis 180 degrees); and finally the declination error.

Other Models. The space eikonometer described previously necessitates a large room. The instrument has been simplified by replacing the actual cords in space by photographic reproductions incorporated in a Vectograph transparency [140] which utilizes the principles of Polaroid. This transparency is placed in a suitable housing about 40 cm. from the patient's eyes, and lenses are placed between the eyes and adjustable units,* an arrangement

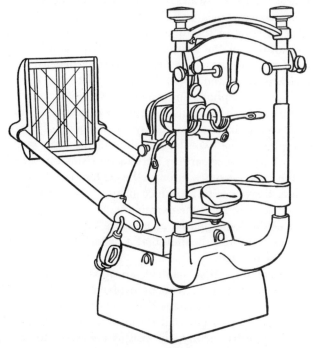

Fig. 150. The space eikonometer using a Vectograph transparency (courtesy of the American Optical Company).

which makes the transparency optically at about 3 meters distance (Fig. 150). The means for obtaining measurements at the reading distance has been omitted. This is justified because of more recent data which show that generally the measurements at distant and near vision are essentially the same.[197] These modifications make for a compact instrument.

THE CORRELATION BETWEEN THE DIRECT COMPARISON AND SPACE EIKONOMETERS

In a separate study,[186] a number of subjects were tested on both the direct comparison eikonometer and the space eikonometer. The subjects were

* This arrangement also improves the optical qualities of the adjustable magnification units, for then little or no power is introduced for different settings of the unit (p. 128).

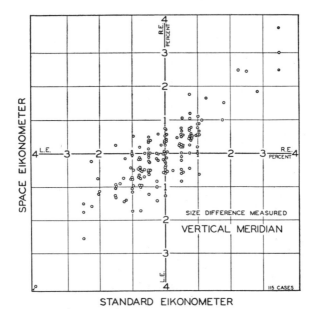

Fig. 151. Scatter representation of data obtained from measurements on the standard eikonometer and on the space eikonometer.

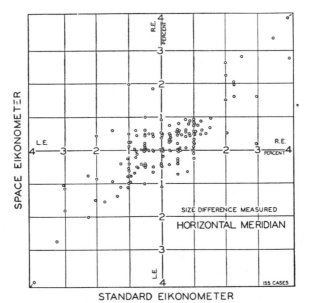

Fig. 152. Scatter representation of data obtained from measurements on the standard eikonometer and on the space eikonometer.

Table 21

TABULATION OF THE NUMBER OF SUBJECTS WHOSE MEASUREMENTS ON THE DIRECT COMPARISON EIKONOMETER AND ON THE SPACE EIKONOMETER AGREED WITHIN SPECIFIED AMOUNTS (156 SUBJECTS)

DIFFERENCE BETWEEN MEASURE-MENTS FROM THE TWO INSTRUMENTS, PER CENT	VERTICAL MERIDIAN			HORIZONTAL MERIDIAN		
	Number of Subjects	Percentage of Subjects	Cumulative Percentage	Number of Subjects	Percentage of Subjects	Cumulative Percentage
0 -0.25, inclusive	67	43	43	64	41	41
0.25–0.50	40	26	69	34	22	63
0.50–0.75	25	16	85	19	12	75
0.75–1	13	8	93	15	10	85
1 –1.25	5	3	96	10	6	91
1.25–1.50	4	2	98	6	4	95
1.50–1.75	1	1	99	1	1	96
Over 1.75	1	1	100	7	4	100

largely routine clinical patients who had been referred for such tests. So far as possible, the two tests were conducted independently of each other, the test with the direct comparison eikonometer being made first. The recorded results of this examination were sent with the subject referred for the second test and remained sealed until the conclusion of the second test. Care was taken that the subject was tested on each instrument with the same properly adjusted spectacles or trial case lenses. The examinations were made only for distant vision.

Figures 151 and 152 are scatter plots of the comparative results for the vertical (axis 180 degrees) and horizontal (axis 90 degrees) meridians. The abscissas are the measurements obtained on the direct comparison instrument, and the ordinates those of the space eikonometer. The more nearly the points on these diagrams fall on a straight line, the higher is the correlation between the results on the two instruments. An inspection of these charts shows clearly that there is a good correlation, since the points tend to cluster about a 45 degree line on each graph.

Studied statistically, one finds highly significant correlations, with standard deviations (σ) of 0.5 and 0.6 per cent difference in magnification for the vertical and horizontal meridians, respectively. This means that the two measurements obtained by 68 per cent of the subjects agreed within 0.5 and 0.6 per cent magnifications. A further breakdown of the data is shown in Table 21.

Usually routine clinical patients are tested within a precision of only 0.5 per cent magnification on the direct comparison instrument. The fact that the data cluster about the 45 degree line indicates a 1:1 ratio between the data from the two instruments. Thus we can conclude that the two instruments are measuring the same quantities accurately.

CHAPTER 20

The Origin of Magnification Differences
Between the Images of
the Two Eyes

INTRODUCTION

W HEN THE CRYSTALLINE lens of an eye has been removed surgically because of pathologic changes, the eye is then said to be *aphakic,* a
condition that renders it hyperopic (farsighted) by about 12 diopters compared to its original refractive error. This farsightedness can be corrected
by an ophthalmic lens placed in front of the eye, but this correction results
in a marked increase in the magnification of the retinal image.

The reason for this increased magnification will be clear from the following. Figure 153 illustrates a normal eye in which the crystalline lens
is to be removed. The optical effect of this removal is as though a thin nega-

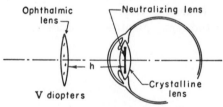

Fig. 153. Equivalent optical relationships in a corrected aphakic eye.

tive (diverging) lens had been inserted at the optical center of the crystalline lens of such a strength as to neutralize the power of that lens completely. The resulting hyperopia would then be corrected by an ophthalmic
lens in front of the eye of such a positive power as to neutralize the effect
of the inserted negative lens. Now the ophthalmic lens and the inserted
lens together constitute a telescopic system, and such a system will introduce a change in the magnification of the retinal image. The resultant optical system is as though a small telescope had been placed before an otherwise normal eye.

Let V be the vertex power (diopters) of the correcting lens that is placed
a distance h (meters) from the inserted lens, then the magnification can
be computed from (p. 122) $M = 1/(1 - Vh)$. On the average the power

of the correcting lens V will be about $+12$ diopters, and the distance of this lens from the position of the optical center of the crystalline lens may be taken as 20 mm., so that the telescopic magnification for a distant object will be about 1.32 and the magnification of the retinal image will therefore be increased by about 32 per cent. The part played by the curvatures and thickness of the correcting lens in the magnifying effect must also be added to this figure.

Now when the crystalline lens of only one eye of an individual is removed, and the refractive errors of both eyes are fully corrected, there will be a marked difference in the magnification of the images of the two eyes. This difference disturbs binocular vision and makes fusion of the images of the two eyes possible only in the very central regions of the retinas (pp. 64 and 152). The actual difference in magnification will, of course,

Table 22

REPRESENTATIVE DATA FOR THE DIFFERENCES IN THE MAGNIFICATION OF THE IMAGES
OF THE TWO EYES AS MEASURED ON THE EIKONOMETER IN
CASES OF CORRECTED UNILATERAL APHAKIA

SUBJECT	REFRACTIVE CORRECTION	VISUAL ACUITY	PER CENT MAGNIFICATION NECESSARY TO EQUALIZE SIZES OF IMAGES IN THE TWO EYES
A. S.	R: $-6.00\ -0.75 \times 15$ L: $+10.00$ S	20/15 20/15	axis 90: R 33 180: R 33
E. E. A.	R: $+1.00\ -2.00 \times 98$ L: $+12.00\ -1.50 \times 70$	20/20 20/20	90: R 21 180: R 25
W. T. C.	R: $+12.50\ -1.00 \times 120$ L: $+1.25\ -1.25 \times 90$	20/15 20/20	90: L 28 180: L 27

depend upon the original refractive errors of the two eyes and their origin prior to the removal of the crystalline lens from one eye. Table 22 gives data representative of actual measurements of the differences in magnification between the images in the two eyes in several individuals with corrected unilateral aphakia.

The problem of the resultant difference in magnification of the retinal images in cases of corrected unilateral aphakia has, of course, been understood for many years, and the uncertain binocular vision resulting has usually been attributed to that fact.

It is reasonable to suppose in this case that the disturbance to binocular vision is due to the difficulties in fusing the larger image of the aphakic eye with that of the other eye. At any given visual angle, the difference in image size constitutes a disparity between the images of the two eyes. The degree to which these images can or cannot be fused depends on the comparative size of Panum's fusional areas and the retinal image disparity for that angle. From the data discussed on p. 64 it was shown that the percentage value of the size of these areas in relation to the corresponding visual angle drops rapidly from the fovea to about 4 to 5 degrees, beyond which the data seem to approach a minimal value of about 3 per cent of the visual angle. These values would be equivalent to the maximal per cent image magnification difference within which the images of the two eyes would be easily fused. Thus, if the difference is more than 3 per cent, these retinal images can be fused only within the visual angle of 4 degrees of the fovea. These data pertain to the horizontal meridian. For the vertical meridian they are probably relatively smaller. A difference of 30 per cent results in disparities far outside Panum's areas over the entire binocular visual field, except for a very small region about the fovea. We can conclude, therefore, that with the failure to fuse the images, except near the maculas, the individual is confronted with a marked confusion of images over most of the binocular visual field, and, if simultaneous vision is maintained, this fact signifies an impairment of vision that cannot easily be tolerated.

Attempts have been made at different times to correct for these differences with special telescopic optical systems designed on a purely theoretical basis (for example, Erggelet[64]).

That smaller differences in magnification could also be a factor in the maintenance of normal binocular vision has not, however, been appreciated. Donders had written as long ago as 1864 that differences in magnification of the retinal images could be expected when astigmatism is corrected by cylinders. Erggelet[67] later even calculated that a difference of 4.1 per cent to 5.4 per cent would occur for a corrected astigmatic error of 4 diopters. He expressed the opinion, however, that little importance could be attached to a difference so small. The general failure to attach significance to differences of this magnitude must be attributed to the fact that the high sensitivity of the eyes to differences in magnification (0.25 per cent) was not known. No method of determining this sensitivity had been devised. Certainly other anomalies of body function four to five times the thresholds, as in the case of astigmatism, for example, are significant. Actually, individuals are rarely found for whom differences in magnification greater than 5 per cent to 6 per cent are measured and who at the same time show normal binocular visual function. For larger differences there may be found poor prism vergences, frequent suppression of the image of one eye, poor stereoscopic vision, and ocular discomfort when the refractive errors are fully corrected by spectacles.

RETINAL IMAGE MAGNIFICATION AND AMETROPIA

Because a magnification of the retinal image would have a bearing upon visual acuity, the question of whether the eye corrected by an ophthalmic lens would have a higher or lower visual acuity than would the normal eye is frequently discussed in textbooks on ocular refraction. Certainly a difference of 4 or 5 per cent change in visual acuity could hardly be perceptible, but a 25 per cent increase in the corrected aphakic eye would be appreciable.

From the point of view of efficient binocular vision, where the sensitivity to differences in magnification of the images of the two eyes is of the order of 0.2 to 0.5 per cent, differences of 5 per cent are very important. The correction of the refractive errors in the two eyes must be treated with strict regard to those conditions affecting the relative magnification of the retinal images. To a considerable extent we can say that the difference in magnification will be associated with unequal refractive errors of the two eyes. Much depends, however, on the *origin* or, better, the *seat* of the refractive errors (ametropias).

We can think of an ametropia as being due to two anomalies: (1) an error in the overall length of the eyeball (called an axial ametropia), in which an excessive length would result in myopia or nearsightedness, and (2) an error in the dioptric powers of the various optical constituents of the eye (called a refractive ametropia), which might be due to changes in (*a*) the curvatures of the surfaces of the cornea or of the crystalline lens;

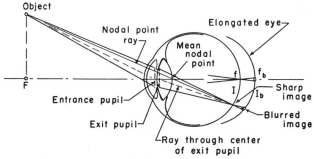

Fig. 154. Schematic drawing showing that the size of the image in an uncorrected axially elongated eye is larger than that of the normal eye.

an increased curvature (shorter radius) would result in myopia; (*b*) the index of refraction of the several media; an increased index of the crystalline lens would also cause myopia, but that of the vitreous humor would cause a small hyperopia (farsightedness); (*c*) the position of the crystalline lens; a forward displacement would introduce hyperopia.

In any given case the ametropia may be due to a combination of these factors. Obviously astigmatism must be a curvature refractive ametropia.

The difference in the magnification of the retinal image of the uncorrected and of the corrected ametropic eye as compared to that of the eye were it normal will be different in these two types of ametropia.

Uncorrected Ametropia—Blurred Imagery. If the length of the eyeball is changed, (say) is elongated, the eye becomes nearsighted (myopic), and the dioptric image will lie in front of the retina (Fig. 154). If the object is a point source of light, the image falling on the retina will be a small disk of light, the diameter of which depends upon the diameter of the pupil and the degree of the myopia. We can assume without loss of generality that the effective part of this blur circle or disk is at its center, a position determined by that ray of light from the center of the exit pupil through the sharp image. Because the exit pupil lies anteriorly to the second nodal point by about 3.8 mm., the size of the blurred image of the object will be larger in an uncorrected axially myopic eye than that in the unelongated or normal eye.

For a distant object the distance of the sharp image from the second nodal point on the axis will be equal to the focal length (f) of the eye; and $f = 1/\phi_0$, where ϕ_0 is the total dioptric power of the eye alone. Now if the eye is elongated by a distance ($\triangle f$), the ametropic (myopic) error ($\triangle D$) caused by the elongation is related to $\triangle f$ approximately by ($\triangle f$) = $-(\triangle D)/\phi_0^2$. From similar triangles in the figure, we have that the ratio of the size of the blurred image, I_b, to that of the sharp image, I, is $I_b/I = (f + s + \triangle f)/(f + s)$, in which s is the separation of exit pupil and second nodal point.

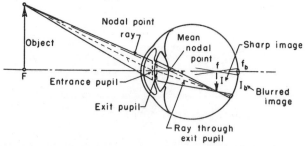

Fig. 155. Schematic drawing showing that the size of the blurred image in an uncorrected refractive ametropic eye is practically the same as the size of the sharp image in the normal eye.

From this we find that the per cent change in magnification of the image due to the elongation will be $\triangle M$ per cent = (100) ($I_b - I$) $/I$ = (100) ($\triangle D)/\phi_0(1 + \phi_0 s)$, in which a positive $\triangle D$ is diopters of myopia. Substituting numerical values, we find that the per cent change in magnification is approximately 1.4 per cent per diopter of ametropia, an increase in uncorrected axial myopia and a decrease in uncorrected axial hyperopia. Thus, there is a change in the magnification of the image in the *uncorrected axial* ametropic eye compared to that of the normal eye.

If the ametropia of the eye is due to a refractive type of change in the dioptric surfaces or media, the dioptric power and therefore the focal length of the eye is changed. In Fig. 155, if the power of the eye increases so that it becomes myopic, the image of a distant object moves in front of the retina, and has a different size from that in the normal eye. For small changes in power we can assume that the positions of the nodal points and of the entrance and exit pupils are unchanged. If ϕ_0 represents the power of the normal eye and ϕ_x represents that of the ametropic eye, then the ratio of the size of the sharp image, I', to that of I, were the eye normal, will be $I'/I = \phi_0/\phi_x$. The size of the blurred image, I_b, on the retina compared to that of the sharp image I' will be given by $I_b/I' = (1/\phi_0 + s)/(1/\phi_x + s)$ $= (1 + \phi_0 s)\phi_x/(1 + \phi_x s)\phi_0$ where, as before, s is the separation of the exit pupil and the second nodal point. The ratio of the size of the blurred image on the retina to that of the image of the normal eye, I, can be found by eliminating I' from the foregoing two expressions; namely, $I_b/I = (1 + \phi_0 s)/(1 + \phi_x s)$, which differs little from unity. The per cent difference in magnification, however, would be $\triangle M$ per cent $= (100)(I_b - I)/I = -(100)(\phi_x - \phi_0)s/(1 + \phi_x s)$. This amounts to about -0.3 per cent per diopter refractive ametropia, which is almost negligible. Again, a positive $\triangle D = \phi_x - \phi_0$ would represent a myopic change, in which case the blurred image is slightly *decreased*. The small forward displacement of the nodal points with increased power will tend to reduce even this difference.

Thus the size of the blurred image in a refractive type of ametropia is essentially the *same* as that of the sharp image were the eye emmetropic. If the eye accommodates while observing a given object, the size of the blurred image of that object remains essentially the same as that of the original sharp image. See also Emsley[63] for a discussion of this general problem.

Corrected Ametropia. When the ametropia of an eye is corrected by an ophthalmic lens, the relationship between the magnification of the dioptric image on the retina compared to that of the emmetropic eye and the type of ametropia is exactly reversed from that just described for uncorrected ametropia. Now the greater difference would be expected in the refractive type of ametropia but not in the axial type. This will be clear from the following.

The total power ϕ of the combined ametropic eye of power ϕ_x and the correcting lens of vertex power V will be $\phi = \phi_x + V - (\phi_x V)h$, where h is the separation of the lens and eye (actually the distance between the second principal plane of the lens and the first principal plane of the eye). The quantities ϕ, ϕ_x and V will be in diopters, h in meters. Now, ophthalmic lenses are worn at a position not far from the anterior focal point of the eye. If the separation h is made equal to the anterior focal length of the eye, that is, $h = 1/\phi_x$, the total combined power of lens and ametropic eye will obviously then be equal to ϕ_x. Thus the combined power of the eye and lens will be equal to the power of the ametropic eye itself.

According to paraxial-ray theory, the magnification M_0 of the retinal image i of an object of size O at a finite distance u from the eye will be given by $M_0 = i/O = -1/(1 - \phi u)$, where ϕ is the power of the eye. Thus if i_0 and ϕ_0 are the image size and power of the normal or emmetropic eye, respectively, the magnification will be $i_0/O = -1/(1 - \phi_0 u)$. For the ametropic eye of power ϕ_x corrected by an ophthalmic lens, the magnification of the retinal image, i_x, would be $i_x/O = -1/(1 - \phi_x u_x)$, where u_x is the object distance from the lens. The ratio, R, of the size of the retinal image, i_x, of the corrected ametropic eye to the size of the image of the normal or emmetropic eye i_0 will, therefore, be $R = i_x/i_0 =$

$(1 - \phi_0 u)/(1 - \phi_x u_x)$. If the object distance is large, this ratio reduces to $R = \phi_0/\phi_x$, the ratio of the two powers.

Clearly, in the case of axial ametropia, where only the length of the eye has been altered, the power of the ametropic eye is the same as that of the emmetropic eye; namely, $\phi_x = \phi_0$, and, therefore, $R = 1$. In other words, this states that *if the correcting lens is placed before the eye so that the second principal plane coincides with the anterior focal point of the axial ametropic eye, the size of the image on the retina will be the same as though the eye were normal, that is, emmetropic.* The case for an axial myopia can be visualized from Fig. 156.

This proposition was first stated by Knapp and by Giraud-Teulon about 1870. Much confusion exists in the literature regarding this law, for it is frequently assumed to hold for *any* ametropic eye that is corrected by an ophthalmic lens.

Just as clearly, in the case of the refractive type ametropic eye, the size of the retinal image of the corrected eye will be different from that image

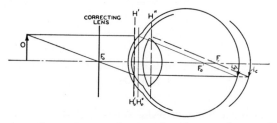

Fig. 156. Schematic axial myopic eye, showing that the retinal image has the same size as though the eye were emmetropic.

were the eye emmetropic, for $\phi_x \neq \phi_0$. We can estimate the magnitude of this ratio from the discussion of the magnification of the image in a corrected aphakic eye. If we know where the seat of the refractive ametropia is, we can use the same formulas. Thus we would find that the per cent change in magnification of the retinal image in the corrected eye to that of the normal eye would be approximately 1.5 per cent per diopter correction in the case of corneal astigmatism, to 2 per cent for a refractive error arising at the crystalline lens.

In the use of the two eyes in binocular vision, it is the unequal refractive errors in the two eyes that will determine whether one could expect a difference in magnification of the dioptric images on the retinas of the two eyes. We cannot know in any given subject whether the ametropias in the two eyes are axial or refractive, except perhaps in certain cases of high myopia, where certain structural changes in the retina can be observed with the ophthalmoscope. Astigmatism is obviously a refractive ametropia due to a curvature deformation, the greater part being usually corneal. The magnification difference due to corrected astigmatism would be a meridional difference, with axis corresponding to that of the astigmatism.

We of course do not know the position of the anterior focal point of a given eye, so that generally the correcting lens will not be placed at that point. The change in magnification of the retinal image will be about 0.1 per cent per diopter correction per millimeter displacement from this position, regardless of whether the ametropia is due to axial or to refractive anomalies.[58] Furthermore, no single anterior focal point exists in an astigmatic eye.

VERIFICATION OF KNAPP'S LAW

The theoretical discussion which just preceded has experimental verification in the results obtained on two subjects.[38, 39]

A Study of a Case of Increasing Unilateral Index Myopia. The first was a case of increasing myopia in one eye only which was studied over a period of eight years, the examinations, fortunately, beginning prior to the onset of the myopia. During this time the refractive error of the right eye changed from a small hyperopia of +0.50 diopter to a myopia of −7.50 diopters, while the refraction of the left eye remained essentially unchanged. The correction of this increasing myopia and the resulting increasing anisometropia was accompanied by a proportionate difference in the magnification of the images of the two eyes.

A gradual decrease in hyperopia or an increase in myopia is often observed in patients more than 60 years of age. Because the increase in the refractive power of the eye is usually observed in cases of incipient cataract, the change was considered due to an increase in the index of refraction of the crystalline lens, especially of the nucleus. Later research has confirmed these findings. Actual measurements of the index of refraction of such crystalline lenses are indeed much higher than those of normal lenses. Today most authors in reporting clinical cases of increasing myopia in older people have accepted the explanation of an increased index of refraction of the crystalline lens.

An ophthalmoscopic examination of this subject showed that the media of both eyes were clear. The slit-lamp examination of the crystalline lens of the right eye revealed an increased reflex from the second layer, an increased density and a greater homogeneity in structure of the adult nucleus. The sutures could not be seen and there was a definite brownish reflex from the posterior cortex. The lens of the left eye showed similar, although considerably less marked, signs of incipient nuclear sclerosis of the crystalline lens. These facts justify the assumption that in this patient, who was more than 60 years of age, the change in the ametropia accompanying the nuclear sclerosis was due to an increase in the refractive power of the crystalline lens, and hence the acquired myopia may be considered as an index myopia.

Table 23 gives the data of the refractive errors and the measured difference in magnification of the images in the two eyes, as well as the calculated difference that might be expected. The refractive measurements

Table 23

REFRACTIVE ERROR AND THE ACCOMPANYING DIFFERENCE IN MAGNIFICATION BETWEEN THE IMAGES OF THE TWO EYES AS MEASURED AND AS COMPUTED FOR A PATIENT WITH INCREASING UNILATERAL INDICIAL MYOPIA STUDIED OVER A PERIOD OF EIGHT YEARS

(1)	(2)	(3)	(4)		(5)	(6)	(7)	(8)
			MEASURED DIFFERENCE		COMPUTED DIFFERENCE, PER CENT			
EXAMINATION DATE	REFRACTION	INDICIAL MYOPIA	Meridian	Per cent	Total	Due to Indicial Myopia	Due to Corneal Astigmatism	Due to the Lenses
12-22-36	R +0.50 −0.25 × 175 L +0.50 −0.25 × 80	None	H* V	L 0.6 ± 0.1 R 0.7 ± 0.5	L 0.5 R 0.5	None	L 0.4 R 0.4	L 0.1 R 0.1
2-2-37	R +0.50 −0.25 × 175 L +0.50 −0.25 × 80	None	H V	0.0 ∓ 0.7 R 1.2 ± 0.5	L 0.5 R 0.5	None	L 0.4 R 0.4	L 0.1 R 0.1
8-22-38	R +0.25 −0.50 × 180 L +0.75 −0.25 × 90	−0.25 D.	H V	R 0.4 ± 1.0 R 1.2 ± 1.5	R 0.1 R 1.8	R 0.7	L 0.5 R 0.9	L 0.1 R 0.2
12-27-39	R −1.00 −0.50 × 170 L +0.50 −0.50 × 95	−1.50 D.	H V	R 2.0 ± 2.0 R 3.0 ± 1.0	R 1.6 R 3.9	R 2.7	L 0.9 R 0.9	L 0.2 R 0.2
5-28-41	R −2.25 −1.00 × 100 L +0.75 −0.75 × 90	−2.75 D.	H V	R 5.0 ± 1.0 R 4.0 ± 1.0	R 4.7 R 4.2	R 4.2	R 0.4 0.0	R 0.1 0.0
7-3-42	R −3.50 −1.25 × 95 L +0.75 −0.50 × 95	−4.00 D.	H V	R 9.0 ± 1.0 R 8.0 ± 1.0	R 9.0 R 7.3	R 7.3	R 1.4 0.0	R 0.3 0.0
3-20-43	R −4.00 −1.50 × 95 L +0.50 −0.50 × 95	−4.50 D.	H V	—	—	—	—	—
11-3-44	R −7.00 −1.00 × 90 L +1.00 −1.00 × 90	−7.50 D.	H V	R 15 ± 1.0 R 14 ± 1.0	R 12.7 R 12.4	R 12.6	R 0.1 L 0.2	0.0 0.0

* H = horizontal meridian, axis 90 degrees, and V = vertical meridian, axis 180 degrees

are shown in column (2) for each succeeding date of examination. These measurements of the refractive errors are also represented graphically in Fig. 157, which illustrates the marked change in the myopia of the right eye. It would appear from this figure that the sclerosis of the nucleus of the crystalline lens began rather abruptly in 1938, and that it had increased at a nearly constant rate until 1944. In column (4) of the table the results of the eikonometer measurements are given for the horizontal meridian (axis 90 degrees) and the vertical meridian (axis 180 degrees). The entries are

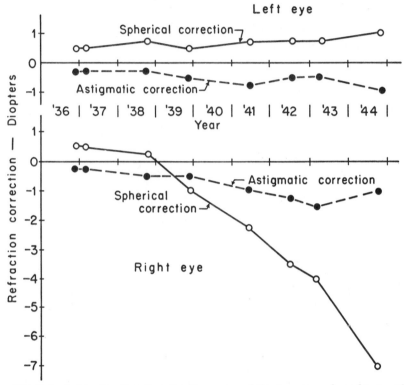

Fig. 157. Spherical and astigmatic refractive errors of the two eyes of a subject with an increasing myopia in one eye associated with nuclear sclerosis.

the per cent magnification needed in a given case to equalize the sizes of the images of the test details in the meridian indicated. These data were obtained with standard (Tillyer) precision trial case lenses carefully adjusted for the correct distance from the eyes, and these lenses fully corrected the refractive errors. The eikonometer results are represented graphically in Fig. 158.

Inspection of the table and the figures relating to the refractive and eikonometer measurements shows that a rapid increase in the difference in the magnifications of the images of the two eyes occurs with the increase in the myopia of the right eye. This increase is in the expected direction. The magnification of the image of the right eye, when the myopia is corrected, decreases relative to that of the image of the left eye, and therefore an increased magnification of the image of the right eye is necessary to equalize the magnification of the images of the two eyes.

This case is especially suitable for the quantitative demonstration of the fact that the correction of a refractive ametropia results in a change in the magnification of the retinal image, because the increasing myopia occurs only in one eye, the refractive error of the other remaining constant, and because the origin of the myopia is known to be due to an effective increase in refractive index of the crystalline lens. These two facts make it possible to calculate the expected increase in difference in magnification, which can then be compared with the corrected myopia.

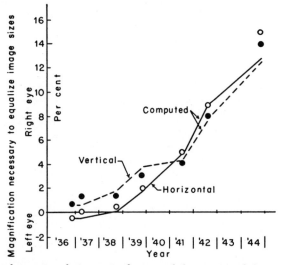

Fig. 158. The change in relative magnification of the images of the two eyes with the correction of an increasing unilateral myopia. The lines are drawn between points corresponding to computed values.

The calculation[38] of the difference in magnification for each examination involves three parts; namely, the determination of (1) that part of the difference due to the correction of the index myopia; (2) that part of the difference due to the correction of the corneal astigmatism, and (3) the modifications in the differences due to the optical properties of the particular trial case test lenses used in the examination.

The results of these calculations are shown in columns (5) to (8) of Table 23. The measured and the computed values are given in columns (4) and (5), which are placed side by side to facilitate comparison. These results are also shown graphically in Fig. 158 by the lines. The close agreement between the measured and the computed difference is evident from the table and the graph. This agreement is in accord with the original assumption made on the basis of the clinical evidence, that the myopia in this case was due to an increase in the index of refraction of the crystalline lens. More important, it demonstrates that a refractive anisometropia, when corrected, is accompanied by a change in the magnification of the retinal image.

A Case of Axial Anisometropia. In contrast to the previous example is the following case of a young individual (22 years). The ophthalmic examination revealed that both eyes were externally normal and the media were clear. The fundus of the right eye showed no pathologic changes. In the fundus of the left eye there were signs of myopic stretching. The refraction and visual acuity were as follows: R.E. +0.50 D. sph. ⌒ −0.50 D. cyl. ax. 135 degrees = 20/15; L. E. −2.75 D. sph. ⌒ −0.50 D. cyl. ax. 105 degrees = 20/15. There was no significant muscle imbalance, and the patient had normal stereopsis with the refractive correction. The examination on the eikonometer gave these results: On the standard eikonometer: (distance vision) ax. 90 degrees: L.E. 0.2 per cent ±0.7 per cent; ax. 180 degrees: 0 per cent ±0.5 per cent. On the space eikonometer: ax. 90 degrees: R.E. 0.4 per cent ±0.5 per cent; ax. 180 degrees: L.E. 0.4 per cent ±0.5 per cent. Because of the absence of a significant difference in magnification between the images of the two eyes, we were forced to conclude that in this case the refractive error of the left eye was axial in nature, a conclusion which was suggested by the clinical appearance of the fundus.

THE RELATIVE INCIDENCE OF AXIAL AND REFRACTIVE TYPES OF AMETROPIA

Spherical refractive errors, according to much of the literature and to most textbooks, are usually regarded as axial ametropias. No doubt that view arose from studies of the sections of excised myopic eyes, and also from the pathologic changes in the retina in highly myopic eyes as observed with the ophthalmoscope.

Within recent years data have been accumulating on this problem that tend to show that axial anomalies account for only part of the spherical ametropias, and that combinations of the axial and refractive types are even more frequent than purely axial ametropias, especially in small or moderate errors. Most of these deductions are based upon calculations made from measurements of the corneal and lenticular curvatures, depth of anterior chamber, and so forth, and using assumed values for the indices of refraction of the ocular media. Figure 159 is a graph based on the calculation of the Russian ophthalmologist, Tron,[227] which shows the incidence of axial and refractive ametropias as computed by him in a study of 243 eyes. The results on ametropic eyes, when compared statistically with computations on normal (emmetropic) eyes, show that combinations of axial and refractive ametropia account for a large proportion of the refractive anomalies, except for high myopia and high hypermetropia.

In general, it has been also pointed out that the variations in axial lengths found in eyes with refractive errors are as great as the variations found in the axial lengths of emmetropic eyes. As an example, Fig. 160 is a graph showing the range of variations in calculated axial length of eyes for different refractive errors, based upon calculations by Paul in which a method somewhat different from Tron's was used. The solid line in the graph represents that relationship for which the ametropia is fully accounted for by an axial anomaly. More recently, Stenstrom determined the axial length of 1000 living eyes, using the roentgenographic method of

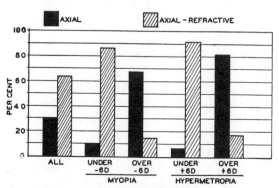

Fig. 159. Results found by Tron[227] on the incidence of axial and combination of axial and refractive ametropia according to the different degrees of refractive errors of the eye.

Rushton. While generally he found a significant correlation between refractive error and axial length, this was markedly higher for the cases of more pronounced myopia and hypermetropia. His results also suggest that only ametropic eyes of more than 8 diopters have axial lengths which fall outside the range of variation of emmetropic eyes. These findings are consistent also with those of Goldmann and Hagen, Deller, O'Connor and

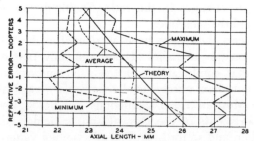

Fig. 160. Graph redrawn from data given by Paul showing variation in computed axial length of eyes having different refractive errors.

Sorsby, and others. While subject to the errors of measurement, calculation and interpretation, the results illustrated suggest that the refractive ametropia plays an important part in the origin of spherical errors except in cases of high nearsightedness or high farsightedness.

One cannot predict from the spherical anisometropia present in a given individual, therefore, what difference in magnification of the images of the two eyes might be anticipated when the refractive errors are corrected by ophthalmic lenses. Astigmatism, of course, is entirely a refractive type of ametropia, and differences in magnification of the dioptric images could be predicted.

ANISEIKONIA

While we have discussed the relative dimensions of the dioptric image falling on the retina of the ametropic eye as compared to those of the otherwise normal emmetropic eye, actually we must be concerned with the physiologic or the functional dimensions of those images as transmitted by the visual pathways to the cortex. These in turn will depend upon the number of retinal elements upon which the dioptric image falls. Thus the functional size of the image will depend upon the relative "packing" or the relative "population" density of corresponding retinal elements. The extent to which Knapp's law holds functionally for the relative size of the image of the corrected ametropic eye compared to that if the eye were normal will depend upon the population density of the retinal elements, which even more broadly includes the entire visual processes with the multiplication of pathways. The ratio between the functional magnification of the corrected ametropic eye and that if the eye were emmetropic will be $R_f = (\phi_0/\phi_x) (d_0/d_x)$, where d_0 and d_x are the densities of the retinal mosaic of the emmetropic and ametropic eyes, respectively. Knapp was aware of this aspect of his proposition and assumed that $d_x = d_0$.

Though the dioptric images in the two eyes may be the same size, if the population density of the retinal elements of one retina is different from that for the corresponding retinal elements of the other, then the dioptric image in one eye will cover more retinal elements than will that in the other, so that functionally there will be a difference in the relative dimensions of the functional images from the two eyes.

Clinically it has been found that in a large proportion of those in whom significant differences in magnification are measured those differences are associated with the refractive corrections. However, significant differences are sometimes measured in emmetropes[123] and isometropes (those with the same refractive error in the two eyes). In about a third of the cases, differences were measured which are in part seemingly unrelated to the dioptric characteristics of the anisometropia present.[187]

One must take into account, therefore, the dimensional factors of the percipient retinal elements of the two eyes and their functional organization (Tschermak). In dealing with the relative magnification of the images of the two eyes we are dealing not only with the dioptric factors involved in the optical formation of images on the retinas of the two eyes, but also with the modifications imposed upon those images by the anatomic, physiologic and perhaps psychologic properties of the entire binocular visual apparatus. Again, functionally, we are concerned not with the dioptric image on the retina alone (the retinal image), but rather with those "images" at the terminal regions of the neurologic visual pathways in the brain. We might therefore call these terminal neurologic "images," *cortical images,* or as an all-inclusive term, just *ocular images.* Certainly they cannot be called "perceptual" images, for perception has not yet taken place, and normally there can be only a single perceptual experience. The basic characteristics of these images, of course, will conform to the patterns of the dioptric images on the retinas.

If we can correct or eliminate the differences in the retinal image sizes due to the geometric arrangement of the objects in space (such as in asymmetric convergence), any remaining difference in the relative sizes of the *cortical* images represents an anomaly in the total binocular visual apparatus —eyes plus lenses. This anomaly has been named *aniseikonia,* a term coined by Dr. Walter B. Lancaster[137] in 1932. Derived from Greek word roots, it means literally "not-equal-images." Aniseikonia therefore. is that *anomaly* in the functional organization of the images from the two eyes evidenced by a difference in the relative magnifications of the *cortical* images of the two eyes—a difference which may be due to anomalies in the dioptric characteristics of the eye (and correcting ophthalmic lenses), to the anatomic dimensions of the organization of the retinal elements and of their neurologic connections to the brain, or to both. It is incorrect to include in aniseikonia those differences in the sizes of the images due to geometric factors in the particular location or orientation of objects in space, but the term must refer rather to the *anomaly* in these sizes over and above any differences due to geometric space factors. In general, aniseikonia would, therefore, be associated with a false stereoscopic localization and an apparent distortion of objects in space regardless of their real positions or orientations.

Conceivably, dimensional differences between the corresponding parts of the cortical images from the two eyes could be irregular, as they would undoubtedly be in cases of a retinal metamorphopsia. There are reasons for believing, however, that the resultant functional differences in the relative magnifications of the cortical images of the eyes, if they exist, are generally regular. The relative magnifications may be unsymmetric, as the evidence from the shape of the longitudinal horopter would suggest, or as would be produced by prismatic elements in the dioptric systems.

For most purposes, we can consider the differences as (1) overall, being the same in all meridians, in the same sense that the focal power of a spherical lens is the same in all meridians; (2) meridional, in which the difference is greatest in one meridian (least at right angles), in the same sense as is the focal power of a cylindrical (or astigmatic) lens; the meridian of this magnification may, of course, be oblique, not horizontal or vertical; and (3) unsymmetric, in which there is a regular change in the magnification difference in one meridian, as would be produced by the unsymmetric magnification of a prism before the eye.

CHAPTER 21

The Stability of Corresponding
Retinal Points

INTRODUCTION

IT SHOULD BE clear at this point that the existence and the persistence of aniseikonia depend upon whether the functional organization of the corresponding retinal points of the two eyes is stable or subject to modification or adaptation to conform to new demands. This question of the stability of corresponding points is an important one, for upon it depends so much of our understanding of the nature of the visual processes, of binocular vision and space perception. Involved in the general problem are the old questions of whether the organization of corresponding points is anatomically innate with fixed and invariant neural connections, or whether this organization can be changed to meet new needs. Can the functional associations be changed by a process of relearning? Is the organization poorly developed or loosely bound at birth, and does it then through experience gradually attain a stable and fixed status later in life?

The school of thought which originated with Hering and was elaborated by Hofmann, Tschermak, and others, stressed the concept of an innate and fixed relationship between corresponding retinal points.[231] Other schools have sought to show that the association is dynamic and plastic and is capable of being reorganized to meet the demands imposed upon it. Jackson,[125] for one, expressed the belief that, especially in youth, it is possible for the organization of corresponding points to be readjusted to overcome any aniseikonia that might be introduced by the correction of unequal refractive errors between the two eyes and even in the cases of corrected unilateral aphakia (!). The existence of the so-called "anomalous correspondence" in individuals with longstanding concomitant strabismus has been used as an argument for insisting on the instability of corresponding retinal points. However, many, and more recently, Burian,[36] have argued that this is not a true change in correspondence of the two retinal organizations but rather that it represents a learned directional association between a peripheral area of one eye and the fovea of the other eye.

The researches on several problems relating aniseikonia to binocular stereoscopic spatial perception bear on this problem of the stability of corresponding retinal points. In particular we can discuss three of these: (1) the incidence of aniseikonia in a group of subjects highly selected on the basis of their having normal eyes; (2) the effect of prolonged wearing of afocal magnification lenses which artificially introduce an aniseikonia, and (3) the correlation between the aniseikonia measured on clinical subjects and that estimated on the basis of the refractive errors in the two eyes.

ANISEIKONIA IN SELECTED PERSONS
WITH "NORMAL" EYES

To determine, among other things, the incidence of aniseikonia in persons highly selected as regards visual characteristics, 280 cadets and instructor pilots at the United States Naval Air Bases at Pensacola, Florida,

Table 24

SUMMARY OF THE OPHTHALMOLOGIC CHARACTERISTICS OF 280 CADETS AND INSTRUCTOR PILOTS TESTED FOR ANISEIKONIA

TEST		MEDIAN	APPROXIMATE STANDARD DEVIATION	RANGE
Age, years		23	1.5	20 to 28
Visual acuity (Snellen)		20/15 (minus)	—	20/15 plus to 20/20
Stereoscopic acuity	Cm.	11	5	2 to 26
	Sec.	20	10	0.5 to 50
Refractive error, diopters		+0.25	*	−0.50 to +2.00
Lateral phoria, prism diopters		1	1.5	0 to 6
Vertical phoria, prism diopters		0	0.25	0 to 0.75

* A very skew distribution

were tested on the eikonometer.[49] Here was a group of young men selected on the basis of low refractive errors, small muscular imbalances and keen vision. These men also had completed successfully at the minimum their primary flight training and therefore can be said to have had a well-developed visuomanual coordination.

The ophthalmologic characteristics of these men are summarized in Table 24. All the visual tests were made for a visual distance of 20 feet (about 6 meters). In this the approximate standard deviation indicates the variation of the characteristic from the mean within which about 68 per cent of the men were included. The stereoscopic acuity was measured on the standard Howard-Dolman apparatus. The refractive errors given here are the maximum to be found in either eye of each subject and were determined with the eyes under cycloplegia. The degree to which anisometropia was present was not available.

The eikonometer test was made by the direct comparison method only, since the space eikonometer had not been sufficiently developed for use at that time.* All subjects were tested without correcting lenses. A number of the subjects were given repeat tests. Figure 161 shows the cumulative percentage curves for the differences in magnification of the images as found in the vertical and horizontal meridians.

Inspection of these curves shows a very low incidence of significant aniseikonic errors. In the vertical meridian, 94 per cent of the subjects had differences of 0.25 per cent or less; in the horizontal meridian, where greater differences might be anticipated, 85 per cent of the subjects had differences of 0.25 per cent or less. These values are on the whole only slightly if any greater than the precision of the measurements as determined by the method of limits.

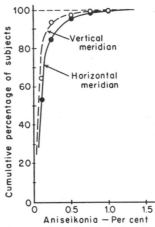

Fig. 161. Cumulative frequency curves showing the percentage of subjects whose measurements were less than the per cent difference in magnification between the images of the two eyes as measured on the direct comparison eikonometer.

The results from this study are evidence that generally persons with low refractive errors, high visual acuity with unaided vision, and low phorias show a low incidence of significant aniseikonia, that is, differences in magnification of the images of the two eyes. In some respects this is a striking conclusion, because at no other place in the body are the two contralateral organs so precisely equalized. But conversely no other organs need such a high precision of organization as do the eyes if there is to be the highest development of accurate stereoscopic spatial localization. Nevertheless, this result certainly suggests the question as to how this precision has come about and how it is maintained.

STUDIES WITH ARTIFICIAL ANISEIKONIA

An obvious approach to a study of the possible actual compensation for the functional differences in magnification of the images of the two eyes

* Space eikonometer tests on less highly selected personnel were made by Elliot.

and the possible adaptation of the eyes to the distortion of stereoscopic spatial localization resulting from aniseikonia, as it bears on the problem of the stability of corresponding points, is to introduce and maintain an artificial aniseikonia for a period of time. Such experimental work has not been pursued as much as it should have been, possibly because in a large part subjects are reluctant to endure the inconvenience and the scheduled routine measurements necessary. Especially difficult is it for those unaccustomed to wearing spectacles.

The artificial aniseikonia is produced by attaching an afocal magnification lens over the spectacle lens of one eye, or, in the case of no spectacles having been worn previously, the lens is incorporated in one eye-wire and a plano-lens in the other of a pair of spectacles. Because of their manifest effect upon stereoscopic spatial localization, meridional lenses were used, and for simplicity these would be placed at either axis 90 degrees (to magnify the image in one eye in the horizontal meridian) or axis 180 degrees (to magnify in the vertical meridian) or two lenses were placed with axes oblique before the two eyes. Burian[35] has carried out the more extensive study with meridional afocal magnification lenses at axis 90 degrees. This is reported in the next section.

Meridional Artificial Aniseikonia in the Horizontal Meridian. Three observers wore meridional magnification lenses at axis 90 degrees in front of one eye for periods of eight to ten days. Preceding, during, and after this time, measurements were made two or three times a day on three instruments, the horopter apparatus, the direct comparison eikonometer and the space eikonometer,* all of which have been described in previous chapters of this book. The settings of the wires on the horopter apparatus for the apparent frontoparallel plane, the appearance of the test elements of the space eikonometer, and the apparent orientation of a tilting plane apparatus depend upon stereoscopic space localization, for the measurement of the manifest aniseikonia at any time.

The procedure was a simple one. Before the lens was worn, measurements were obtained on four to seven days, early in the morning and late in the afternoon. These measurements established the subject's normal aniseikonic condition. When the lens was attached to introduce the artificial aniseikonia, and after the period when it was removed, the same routine of measurements was followed. One of the observers also regularly made a set of measurements at night before retiring. During the period that the lens was worn, the observers were never for a single waking moment without it. If the spectacles had to be removed, one eye was always closed until the glasses could be put on again. In the morning as a rule, one eye was occluded until the first measurements could be obtained. Each subject kept a diary to record the visual experiences in his activities day to day. Immediately after the lens was removed at the end of the run, measure-

---

* Data were also obtained upon a tilting plane type of instrument, but these proved on the whole unreliable.

ments were routinely continued until the subject's normal aniseikonic condition was obtained. This end period took from four to ten days, so that the entire experiment required three to four weeks.

The three observers were nonpresbyopic, all had normal visual acuity when corrected and normal binocular vision. One (H.M.B.) was a myope, the second (R.E.B.) a hyperope and the third (M.E.B.) an emmetrope. During the preliminary period the emmetrope wore spectacles with plano-lenses, to which the magnification lens was later added.

Adaptation for the Distortion of Stereoscopic Spatial Localization. All three subjects reported the typical distorted appearances of the surroundings (Chapter 13) when the magnification lens was first attached to their spectacles. If the lens was before the right eye, objects on the right side of the visual field appeared farther away and larger than those of the same relative location on the left side. A flat desk top appeared tipped down on the right side, up on the left; a front wall appeared farther away on the right, nearer on the left; the ground upon which the subject walked appeared to be slanted downward on the right and upward on the left, as though he were walking on a side hill. His right hand held in front appeared larger than his left hand. At the same time objects appeared distorted in shape. Square or rectangular objects such as the desk top or magazines on it appeared trapezoidal; round objects appeared egg-shaped. The subject saw his face distorted in a mirror. The spatial distortion was more pronounced for comparatively near vision than for distant, and often it seemed also more marked when attention was given to the shapes of objects and when single objects were fixated than when the eyes were allowed to rove quickly from one object to another.

However, with continued wearing of the lens, the observers became less and less aware of the distortion and usually after three to four days it was not evident in familiar surroundings. During the last few days before the lens was removed, the subjects found it usually impossible to detect the distortion of space in those surroundings, even with strict attention to specific objects. As far as the ordinary surroundings or those encountered in homes and offices were concerned, the *adaptation* to the artificial aniseikonia seemed complete after a week's wearing of the lens.

However, when the subjects walked into the fields or on a hill with high-grown grass, that is to say, found themselves in surroundings with few empirical clues to space localization, the distortion immediately reappeared. This phenomenon occurred time after time, irrespective of how long the lens had been worn. These results suggest that one is able to adapt to an artificial aniseikonia in the sense that objects are seen in their correct shape and localization as long as the surroundings contain empirical clues in sufficient number or intensity to dominate the stereoscopic perception of space. This adaptation does not mean, however, that the aniseikonia no longer is present. The reappearance of the distortion in surroundings which demand stereoscopic localization implies that, though an adaptation to the distortion occurred, the difference in magnification of the images had not been compensated. This fact is quantitatively proved by the correlation between the direct comparison eikonometer and the space eikonometer (p. 254).

The phenomenon of the *adaptation* for the incorrect stereoscopic localization is entirely consistent with the experience of ophthalmologists, that patients given spectacles for the first time or given changes in refractive correction frequently report a distortion and discomfort from wearing the spectacles, but usually "get accustomed" to them in a week or ten days.[62]

All three observers reported that the wearing of the lens caused some ocular discomfort, though this varied between the observers. The discomfort, especially at the beginning, consisted of slight headaches, feelings of eyestrain and some irritability and nervous tension. The intensity of the symptoms seemed to become less the longer the lens was worn. Generally the subjects could go about their duties without inconvenience, for the spatial distortions did not interfere materially with tasks that involved the finer visuomanual coordination. There was no evidence that a loss of stereoscopic depth discrimination occurred, even after the distortion of space was no longer generally apparent in familiar surroundings. Thus the disappearance of the distortion with the prolonged wearing of the lens is not an overt suppression of stereoscopic vision, at least in the central portions of the binocular field, for there stereoscopic depth differences can still be readily appreciated.

When the lens was finally removed, a considerable distortion of space was immediately evident, but this distortion was in the direction opposite to that which had appeared when the lens was first worn. The return to normal, while usually taking several days, was a little more rapid than the process whereby the subject became adapted to the lens. Again, the distortion was more marked in surroundings where there was a paucity of empirical clues to space localization. Schwarz has already described a similar adaptation to the spatial distortions caused by prisms. After the prisms had been worn for some time, the distortion that had been noticed at first gradually disappeared. Upon the removal of the prisms, a distortion reappeared, but its direction was opposite to the one first experienced, and this likewise gradually disappeared. Psychologic experiments of a different order which show this type of *aftereffect* phenomena have been described by Hofmann and Bielschowsky,[120] Gibson,[89] and Köhler and Emery. Larrabee and Bronk have attempted to find the mechanism for such effects in the sympathetic ganglia. This problem cannot be considered further until we review the quantitative results.

Quantitative Results. All three subjects as they continued wearing the lenses tended to respond to the artificial aniseikonia in the same fashion, although the magnitude of the reaction was often markedly different. We can list the essential results of the data as follows. (1) From the first day after attaching the lens, there was for two observers a small but definite reduction in the manifest aniseikonia. The change was greatest during the first few days and then the manifest values seemed to reach a stable value in six to eight days. One subject showed no such reduction. (2) A consistent diurnal variation was found in the manifest aniseikonia, being greater early in the morning and smaller at the end of the day. (3) High correlations were found in the aniseikonia as measured on all the instruments. (4) No significant change was found in the sensitivity of the subjects to the measurement of the manifest aniseikonia during the course of the experiment.

Typical results are shown graphically in Figs. 162 and 163. The first illustrates the data obtained by one subject by the settings of the apparent frontoparallel plane on the horopter apparatus, when a 6 per cent meridional afocal magnification lens is worn with axis 90 degrees before the right eye. On the abscissa are plotted days during the experiment, and on the ordinate are plotted the corresponding manifest per cent difference in magnification of the images of the two eyes in the horizontal meridian obtained from the degree of rotation of the horopter curve from the objective frontoparallel plane.

During the four days prior to wearing the lens, the data show an initial aniseikonia of about 0.70 per cent, the image of the left eye being the larger. The points are for the data as obtained in the early morning and late afternoon. On the fourth day, the 6 per cent magnification lens was placed before the right eye, and data on the horopter apparatus were immediately obtained. With this lens the manifest aniseikonia was about 5.15 per cent, the right eye image being the larger, and thus the total change agreed well with the magnification of the lens. On subsequent days the manifest aniseikonia decreased, but appeared to reach a stable value at about 4 per cent about the seventh day. On the thirteenth day the lens was removed and immediately data were obtained; the manifest aniseikonia was about 2.2 per cent, the image of the left eye being the larger, corresponding to a change of 5.1 per cent. Subsequently this decreased, and on the fifth day after removal of the lens the relationship between the two eyes was the same as that at the beginning of the experiment.

Figure 163 illustrates the data as measured both on the horopter apparatus (which is here essentially the same as the space eikonometer) and on the direct comparison eikonometer for another subject who wore a 3 per cent lens before the left eye. Essentially the trend in this figure is the same as that shown in Fig. 162.

The average decrease in the manifest aniseikonia differed for the three subjects, there being almost no decrease for the third subject, who was emmetropic. Also the amount of decrease in the first two differed somewhat depending upon whether the lens was worn before the right or left eye. Similar results had previously been found with some subjects when tested on the large horizontal tilting plane[4] and in the leaf room,[186] in that they would not respond equally to magnification lenses placed before the right and then the left eye. However, with the apparent frontoparallel plane test on the horopter apparatus, all three subjects responded precisely to the

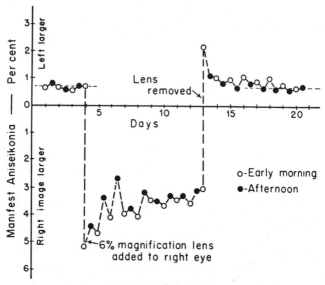

Fig. 162. The manifest aniseikonia measured twice daily in the course of a continuous wearing of a meridional afocal magnification lens before one eye in the horizontal meridian. Data (H.M.B.) from the apparent frontoparallel plane in the horopter apparatus.

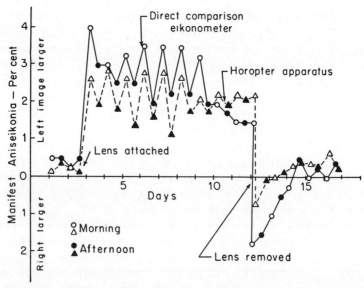

Fig. 163. The manifest aniseikonia measured twice daily in the course of the continuous wearing of a meridional afocal magnification lens before one eye in the horizontal meridian. Comparative data (R.E.B.) obtained by the apparent frontoparallel plane on the horopter apparatus and by the eikonometer.

magnification of the lens used, whether it was placed before the left or the right eye (p. 29 and following).

Measurements on the direct comparison eikonometer and on the space eikonometer showed that no changes whatsoever in the manifest aniseikonia took place in the vertical or oblique meridians of the eyes during the experiments. The trend of the data is essentially the same when obtained on all three instruments, though each of these instruments depends on somewhat different functions of the eyes. With the horopter apparatus, fixation is constantly maintained on the central (fixation) wire, all others being observed in more peripheral vision but set by means of stereoscopic vision. In the space eikonometer, while essentially the same subjective criterion is used with stereoscopic vision, the observer is free to let his fixation rove over the test elements. In the direct comparison eikonometer, stereoscopic vision is not involved, for direct comparison of the relative sizes of the images is made. The correlation between the three instruments was quite high,[35] although somewhat less so during the time the lenses were actually worn. From these correlations, there is little doubt that all three instruments are measuring essentially the same quantity.

The Diurnal Effects. The manifest aniseikonia while the lenses were worn as measured on all three instruments was generally found greatest in the early morning and least at night. There was also evidence that it was significantly greater in the morning if an occluder was worn over one eye from the moment the subject awakened until the first measurements were taken. This difference between morning and evening measurements was most marked in the first few days after the lens was attached, and toward the end of the period of wearing the lens the differences became less and in some cases became hardly significant. The variation between morning and evening measurements was different for the three observers, and for one, the variations were comparatively small. Nevertheless, this diurnal effect is very important to keep in mind in trying to understand the mechanism for any compensatory process in the organization of corresponding retinal points involved here.

Meridional Artificial Aniseikonia in the Vertical Meridian. The apparent distortion in the stereoscopic perception of space caused by the wearing of a meridional lens at axis 90 degrees before one eye, as has been made clear, is a geometric phenomenon that arises because the horizontal disparities between retinal images of all objects in space have been changed. The adaptive and compensating processes of the visual system to prolonged wearing of the lens may be different in this case from that in which the lens is worn at axis 180 degrees to magnify the retinal image of the eye in the *vertical* meridian only. The apparent false spatial perception in this case is the *induced* effect phenomenon and is not geometric in origin in the same sense as that produced by the lens worn at axis 90 degrees.

Data on this problem[168] have been obtained so far on only two subjects.

Daily measurements were made on the direct comparison eikonometer and the space eikonometer during the course of the experiments, and the procedure was essentially the same as that described previously for the lens worn at axis 90 degrees. A distortion of space was as evident in this case as in the former, and the subjects reported about the same experiences while wearing the lens. Again, after the fifth day, the subject became unaware of the distortion in familiar surroundings, but it would always be apparent in the leaf room or in surroundings where the empirical clues for spatial localization were weak.

The results of one subject who wore a 2 per cent meridional afocal magnification lens before the left eye at axis 180 degrees are shown in Fig. 164.

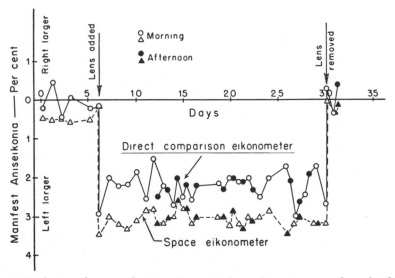

Fig. 164. The manifest aniseikonia in the vertical meridian as measured on the direct comparison and space eikonometers in an experiment in which the subject (E.J.B.) wore a 2 per cent meridional afocal magnification lens at axis 180 degrees before the left eye over her regular refractive correction.

This subject was a corrected myope (—2.50 spheres O.U.). The lens was worn for twenty-four days, during which time the same precautions to prevent binocular vision except through the lens were taken as in the previously described experiments. In the graph the abscissas are the days and the ordinates are the results of the measurements showing the manifest aniseikonia in the vertical meridian.

The measurements in the horizontal meridian showed no change throughout the experiment. The displacement of the data points obtained on the space eikonometer from those obtained on the direct comparison eikonometer may be accounted for by a constant difference of about 0.5 per cent between the two particular instruments used. Irrespective of this, however, it is clear that no significant decrease or trend in the manifest aniseikonia occurred during the period the lens was worn. Generally similar results were obtained by the other subject.[*]

Meridional Artificial Aniseikonia at Oblique Axes. One subject[168] obtained data on the space eikonometer with the continued wearing of a meridional afocal magnification lens before each eye placed at symmetrically oblique axes. The lenses were R.E.: 2 per cent axis 45 degrees, and L.E.: 2 per cent axis 135 degrees. These lenses, being equal and their axes being symmetrically placed, cause no aniseikonic difference in the vertical and horizontal meridians. They do, however, introduce a rotary deviation of the images of lines of all meridians of space not 45 degrees and 135 degrees (p. 166). Functionally it is this effect upon the images of vertically arranged objects that is important, for stereoscopically these will appear incorrectly oriented in space (p. 147).

The subject reported an extreme amount of spatial distortion of the type characteristic of lenses placed obliquely. Unlike the other cases of artificial aniseikonia, this distortion was only slightly less after a week, and even at the end of the twenty-seven days during which the lens was worn, there was some spatial distortion in the most familiar of surroundings. The subject also reported a sense of eyestrain which persisted during the entire course of the experiment, with "a constant and at times overwhelming desire to remove" the glasses.

The small angular rotary deviation between the images in the two eyes of vertical lines caused by the lenses when the images are fused is a *declination error*, δ, and this can be measured on the space eikonometer. The results obtained by the subject who wore the obliquely placed lenses for twenty-seven days are illustrated in Fig. 165. In this graph, again the abscissas are the days measured from the beginning of the experiment, and the ordinates are the corresponding measurements of the manifest declination error, δ, in degrees as measured on the space eikonometer. The meridional lenses worn should introduce a declination error of about 1.1 degrees. The graph shows that this amount was substantially measured when the lenses were first attached to the spectacles. However, it is evident that the manifest error decreased to about 0.6 degree about the fifth day after attachment of the lenses, after which it fluctuated about an essentially constant value throughout the rest of the experiment. When the lenses were removed, a manifest declination error of about 0.4 degree was measured in the direction opposite to that introduced by the lenses. This, however, disappeared in several days, and the normal error returned.

The decrease in the manifest declination error suggests a compensatory process which reduces the degree of the error introduced by the lenses. In this case, however, we can account for this effect entirely upon the basis

[*] One subject[168] obtained data also with the induced effect S-curve, measuring in each case the amount of the displacement of the center of symmetry of the curve (p. 196) as a measure of the manifest aniseikonia. This is a very important approach to the problem, and while the results were quite variable for this subject, no compensatory effect to the lens was evident.

of a change in the cyclofusional positions of the eyes. In Chapter 10, it was shown that a cyclofusional movement could occur when meridional magnification lenses are placed at oblique axes before the eyes. The magnitude of these movements depended upon the degree of the declination error introduced and the spatial configurations of objects in space, and they served the purpose of keeping the images of all configurations of the visual field on a whole as near as possible on corresponding retinal elements. However, vertical configurations appeared to exert a greater stimulus for these movements than did horizontal configurations. The important factor shown in the present experiment is that the final cyclotorsional positions of the eyes tend to become conditioned by the prolonged wearing of the lenses, so that these are even maintained for a short time after the lenses have been re-

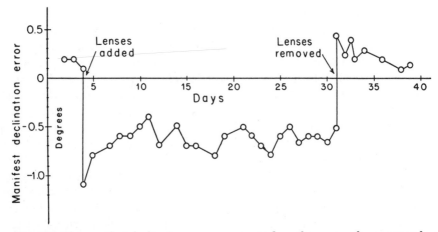

Fig. 165. The manifest declination error as measured on the space eikonometer when the subject (P.W.M.) wore 2 per cent meridional afocal magnification lenses before the two eyes at oblique axes.

moved.* Because the magnitude of the declination error introduced is of the order of 1 arc degree, it is obviously not possible to measure any change in a cyclophoria of the two eyes by ordinary means in this experiment.

General Comment. From the few cases described, it is impossible, of course, to draw definitive conclusions on the problem as to what extent the functional organization of corresponding points can be changed in the interest of overcoming aniseikonic errors. Much more work is required. However, they do provide us with certain evidence that may be quite representative.

A change in the functional organization could come about in several ways. First, changes in the optical systems could take place, such as displacements of the crystalline lens or changes in its curvatures. The effect of these changes would not be very large, however. Second, actual realignments of

* The possibility that the partial compensation for the declination error introduced by the lenses is due to a psychologic "aftereffect" must be mentioned here.

cortical neural connections within the visual cortex could occur if the corresponding terminal points retain their same psychical counterparts. Third, changes in the psychical counterparts relative to the fixed anatomic organization of the neurons from the two eyes might be possible. This last category was the basis for Wundt's conclusion that the disappearance of a retinal metamorphosis in one of his eyes was proof of the empiristic hypothesis of corresponding retinal points and spatial localization.

From the experiments with prolonged wearing of meridional afocal magnification lenses we do know that when a subject with normal binocular vision wears before one eye a meridional lens at axis 90 degrees or axis 180 degrees for several days, he at first experiences a typical and usually marked distortion of objects in his surroundings. The longer the lens is worn, the less evident the distortion becomes, and finally it is absent as long as the subject remains in familiar surroundings in which there are an abundance of objects which provide empirical clues for spatial localization. Thus, in normal surroundings there is a complete *adaptation* to the stereoscopic stimuli that would ordinarily result in a distortion of space. If, however, these empirical clues are few or weak in other surroundings, the distortion reappears immediately. This is to be expected because actual measurements made on the direct comparison and space eikonometers (in which these empirical clues are almost absent) show that the greater part of the artificial aniseikonia is still present, regardless of how long the lenses have been worn. One must conclude that the absence of spatial distortion does not preclude the existence of aniseikonia.

As to the nature of this adaptation we should have to conclude that it results in a conditioning process involving space localization based wholly upon empirical factors. We are almost forced to the conclusion that such a change fits only the picture of a psychical change in the frame of reference for binocular visual egocentric localization—in these cases as a rotation of the binocular field of view about the fixation point, a change always dependent upon the visual factors of empirical spatial localization. This would be essentially the same whether the axis was 90 degrees or 180 degrees. In spite of such a change in reference, however, the stimuli for an incorrect stereoscopic spatial localization will nevertheless be present.

This type of adaptive process which is effective for the axis 90 degrees and axis 180 degrees cases would not be effective in the case where meridional lenses are placed obliquely. It is here that the adaptive process actually seems to fail or at least is much slower to manifest itself.

The fact that the manifest aniseikonia in the case of meridional lenses at axis 90 degrees as measured actually seemed to decrease to a stable value with continued wearing of the lens constitutes a more difficult problem. Is it evidence of a specific partial *compensation* of the aniseikonia introduced? Second, we must keep in mind that the amount of this compensatory effect appears to be different depending upon which eye is magnified, although the variation was not found in one of the three subjects, whose eyes were emmetropic. Third, no compensatory effect is found for the wearing of the lens at axis 180 degrees on the basis of two subjects whose data have been reported. Were it not for the parallel changes in the data of the direct comparison eikonometer to those of the space eikonometer, we might feel justified in considering the effect as being a memory "hold-over" from the *adaptive* process, since it is improbable that all empirical space clues are absent in the space eikonometer. The direct comparison eikonometer, however, depends only on the discrimination of differences in subjective direction, and depth localization is not a factor. The fact that the compensatory effect does not seem to occur with lenses placed at axis 180 degrees suggests that the *compensatory* effect for lenses at axis 90 degrees is associated with the binocular stereoscopic function.

We can, of course, conjecture that this decrease in the manifest aniseikonia represents a true physiologic process tending to compensate for the artificial aniseikonia introduced. This process would also account for the low incidence of aniseikonia found among emmetropes. The process conceivably would have definite limits and in fact these limits in terms of per cent magnification difference between the images of the two eyes would be small. In the cases of H.M.B. and R.E.B., both of whom have moderate ametropia and anisometropia, this process may have already taken place in one direction. Hence, lenses before one eye or the other might easily show a difference in the degree to which further compensation could take place. Moreover, in the case of the emmetrope (M.E.B.), in spite of the fact that the evidence for a compensatory process was small, it was, nevertheless, more nearly equal for the lens worn before either eye. A stumbling block to this hypothesis is the failure of a compensation to appear for the lenses placed at axis 180 degrees. It is useless to conjecture further on this problem until many more data are available. The present discussion is merely an attempt to account for the data now available.

MANIFEST ANISEIKONIA AND REFRACTIVE ERRORS

A study of the data obtained in the clinic suggests that in a large percentage of patients the manifest aniseikonia as measured agrees in type and in approximate amount with that which might be expected on the basis of the corrected anisometropia present. The implications of such evidence are important in the problem of the stability of corresponding retinal points, for many of these patients must have been subject for long periods to the aniseikonia introduced by the corrections.

We cannot know in any given case, of course, whether the spherical ametropia is axial or refractive, except in certain cases of high myopia (nearsightedness), in which there may be observable structural changes in the fundus. Hence we cannot predict the presence of aniseikonia from the simple spherical anisometropia present. Astigmatism obviously is a refractive ametropia in one meridian, the greater part of which can usually be measured directly by means of the ophthalmometer. In this case we can calculate what the expected change in magnification of the image on the retina might be.

Most persons whose eyes are suitable for a study of this kind have spherical anisometropia combined with astigmatic errors. Then it is not possible to predict the difference in magnification of the dioptric images of the two eyes that might be expected on the basis of the computation.

Declination Errors. Nevertheless, it is possible to study an aspect of this problem that is independent of the spherical anisometropia, and that depends only upon the astigmatic errors, if the axes of those errors are oblique and different in the two eyes.[196] We have seen (p. 264) that the correction of astigmatism with cylindrical lenses results in a meridional magnification (or diminution in the case of a negative cylinder) of the retinal image, at right angles to the axis of the cylinder. If this meridional magnification is at an oblique axis, the images of objects arranged vertically in space will undergo a small rotary deviation[155] which we have called a *declination error* (Appendix I, p. 307). Declination errors between the two eyes cause a particular type of incorrect *apparent* spatial localization, in that objects appear inclined with tops away from or toward the observer. This declination error can be measured on the space eikonometer.

A project was set up whereby a study of the declination errors between the images of the two eyes could be made on several hundred clinical subjects. Especially tested were those subjects whose refractive corrections included astigmatic errors at oblique axes. The measurements were, of course, only a part of the complete test made with the space eikonometer.

The patients were tested only after their refractive errors had been carefully corrected either with trial case lenses, or with their own spectacle lenses if no change in refractive correction was necessary. In the majority of the cases the spectacles worn by the patient in the test were standard Tillyer lenses. These particular lenses were used because their relative magnification properties are readily available in prepared tables. The distance of the eye-wires from the corneas of the eyes was measured. In order to find the origin of the astigmatic errors, the curvatures of the corneas were measured with the ophthalmometer.

The ages of the patients ranged from 17 to 70 years, the average age being about 40 years. A record was made of the age at which spectacles were first worn, the length of time they had been worn prior to the examination and how constantly they had been worn.

A total of 419 subjects were tested. Of these, 30 were considered to have normal eyes because they had small or no refractive errors, did not wear and had not worn glasses, had a visual acuity in each eye of 20/20 or better (Snellen notation), had heterophorias within the normal limits and, moreover, did not complain of any ocular symptoms. Of the subjects, 80 had no astigmatic errors, had astigmatic errors which were within 10 degrees of axis 90 degrees or axis 180 degrees or had errors equal in amount in the two eyes with parallel axes. The remaining 309 subjects definitely had astigmatic corrections, the axes of which were oblique, that is, deviating from the horizontal or the vertical axis by at least 10 degrees.

Incidence. The incidence of declination errors between the images of the two eyes for each of the three groups is illustrated graphically in Fig. 166. The ogive curves indicate the percentage of subjects whose measured declination error was equal to or less than any specified amount. Thus, for the range of declination error of 0.20 degree and less, there were 97 per cent of the normal group, 80 per cent of clinical subjects with astigmatism of the "nonoblique" type and 54 per cent of the subjects with astigmatism in oblique axes. For the group having normal eyes, the average declination

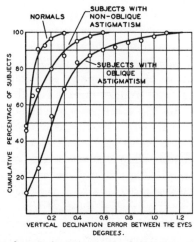

Fig. 166. Cumulative distribution (ogive curve) of the percentage of subjects for whom the measured declination errors were equal to or less than given amounts.

error was essentially zero, with an average sensitivity to changes in the declination of the order of ±0.1 degree. Thus, 90 per cent of these subjects had a declination error between the images of the eyes equal to or less than the average sensitivity of the group. In the 80 subjects with nonoblique astigmatism, a generally higher incidence of declination errors was found, though even here 50 per cent of these patients had no measurable error. The 309 subjects with astigmatism at oblique axes showed, unmistakably, a much higher incidence of declination errors, scarcely 10 per cent having no measurable error.

Sensitivity. The ability of subjects to recognize changes in the declination between the images of the two eyes by means of the apparent incorrect localization of the cross of the space eikonometer can be found by the limits within which the cross appears oriented correctly, the sensitivity being written as one half of that range.

For the group of subjects considered to have normal eyes the average sensitivity, by the method of limits, was ±0.1 degree (see also p. 239). The approximate cumulative distribution of the sensitivities for the normal group is shown in Fig. 167. In terms of stereoscopic acuity, the high sensitivity of ±0.1 degree would correspond to about 35 seconds of arc between the retinal images of the two eyes at an angular distance of 5 degrees above and below the visual plane. An apparent inclination of the cross of the space eikonometer for an observation distance of 3 meters, corresponding to a 0.10 degree δ, would be about 5 degrees.

In an entirely separate project conducted by Dr. Henry A. Imus during the War, 300 men of military age, whose ocular characteristics were scarcely less normal than those of the thirty described previously, were studied for sensitivity to changes in the declination on the space eikonometer. Each subject made five settings (adjustments) of the geared lenses so that the cross appeared correctly oriented. The cumulative distribution of the mean deviations from the median of the five settings for the group is also shown

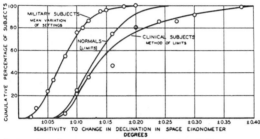

Fig. 167. Cumulative distribution (ogive curves), for different groups of subjects, of their sensitivities to declination errors between the two eyes as measured on the space eikonometer.

in Fig. 167. The sensitivity obtained by the method of limits is nearly twice that obtained by the method of mean variation of settings.

The cumulative distribution curve of sensitivities for the clinical subjects is also shown in Fig. 167. It will be noted that the sensitivity in this group is only slightly poorer than that of the normal subjects, except when the declinations become larger. This fact must be taken into account when studying the significance of declination errors.

Repeatability of Measurements. The reliability of the measurements of the declination error between the images of the two eyes depends upon how well the data repeat after a lapse of time. It was difficult to make a statistical study of repeatability on clinical subjects because the time which elapses between tests varies so greatly. There is always the possibility that changes in the refractive correction have also occurred when the time between tests is long.

Several trained subjects with fairly normal eyes found over several months a maximal day-to-day variation in the measurements of the order of ±0.15 degree, while the average variation from the mean for the measurements over the period was about ±0.05 degree.

Typical repeatability data on clinical subjects are given in Table 25. On the whole, it can be said that the measurements seem to repeat well.

The Correlation Between the Measured Vertical Declination Error and That Calculated From the Astigmatism. The declination error which might be predicted on the basis of the change in magnification introduced by the

Table 25

REPEATABILITY MEASUREMENTS OF THE DECLINATION ERROR ON CLINICAL SUBJECTS

CASE NO.	DATE OF EXAMINATION	REFRACTIVE CORRECTION	DECLINATION ERROR, DEGREES	
			Measured	Predicted
1	10/16/41	R +1.00 D. sph. ◌ −5.00 D. cyl., ax 70 L +1.00 D. sph.	+0.40 ±0.20	+1.10
	9/11/42	R +1.00 D. sph. ◌ −5.00 D. cyl., ax 72 L +1.50 D. sph. ◌ −0.50 D. cyl., ax 80	+0.55 ±0.20	+0.95
2	10/18/41	R +1.75 D. sph. ◌ −1.75 D. cyl., ax 150 L +1.25 D. sph. ◌ −1.00 D. cyl., ax 30	−0.30 ±0.20	−1.20
	11/22/41	R +1.75 D. sph. ◌ −1.75 D. cyl., ax 150 L +1.25 D. sph. ◌ −1.00 D. cyl., ax 30	−0.40 ±0.20	
	4/13/44	R +1.50 D. sph. ◌ −2.00 D. cyl., ax 155 L +0.75 D. sph. ◌ −1.00 D. cyl., ax 20	−0.55 ±0.15	−1.15
3	1/8/42	R +2.00 D. sph. ◌ −3.00 D. cyl., ax 100 L +3.25 D. sph. ◌ −2.50 D. cyl., ax 85	−0.70 ±0.50	−0.65
	5/6/42	R +2.00 D. sph. ◌ −3.50 D. cyl., ax 100 L +3.25 D. sph. ◌ −2.50 D. cyl., ax 85	−1.00 ±0.25	−0.70
4	2/26/42	R −4.25 D. sph. ◌ −0.50 D. cyl., ax 15 L +2.00 D. sph. ◌ −7.00 D. cyl., ax 100	+0.55 ±0.55	+1.15
	3/12/43	R −4.25 D. sph. ◌ −0.50 D. cyl., ax 15 L +2.00 D. sph. ◌ −7.00 D. cyl., ax 100	+0.75 ±0.20	
5	3/28/42	R +1.00 D. sph. ◌ −0.75 D. cyl., ax 150 L +1.37 D. sph. ◌ −0.75 D. cyl., ax 30	−0.40 ±0.20	−0.65
	8/8/42	R +1.25 D. sph. ◌ −1.00 D. cyl., ax 140 L +1.00 D. sph. ◌ −0.75 D. cyl., ax 40	−0.55 ±0.20	−0.85

corrected astigmatism can be simply computed, if we know the dimensions of the refractive lenses used in the correction and the distances of the lenses from the eyes and have information as to the origin of the astigmatic error. The astigmatism due to the corneal curvatures can be measured by the ophthalmometer. That part of the subjective astigmatism which cannot be accounted for by the corneal astigmatism must be assumed to be lenticular in origin and correspondingly will be located at an average distance of

5.3 mm. (reduced distance) behind the cornea (Fig. 168). If the subjective and the corneal astigmatism have the same axes, the percentage of meridional magnification (or diminution), m per cent, can be found with sufficient accuracy from the formula m per cent $= (\triangle D_1)t/1.5 + Ah + 0.53 [A(1 - Ah/100) - C]$ in which $\triangle D_1$ is the dioptric difference between the curvatures of the front, toric surface of the ophthalmic lens; t is the thickness of the lens, in centimeters; A is the prescribed correction for the astigmatism, in diopters; h is the distance from the vertex of the lens to the pole of the cornea, in centimeters, and C is the corneal astigmatism in diopters. If the toric surface of the lens is the front surface, $\triangle D_1$ will be equal to A. The quantity $(1 - Ah/100)$ corrects for the effectivity of the lens at the cornea. The axis of the meridional magnification will be the same as the axis of the astigmatic correction written as plus cylinders. The declination error, δ, can then be computed from $\delta = 0.28\ m \sin 2\ \phi$, where ϕ is the angular position of the axis of the meridional magnification.

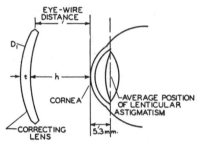

Fig. 168. Quantities used in computing the meridional magnification of the retinal image due to a lens correcting astigmatism.

If the axes of the corneal and the subjective astigmatism differ considerably, it is best to compute the magnifications of two separate systems: (1) the system comprised of the correcting ophthalmic lens and the crystalline lens of the eye and (2) the system comprised of the cornea and crystalline lens of the eye. Then m_1 per cent $= \triangle D_1 t/1.5 + A(h + 0.53)$, and m_2 per cent $= -0.53\ C$. The declination error will be the sum of the errors for each of these magnifications.

The total declination error between the eyes will be the sum of the errors in each eye. This computed value, δ_c, represents the declination error between the images of the two eyes to be expected on the basis of the dioptric meridional magnifications introduced by the corrected astigmatism of the eyes. Table 26 illustrates the data in several typical cases.

The theoretical declination errors were calculated for all the subjects measured. The possible relationship between the measured errors, δ_m, and the calculated errors, δ_c, can be best visualized from a scatter chart shown in Fig. 169 for the 396 subjects. Even a cursory inspection of this chart shows unmistakably a positive correlation. The majority of the data points fall in the upper right and lower left quadrants of the graph, this distribu-

Table 26

CALCULATED AND MEASURED DECLINATION ERRORS BETWEEN IMAGES OF THE TWO EYES
OF SELECTED SUBJECTS WITH ASTIGMATISM AT OBLIQUE AXES

CASE NO.	AGE	REFRACTIVE CORRECTION	OPHTHALMOMETER MEASUREMENT	DECLINATION ERROR, DEGREES	
				Calculated	Measured
1	30	R −0.75 D. sph. () −1.25 D. cyl., ax 155 L +0.75 D. sph. () −1.00 D. cyl., ax 177	−1.12 D. cyl., ax 155 −1.12 D. cyl., ax 180	−0.40	−0.30 ± 0.20
2	44	R +0.62 D. sph. L +0.75 D. sph. () −0.50 D. cyl., ax 40	−0.75 D. cyl., ax 180 −1.00 D. cyl., ax 180	−0.20	−0.20 ± 0.20
3	34	R +2.25 D. sph. () −1.50 D. cyl., ax 40 L +2.00 D. sph. () −1.50 D. cyl., ax 145	−1.25 D. cyl., ax 30 −1.75 D. cyl., ax 150	+0.95	+0.40 ± 0.20
4	33	R Plano () −0.75 D. cyl., ax 60 L Plano () −1.50 D. cyl., ax 155	−1.00 D. cyl., ax 25 −2.00 D. cyl., ax 155	+0.55	+0.55 ± 0.15
5	30	R +2.50 D. sph. () −3.25 D. cyl., ax 15 L +2.75 D. sph. () −3.50 D. cyl., ax 140	−3.37 D. cyl., ax 15 −3.50 D. cyl., ax 150	+1.40	+1.00 ± 0.20
6	25	R −1.00 D. sph. () −3.50 D. cyl., ax 170 L −1.00 D. sph. () −4.00 D. cyl., ax 17	−3.25 D. cyl., ax 170 −3.50 D. cyl., ax 3	−1.45	−0.50 ± 0.10
7	23	R +1.25 D. sph. () −0.50 D. cyl., ax 170 L +3.25 D. sph. () −5.00 D. cyl., ax 25*	−1.50 D. cyl., ax 172 −6.50 D. cyl., ax 19	−1.60	−1.00 ± 0.30
8	48	R +1.00 D. sph. () −1.00 D. cyl., ax 180 L +5.00 D. sph. () −5.00 D. cyl., ax 42	−1.25 D. cyl., ax 180 −5.00 D. cyl., ax 42	−1.80	−1.10 ± 0.30
9	62	R −0.50 D. sph. () −1.25 D. cyl., ax 70 L −4.50 D. sph. () −1.50 D. cyl., ax 115	−1.00 D. cyl., ax 45 −0.75 D. cyl., ax 150	+0.80	+0.95 ± 0.25

* This astigmatism resulted from corneal ulcers, following an illness at the age of 5 years.

tion indicating that the direction of measured error is statistically the same as that of the computed error.

An analysis of the data may be summarized as follows:

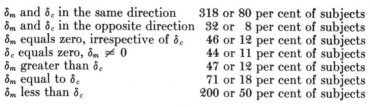

δ_m and δ_c in the same direction   318 or 80 per cent of subjects
δ_m and δ_c in the opposite direction   32 or   8 per cent of subjects
δ_m equals zero, irrespective of δ_c 46 or 12 per cent of subjects
δ_c equals zero, $\delta_m \neq 0$ 44 or 11 per cent of subjects
δ_m greater than δ_c 47 or 12 per cent of subjects
δ_m equal to δ_c 71 or 18 per cent of subjects
δ_m less than δ_c 200 or 50 per cent of subjects

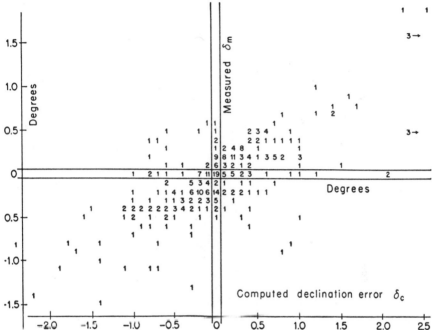

Fig. 169. Correlation between the measured declination error and that computed on the basis of the astigmatism at oblique axes.

The important fact in this study is that for 80 per cent of the subjects the measured declination error between the two eyes was in the same direction as that expected on the basis of the magnification of the dioptric error computed by the astigmatic corrections. Moreover, a statistical treatment of the data gives a Pearson correlation coefficient (r) of $+0.65$, with a probable error of 0.05. The standard error of estimate was ±0.34 degree. For 396 subjects this represents a significant correlation. There is no evidence from the diagram that this correlation is not linear.

Comment. The positive correlation found between the declination error as measured on the space eikonometer and that computed on the basis of the magnifications introduced in the correction of unequal astigmatism between the two eyes is important, for it implies that to a certain extent at least there is a long range stability of corresponding retinal points.

It is at once evident from the scatter diagram that on the average the measured value is smaller than the computed one. However, for 8 per cent of the subjects the measured and the calculated declination errors were in opposite directions and for 12 per cent of the subjects the measured value was greater than the computed value. The fact that the percentage of cases in the two groups is of the same order suggests that a factor independent of the astigmatism enters into the measurements. Questions immediately come to mind whether these results imply (1) that a partial compensatory (or other change) in the organization of corresponding retinal points has occurred in these individuals wearing anisometropic corrections or (2) that the space eikonometer does not measure the true declination error, and if not (3) what are the extraneous factors affecting that measurement?

It may not be possible to separate these problems on the basis of the data so far available, but evidence suggests that cyclotorsional changes in the

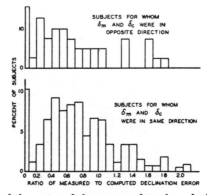

Fig. 170. Distribution of the ratios of the measured to the calculated declination errors.

orientations of the eyes occur in the space eikonometer under the influence of the effect of the corrective lenses and the declination unit which tend to mask the true declination error.[40]

The extent to which the measured and computed values are different can be visualized from the distribution of the ratio of the values. This ratio ($\delta_m : \delta_c$) will be unity if the two values are equal, greater than unity if δ_m is the larger value and less than unity if δ_m is the smaller value. This distribution is shown in Fig. 170 for the two groups of subjects for whom both the measured and the calculated values were in the same and in the opposite direction. As might be anticipated from the scatter chart, the measured value, δ_m, is about 0.6 of the calculated value for the greatest number of subjects. This also is about the ratio found for the subject (p. 283) who wore meridional magnification lenses at oblique axes for almost a month, and in this case the effect was undoubtedly due to the adaptation of the eyes to a new cyclotorsional adjustment.

If one computes the difference between the measured and the calculated declination error, $\delta_m - \delta_c$, and plots this against the calculated value, we also find a positive correlation (Fig. 171). This means that the difference between the measured and computed value increases with the calculated declination error. The effect could be best explained as being due to torsional adjustments of the eyes.

In Chapter 10 it was shown that a cyclotorsion could occur when meridional magnification lenses were placed before the eyes at oblique meridians, with a cross and centered vertical line configuration as used in the space eikonometer.

The fact that the measured declination error, δ_m, in a majority of the subjects is less than the calculated declination error, δ_c, might be expected

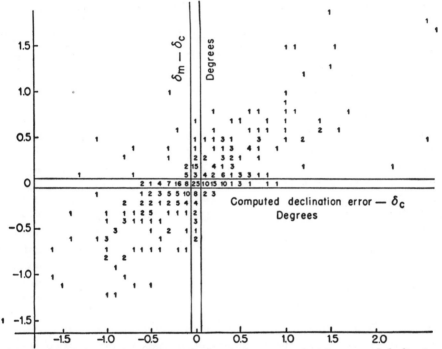

Fig. 171. Correlation of the difference between the measured and computed declination errors to the computed error.

from the point of view of physiologic or anatomic compensation. Yet only a small proportion, 12 per cent, of the subjects showed zero declination error when the calculated values were not zero. There is also the possibility that in these subjects there may be present a basic (not optical) meridional aniseikonic error. A statistical study of data has shown that for at least a third of the patients the measured aniseikonic errors or part of those errors seem to bear no obvious relationship to the refractive errors.[187] Again, it will be recalled from Fig. 166 that for a small percentage of subjects with non-oblique astigmatism, significant declination errors were measured. A possible cyclotropia is believed to be a real factor in the latter cases.

One must allow for the possible existence of a mechanism in the binocular processes which, within certain limits, can actually compensate for effective image magnification differences. This has already been suggested by the experiments on the prolonged wearing of afocal magnification lenses. Burian[35] found that a partial compensation of from one fourth to one third of the image magnification differences was artificially introduced by the lenses at axis 90 degrees after about three weeks.

On 226 subjects with astigmatism at oblique axes for whom δ_m and δ_c were in the same direction, no relation was found between the ratio $\delta_m : \delta_c$ and the age of the subject at the time of examination or the length of time that spectacles had been worn. Perhaps there was a possible trend between the ratio $\delta_m : \delta_c$ and the age at which glasses were first worn; the earlier they were worn, the smaller the ratio tended to be. However, this age was obtained by questioning the subject, and the answer was often only a guess. Moreover, the nature of the refractive correction first worn then was unknown. Only in the case of high astigmatism is there a probability that astigmatic corrections were prescribed at that time.

When relatively small uncorrected refractive ametropias exist, the magnifications of the retinal images as determined by the center of the blur circles are substantially the same as though the refractive errors did not exist (p. 263). From an empirical point of view the more or less fixed relationship in the organization of corresponding retinal elements in the two eyes might conceivably have come about empirically though the images were slightly blurred. However, such high astigmatism in a number of subjects that must have been present at birth would prevent the recognition of detail; yet the measurements on these subjects showed a large declination error between the eyes in the direction indicated by the oblique astigmatism (subjects 7, 8 and 9 in Table 26). On the other hand, there were several subjects whose astigmatism at oblique axes was large, and the measured declination error was found to be zero. In these there were suggestions of faulty stereoscopic vision.

The important inference to be drawn from this study and the correlation found must be that the anatomic and physiologic organization of the two retinas in the binocular processes of vision, for a majority of subjects, must have been determined independently of the development of the refractive errors. The fact that a partial compensation has occurred does not refute this statement. All or part of the distortions of the dioptric images on the retinas, which must take place when the astigmatic errors are corrected by ophthalmic lenses, are present and can be measured on the space eikonometer. Thus, the results of this study would be evidence in favor of the Hering hypothesis of the innate and stable character of corresponding retinal elements.

CHAPTER 22

Eye Movements and Aniseikonia

THE MAGNIFICATION OF EYE MOVEMENTS IN AMETROPIA

WHENEVER THE EYES turn from the fixation of one object to observe another located more laterally, the primary innervations to the extrinsic muscles of the eyes which initiate the necessary eye rotations must depend upon the separation of the retinal images of those two objects. We cannot easily avoid the assumption that associated with retinal elements themselves are some type of "local signs" which in this case can be called *motor values.* These motor values may or may not be identical with or be derived from the "local signs" that give rise to the subjective directional space values[209] (p. 11). It is highly probable, however, that these motor values are empirical, acquired through experience, and are subject to relearning.

Under normal circumstances, the rapid movements of the eyes that take place when they leave one fixation point to arrive at another are markedly precise. However, it is not a perfect excursion, for the ophthalmograph shows that in binocular vision usually one eye leads, making the more accurate movement, while the other eye follows to make a few adjustments at the end of the excursion. Nevertheless, the movements in the main conform to the requirements which must arise from the separation of retinal stimuli. Obviously these will be different if changes are made in the magnification of the retinal images. They will also be different for objects observed in asymmetric convergence, where the angular separations of points on the objects will be different for the two eyes.

When the refractive error of an ametropic eye is corrected by an ophthalmic lens, we must consider not only the effect of change in the magnification of the retinal image, but also the prismatic effects of the lens as the eye moves behind it. The angle through which the eye has to turn to observe an object more laterally located will be larger when the visual field is seen through a positive (hyperopic) lens and smaller when seen through a negative (myopic) lens. The ophthalmic lens always introduces a magnification (or diminution) of all angular rotations of the eyes, irrespective of whether there is any change in retinal image magnification. The effect, a prismatic deviation, will always exist when the visual axis and the optical axis of the lens do not coincide. We can say that the *field of fixation* is proportionally increased with positive lenses and decreased with negative lenses.

The magnitude of the prismatic effect depends upon the angular distance of the peripheral object from the fixation point, the dioptric power of the lens, and the distance of this lens from the center of rotation of the eye. Now the angular magnification of all eye excursions due to a lens of V diopters, placed at a distance h_c (meters) from the center of rotation of the eye, will, for distant vision, be (see p. 125) $M = 1/(1 - Vh_c)(1 - D_1t/n)$, in which D_1 is the front surface power of the lens (in diopters), t is its thickness (in meters) and n is the index of refraction. Approximately the per cent angular increase (or decrease) will be m per cent $= Vh_c + D_1t/n$, in which now h_c and t are expressed in centimeters. The prismatic effect in degrees would be $\triangle = (m)(\alpha)/100$,[*] where α is the angular separation of the two objects being observed or the angle (degrees) in which the eye would turn were the lens not present.

Thus, with a $+4$ diopter lens at 15 mm. from the cornea, and assuming that the center of rotation is 13.6 mm. from the cornea,[56] the angular magnification of all eye movements behind the lens will be about 12 per cent. If the eye turns to observe an object laterally placed 20 degrees from the axis, the eye will have to turn 12 per cent farther or 2.4 degrees (4.2 prism diopters), that is, make a total angular rotation of 22.4 degrees. If the lens were a -4 lens, the effect would be an angular diminution of the rotations; the eye would have to turn only 17.6 degrees. Afocal magnification lenses will also have the effect of necessitating increased excursions of the eyes.

In general we could say that a given movement of a corrected ametropic eye, as initiated by retinal stimuli, which depend upon the size of the retinal image, would not correspond to the required eye movement because of the prismatic effect of the lens. For the axial myopic eye, the size of the image on the retina would be essentially the same as that if the eye were normal, and the eye movements initiated by retinal stimuli would be those for the normal eye. Owing to the proportional diminution of the field of fixation, though, caused by the lens, smaller eye excursions are actually required. One might expect, therefore, an overshooting of all eye movements. The reverse would be anticipated in corrected axially hypermetropic eyes. When the ametropia is refractive in origin, this discrepancy between the innervations for movements and those actually necessary would be smaller, for the size of the image is changed in the same direction as would be the prismatic deviations caused by the lens. However, the discrepancy would never be eliminated automatically because the distance from the lens to the seat of the refractive error (which determines the change in image magnification) will be less than the distance from the lens to the center of rotation of the eye (which determines the change in eye movements).

ANISOMETROPIA

In anisometropia, where the refractive errors in the two eyes are unequal, the problem of the magnification of the eye excursions becomes more marked,

---

[*] This reduces to the usual formula for the prismatic deviation, $\triangle$, of an ophthalmic lens, displaced laterally a distance d, for approximately $\alpha = d/h$, and $\triangle = Vd$, which is prism diopters per centimeter displacement.

for as the eyes turn to observe a more laterally located object, the eyes will have to make different movements. On the basis of Hering's law of equal innervations to the extrinsic muscles, readjustments of the eyes must be made at each change in fixation point. The effect, usually described as a differential prismatic effect involving differential eye movements, obviously increases with the degree of turning of the eyes.

Apart from the problem of ocular readjustments of the eyes for accurate fixation, actually the prismatic effects themselves have been considered a source of ocular discomfort. In fact, for example, von Rohr[210] and Erggelet,[65] among others, considered this effect more a source of eyestrain than differences in magnifications of the retinal images. Especially on looking down to the reading position through anisometropic corrections, the prismatic deviation has been considered a source of discomfort because the prismatic effect may be large compared to the usual small fusional amplitude in vertical prism vergences. "Slab-off" prism segments have been designed for spectacles to offset the prismatic effect at the reading level. Obviously, these are of no aid in other parts of the visual field. Von Rohr designed anisometropic lens units, consisting of small telescopic systems to correct these prismatic deviations for the entire visual field. Whitwell and similarly Weiss have carefully considered the problem of correcting the differential prismatic effects in small amounts of anisometropia, and suggested making the base-curves and thicknesses of the lenses different for the two eyes. These obviously change the angular magnification of the eye movements, but in so doing may and probably do introduce aniseikonic errors also.

The correction of aniseikonic errors in anisometropia, which would occur generally because of refractive types of ametropias, would go far to correct not only the differential prismatic effects of the lenses for all angles in the visual field, but also the discrepancies between initiated and required eye movements. In anisometropia of axial origin and little or no aniseikonia, a correction of the differential prismatic effects with afocal magnification lenses would obviously introduce aniseikonia.

There is evidence that the eyes can become adapted to the differential prismatic effect of anisometropic corrections,[46, 59] so that correct eye movements take place with every excursion. From what has been reported in previous paragraphs, the evidence is that the aniseikonic errors can, if at all, be only slightly compensated for.

ANISOPHORIA

There exists some confusion in the literature regarding the terms "anisophoria," "differential prismatic deviations" and "aniseikonia." Each, of course, describes something entirely different.

Anisophoria (meaning "not the same phoria"), as coined by Friedenwald, is a heterophoria that varies with the direction of fixation; that is, the phoria is different in other parts of the visual field from that found in the primary direction. A phoria measurement requires that binocular vision be suspended by eliminating all stimuli for fusion. Then the nonfixing eye assumes a position that deviates from the direction of the other eye. The angular deviation of direction of the nonfixing eye to the direction it would have were it allowed to see the point of fixation defines the phoria. This angle is expressed in arc degrees or prism diopters (1 arc degree = 1.74 prism diopters). Phorias cannot be measured with high precision, because of the number and variety of nervous factors which cannot be eliminated and which are constantly changing (Bielschowsky[18]).

"Anisophoria is very common—in fact it is the exception to find a patient in whom the phoria is the same in all directions of gaze, especially if the tests are made at large angles of deviation from the primary position . . . ." (Lancaster[138]). Anisophoria is a neuromuscular anomaly and must not be confused (see Friedenwald) with differential eye movements which must occur because of the differential prismatic effect when anisometropia is corrected with lenses and where fusion is maintained. We cannot consider these two in the same category, for it would be analogous to saying that when a prism is placed before one eye the heterophoria changes. Obviously it does not change, without fusion, and with fusion the effect is not a phoria.

When phoria is being measured in various parts of the visual field while the patient is wearing anisometropic spectacles, the manifest measurements do not represent the true phorias in those positions, for the differential prismatic effect of the lenses should be subtracted. This is as necessary as in measuring phoria at central vision where the effect of prisms must be taken into account in order to find the true phoria.

It has been suggested (Friedenwald) that the benefit said to be derived by patients with corrected aniseikonia was actually derived from the fact that they were being corrected for "anisophoria." This followed because in general the aniseikonia would be found in anisometropia where also "anisophoria" (as used by Friedenwald) would be present. The direct comparison eikonometer in this case would actually be measuring "anisophoria." Let us examine this hypothesis.

In the first place we must disentangle the concept of anisophoria from that of differential eye movements. Anisometropic spectacles would introduce differential eye movements if fusion is maintained. We have no way of knowing whether there is or is not anisophoria.

In aniseikonia differences greater than 5 per cent are rarely encountered if binocular vision is normal. But a 5 per cent anisophoria would correspond to 1 degree ($1.7^\triangle$) of anisophoria at a visual angle of 20 degrees. At the average angles at which the eyes would customarily be used, the difference in eye movements due to the anisophoria would be less than the precision of measurements. If these small differences could be a source of ocular discomfort, the effect of ordinary phorias themselves would be intolerable. One cannot easily follow the argument that anisophoria *per se* can be much of a source of ocular discomfort except in cases of muscle paralysis where large phorias and even tropias with the resultant diplopia would be a source of discomfort.

Coming now to the differential eye movements in anisometropic corrections, we are no longer dealing with anisophoria, and this problem, as indicated previously, has been recognized and fully described in the literature since Donders' time.

Differential eye movements are of course normal in the ordinary use of the eyes in near vision, as in reading. These do not normally entail ocular discomfort. In the direct comparison eikonometer, anisophorias are not being measured because fusion is maintained. If the ordinary anisophorias found at 4 degrees visual angle are susceptible of being measured, their effect upon the ability to maintain fusion, even though peripheral, would be of second order compared to the usual phoria that exists in the primary position and which would therefore prevent fusion at all.

For many cases of anisometropia no differences are measured on the eikonometer, whereas if the eikonometer measured differential eye movements alone then differences would be found.

Finally the high 1:1 correlation between the space eikonometer and the direct comparison eikonometer for distant vision shows that differences in magnification of the images are being measured. Phorias are not a factor in stereoscopic spatial perception.[83, 130] It is true that at near vision with the direct comparison eikonometer, high phorias tend to interfere with the measurement and depress sensitivity and reliability. However, these errors do not necessarily correspond to the anisometropia present.

ANISEIKONIA AND DISTURBANCES IN BINOCULAR VISION

Since vision is that complex phenomenon by which physical light stimuli mediated through anatomic structures and physiologic processes result in a visual experience, it would be reasonable to suppose that anomalies in the visual processes themselves would result in disturbances in those experiences. These, in turn, might lead to feelings of eye strain and asthenopia. In evaluating these symptoms we would search for the particular physical or physiologic causes, for one must be on guard to recognize those symptoms undoubtedly psychogenic in origin.

The extent to which aniseikonic errors result in disturbances in the normal function of the visual processes is not easy to determine. But it is no less difficult to account for the visual disturbances due to small amounts of uncorrected astigmatism or of phoria. An ophthalmologist[206] wrote fifty years ago: "It is a self-evident proposition that every glass which we place before the eyes, be it prescribed for the relief of the ciliary muscle, the acquisition of clearer retinal images, or what not, will at the same time change the conditions under which we have been accustomed to view the objects about us, and hence, interfere more or less with the ideation of those objects upon which we have been wont to rely." Usually we seek for the origin of the difficulty in the fatigue of certain muscles, such as the ciliary muscles in the accommodation processes, or in the fatigue of cortical association centers where an excessive expenditure of nervous energy is constantly necessary to overcome muscular anomalies. One must also bear in mind that the extent to which such disturbances in the visual processes' actually result in visual symptoms varies with the individual and his neurologic sensitivity and well-being.

In the aniseikonic problem we are confronted with the facts (to the best of our knowledge on existing data) that (1) individuals with otherwise above normal eyes do not show aniseikonic errors; and (2) a reorganization of the system of corresponding points of the two eyes can be made, if at all, only to a limited extent to meet the changed conditions due to the aniseikonic errors. Aniseikonia then becomes and remains an anomaly in the binocular visual processes, which the individual is forced to accept. It is important to bear in mind the influence of these errors on stereoscopic spatial localization, fusion and fusional movements of the eyes as the possible sources of visual disturbances.

The Theory of the Correction
of Aniseikonia

INTRODUCTION

LET US CONSIDER an ametropic eye fully corrected by a suitable ophthalmic lens. By "fully corrected" we mean that the dioptric image of a given object will be sharply defined on the retina of the eye.

Suppose the object observed is u_1 meters from the front surface of the ophthalmic lens. In general u_1 will be large compared to the distance of the lens from the eye and the thickness of the lens. By the simple Gauss paraxial ray formulas we can trace the optical imagery, the object and image distances, u and v, through the successive surfaces of the lens and eye. We can then write down the expression for the ratio of the size of the retinal image i to the size of the object O; namely,

$$\frac{i}{O} = \left[\frac{1}{u_1} \frac{v_1 v_2}{u_2 u_3} \right] \left[\frac{v_3 v_4 v_5 v_6}{u_4 u_5 u_6} \right]$$

The quantities in the first bracket depend only upon the dimensions of the ophthalmic lens, the object distance and the separation of the lens and cornea of the eye. The quantities in the right hand bracket depend only upon the dimensions and optical properties of the successive media of the eye. We do not know and cannot find the value for this latter bracket in a given case.

Let the dioptric powers of the front and back surfaces of the ophthalmic lens be D_1 and D_2 diopters, respectively; the thickness of the lens, t meters; the index of refraction of the glass of the lens, n; and the distance of the back surface of the lens to the pole of the cornea, h meters. Then from the simple paraxial formulas,* we can reduce the foregoing expression to

$$\frac{i}{O} = \frac{E}{u_1(1 - D_u t/n)(1 - V_u h)}$$

in which E is the second bracket that pertains wholly to the eye, and $D_u = D_1 - 1/u_1$, and $V_u = (D_u + D_2 - D_u D_2 t/n)/(1 - D_u t/n)$.

Now consider the *two* eyes of an individual, the ametropias of which are

---

* These are in this case $1/v_1 - 1/u_1 = D_1$, $u_2 = v_2 - t/n$, $1/v_2 - 1/u_2 = D_2$ and $u_3 = v_2 - h$.

fully corrected by the ophthalmic lenses for the object at the given visual distance. In the eikonometers we can assume the size of the object, O, and the object distances (u_1) to be substantially the same for the two eyes. Using subscripts R and L for the right and left eyes, respectively, we find that the ratio of the sizes of the dioptric images on the two retinas would be

$$\frac{i_R}{i_L} = \frac{(1 - D_u t/n)_L (1 - V_u h)_L}{(1 - D_u t/n)_R (1 - V_u h)_R} \cdot \frac{E_1}{E_2}$$

For an object at a considerable distance (u_1 large) $D_u = D_1$, and $V_u = V_0$, in which V_0 is the vertex power of the ophthalmic lens in diopters. For simplifying the equation we can write the resulting expression,

$$\frac{i_R}{i_L} = \frac{S_R P_R}{S_L P_L} \frac{E_R}{E_L}$$

in which $S = 1/(1 - D_1 t/n)$, and $P = 1/(1 - V_0 h)$. The factors S and P are frequently referred to as the *shape* and *power* factors of the magnification effect of the ophthalmic lens. S depends only upon the front surface power and thickness of this lens, while P depends only upon vertex power of the lens and its distance from the cornea.* S is, of course, equivalent to the magnification of an afocal lens that has the same front surface power and thickness. It is from this relationship that we can consider a correcting ophthalmic lens as a combination of an afocal lens and an infinitely thin power lens attached to the posterior surface of the afocal lens.

ANISEIKONIA

The foregoing ratio of the sizes of the dioptric images on the two retinas, of course, cannot be measured. Only the ratio of the functional and subjective sizes of those images is measured. We have seen that this ratio depends not only on the dioptric factors involved in the correction of the ametropias by lenses, and those involved in optical characteristics of the eyes (E_R/E_L), but also on the population density of the percipient elements[53] of the retinas and their neurologic connections to the cortex.

Thus, if i_R' and i_L' represent the comparative sizes of these *functional* images, we have for their ratio

$$\frac{i_R'}{i_L'} = k \frac{S_R P_R}{S_L P_L}$$

in which k includes the ratio E_R/E_L, and those other anatomic and neurologic factors of the binocular visual apparatus. This ratio of the sizes of the images cannot, of course, be computed without making assumptions regarding the value of k, and must be found by measurement.

The actual procedure in making this measurement with the eikonometer

---

* This simplification in the formula and the notation was suggested by Dr. Edgar D. Tillyer of the American Optical Company.

consists in introducing suitable afocal magnification lenses before the two eyes so that the two images are apparently equal in size. Then we would have

$$\frac{i_{R'}}{i_{L'}} = \left[\frac{M_R}{M_L}\right]\left[\frac{S_R P_R}{S_L P_L}\right]\left[k\right] = 1$$

in which M_R and M_L are the magnifications of the lenses introduced before the right and left eyes, which are necessary to equalize the images of the two eyes. The ratio $M_R : M_L$ is the amount of aniseikonia in *any given meridian.*

It will be clear from this relationship that the magnitude of the *measured* aniseikonia will depend on the dimensions of the correcting lenses and the distances of the lenses from the two eyes. Thus, *we cannot specify the aniseikonia in absolute magnitude, but always in relation to the particular lenses used to correct the refractive errors.* A different measurement might be found depending upon whether the observer is corrected by ophthalmic trial case lenses or by spectacle lenses, though the powers of these two corrections would be identical.

The foregoing discussion must hold true for all meridians if the entire aniseikonia is to be corrected. The ratio $M_R : M_L$ pertains to a single meridian, and therefore in general represents a meridional magnification of the image of one eye compared to the image of the other in that meridian.

SOME PROPERTIES OF MERIDIONAL MAGNIFI-CATION SYSTEMS

The Horizontal and Vertical Components. Points in the image and object planes can be represented in the same plane, since linear dimensions will be proportional to each other according to the angular magnification. In Fig. 172 let 0 be the origin at a point on the plane of symmetry of a meridional magnification lens or lens system.

Consider now any object point P given by the polar coordinates, r, σ, where r is the distance from the origin and σ is the meridian angle measured from the horizontal. For generality suppose the image of the object plane is magnified A times in the meridian θ and B times in the meridian at right angles to θ. The angles θ and $(\theta + 90$ degrees$)$ will be the principal meridians of the magnifying system. The point P will be imaged at a point P', given by the coordinates r', σ', where r' is the distance from the origin and σ' is the image meridian angle. Suppose A is greater than B. In the image plane, P' will then be displaced farther in the meridian θ than in the meridian at right angles to θ. Inspection of the figure shows that

$$r' \cos (\sigma' - \theta) = Ar \cos (\sigma - \theta)$$
$$r' \sin (\sigma' - \theta) = Br \sin (\sigma - \theta) \tag{1}$$

The relationship between r' and r for any meridian angle σ' can be obtained by eliminating $(\sigma - \theta)$ from these equations. One obtains, then,

$$r'^2 = r^2 A^2 B^2 / [A^2 \sin^2(\sigma' - \theta) + B^2 \cos^2(\sigma' - \theta)] \tag{2}$$

If the object figure is a circle of radius r, the image of that circle according to (2) would be an ellipse.

The magnification, M, produced by the lens at the meridian angle σ', will be defined by the ratio of r' to r and will be, therefore, the ratio of the distance of the image point to the corresponding distance of the object point measured from the origin. This magnification can be represented by an ellipse, so that it is convenient to describe the magnification of the image produced by a meridional magnification system as a *magnification ellipse*. It can be shown, moreover, that the magnification of the image through a combination of two or more meridional magnifiers is an ellipse, even if the axes of the two component systems are crossed obliquely. Strictly speaking, the resultant magnification ellipse will be slightly different, depending upon the particular sequence of the component systems.

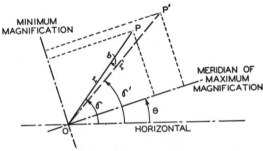

Fig. 172. Representation of points in object and image planes with a meridional magnification lens.

The relationship between the image meridian angle σ' and the object meridian angle σ is also obtained from (1); namely,

$$A \tan (\sigma' - \theta) = B \tan (\sigma - \theta) \tag{3}$$

This relation[223] shows that the difference between the two meridional angles σ' and σ depends upon the ratio A/B, that is, upon the meridional magnification. These two angles will be different for all meridian angles, except when the meridian angle is either one of the principal meridians of the lens, θ or ($\theta + 90$ degrees).

In aniseikonic problems, the properties of the magnification ellipse are usually wanted in terms of the object meridian angle σ instead of the image meridian angle σ'. By eliminating σ' (instead of σ) from equation (1), we find

$$M_\sigma^2 = r'^2/r^2 = A^2 \cos^2(\sigma - \theta) + B^2 \sin^2(\sigma - \theta) \tag{4}$$

This equation does not describe a true ellipse, but if A and B differ by only a few per cent it does so with sufficient accuracy. Equation (4) will be used in the subsequent discussion, to describe the magnification "ellipse."

If the difference between the magnifications A and B is relatively small, the per cent magnifications m, b and a can be used instead of the magnifications M, B and A, respectively. Then, instead of (4) we have

$$m_\sigma = b + f \cos^2(\sigma - \theta) \tag{5}$$

where $f = (a - b)$. Equation (5), of course, expresses the difference between the magnification ellipse and a unit circle for a given meridian σ.

The component magnifications for the horizontal and vertical meridians ($\sigma = 0$ and $\sigma = 90$ degrees) which occur in most problems of aniseikonia will be

$$M_0{}^2 = A^2 \cos^2\theta + B^2 \sin^2\theta$$
$$M_{90}{}^2 = A^2 \sin^2\theta + B^2 \cos^2\theta$$

or when the magnifications are expressed in per cent,

$$\begin{aligned} h &= b + f \cos^2\theta \\ v &= b + f \sin^2\theta \end{aligned} \tag{6}$$

One sees at once that $(h - b) + (v - b) = f$, if f is not too large. That is, the sum of the vertical and horizontal components is substantially equal to the meridional magnification. Figure 173 is a nomograph for finding the horizontal component of a given meridional magnification at an oblique meridian.

It is easy to show from equation (4) that, for any two meridian angles σ and ($\sigma + 90$ degrees), the following is true:

$$M_\sigma{}^2 + M_{(\sigma + 90 \text{ degrees})}{}^2 = A^2 + B^2$$

or approximately, when per cent magnifications are used,

$$m_\sigma + m_{(\sigma + 90 \text{ degrees})} = a + b$$

This states simply that the sum of the per cent magnifications, in any two meridians which are at right angles to each other, is approximately equal to the sum of the per cent magnifications in the principal meridians.

Rotary Deviations. The difference between the image meridian σ' and the corresponding object meridian σ (see Fig. 172),

$$\delta = \sigma' - \sigma \tag{7}$$

will be a rotary deviation of the image meridian from the corresponding meridian of the object.

The magnitude of the rotary deviation can be obtained by eliminating σ' from equations (3) and (7), namely,

$$\tan \delta = -K \sin 2(\sigma - \theta)/[1 + K \cos 2(\sigma - \theta)] \tag{8}$$

where $K = (A - B)/(A + B)$. Again, if the difference between A and B is not large, and if per cent magnifications are used, this may be written

$$100 \tan \delta = -\tfrac{1}{2}f \sin 2(\sigma - \theta) \tag{9}$$

The rotary deviation δ here will be measured positive counterclockwise for either eye, to agree with the positive direction of σ and θ, from the point of view of the observer looking through the lens.

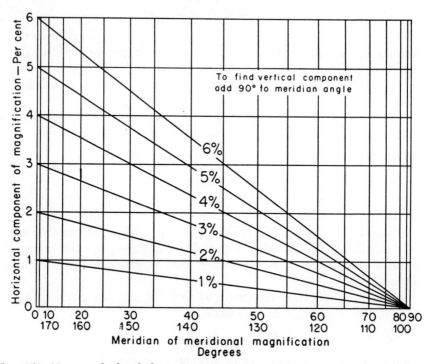

Fig. 173. Nomograph for finding the horizontal component of a given meridional magnification at an oblique meridian.

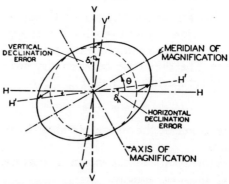

Fig. 174. Magnification ellipse showing the vertical and horizontal rotary deviations (a declination error if the lens is used before the eye) for a meridional magnification at an oblique meridian.

The *vertical* rotary deviation, δ_v, is the deviation of the image of the vertical meridian (when $\sigma = 90$ degrees) (Fig. 174) and is given by

$$\tan \delta_v = -K \sin 2\theta / (1 - K \cos 2\theta)$$

or

$$100 \tan \delta_v = -\tfrac{1}{2}f \sin 2\theta \tag{10}$$

Similarly, the *horizontal* deviation δ_h (when $\sigma = 0$) will be given by

$$\tan \delta_h = K \sin 2\theta/(1 + K \cos 2\theta)$$

or   (11)

$$100 \tan \delta_h = +\tfrac{1}{2}f \sin 2\theta$$

Since δ_v and δ_h will be small, these can be written in degrees simply

$$\delta_v = -0.29f \sin 2\theta$$

and   (12)

$$\delta_h = 0.29f \sin 2\theta$$

No vertical or horizontal deviations exist if the principal meridians of the meridional magnification are horizontal or vertical; $\theta = 0$ degrees or 90 de-

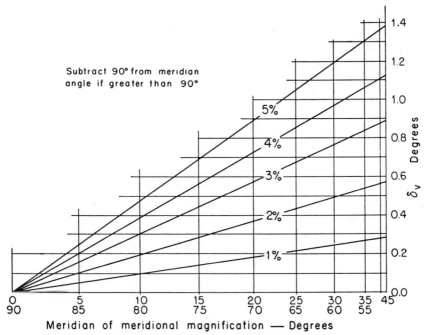

Fig. 175. Nomograph for finding the vertical declination error introduced by a given per cent meridional magnification at an oblique meridian.

grees. Figure 175 is a nomograph which gives the vertical rotary deviation for different meridional magnifications placed at different meridians.

It will be noticed, however, that if $\theta \neq 0$ degrees and $\neq 90$ degrees, the rotary deviations of the vertical and horizontal meridians will be opposite in sign, that is, their directions will be opposite. This describes the well-known scissors effect in the image as observed through cylindrical power lenses and meridional magnifying lenses. The direction of the *rotary deviation for a specified meridian will always be toward the meridian of greatest magnification or away from the meridian of least magnification*. The scissors effect will be evident, however, for any two meridians, except the principal meridians themselves. The spokes of a wheel seen through a meridional magnifier would be unequally spaced, being crowded toward the meridian of the greatest magnification. For small per cent magnifications, the vertical and horizontal deviations will be substantially equal but in opposite directions. The vertical and horizontal declination errors will be maximal when $\theta = 45$ degrees or 135 degrees.

The Declination Error. When the retinal image of an eye is magnified meridionally, the rotary deviation of the image of any given meridian is designated a *declination error*, since it is an error in the normal declination[222] of that meridian. In binocular vision these declination errors are important only to the extent that they are different in the two eyes. It is the vertical declination error that is to be measured on the space eikonometer. Horizontal declination errors have little or no influence upon the binocular space perception, but may under certain conditions cause fusion difficulties when the objects have predominantly horizontal detail.

The Combination of Two Meridional Magnifiers. Problems involving combinations of meridional magnifying systems arise frequently when anisei-

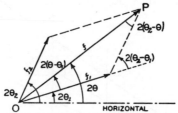

Fig. 176. Parallelogram solution for the resultant of two meridional magnifying systems.

konic corrections are to be determined. Moreover, the aniseikonic error itself can be treated as the combination (a difference) of two magnification ellipses, one for each eye.

A rigorous solution for the resultant magnification ellipse of two meridional magnification systems in sequence gives expressions too unwieldy for general use. It is convenient and sufficiently accurate to use those formulas in which the magnifications have been replaced by per cent magnifications.

The image meridian of the first system must be the object meridian of the second. Rigorously, then, the resultant image meridian angle will be slightly different depending upon the particular sequence of the systems. In most ophthalmic problems this difference may be neglected, so that in the magnification formulas the object meridian angle can be used.

Consider two meridional magnifying systems in sequence, the per cent magnifications for a given meridian σ being given by

$$m_1 = b_1 + f_1 \cos^2 (\sigma - \theta_1)$$
$$m_2 = b_2 + f_2 \cos^2 (\sigma - \theta_2) \tag{13}$$

The resultant "ellipse" will be described by

$$m = m_1 + m_2 = b + f \cos^2 (\sigma - \theta) \tag{14}$$

and the problem will be to find the values of b, f and θ *of* the resultant magnification ellipse, when b_1, b_2, f_1, f_2, θ_1 and θ_2 are given.

The principal meridian angles of this ellipse can be obtained by differentiating m with respect to σ and setting the result equal to zero. One has, then, substituting θ for σ,

$$f_1 \sin 2(\theta - \theta_1) + f_2 \sin 2(\theta - \theta_2) = 0$$

The formula for the principal meridian angles of the resultant magnification ellipse would be given by

$$\tan 2\theta = [f_1 \sin 2\theta_1 + f_2 \sin 2\theta_2]/[f_1 \cos 2\theta_1 + f_2 \cos 2\theta_2] \tag{15}$$

This relation suggests at once the parallelogram law for the addition of vectors (Fig. 176). The resultant meridional per cent magnification f according to this would (by the sine relationship between the sides and opposite angles of a triangle) be given by

$$f/\sin 2(\theta_2 - \theta_1) = f_1/\sin 2(\theta - \theta_2) = f_2/\sin 2(\theta - \theta_1) \tag{16}$$

By applying the rule of p. 307, the resultant overall per cent magnification b would be given by

$$b = (b_1 + b_2) + \tfrac{1}{2}(f_1 + f_2 - f) \tag{17}$$

Thus by means of formulas (15), (16), and (17), the equivalent of two magnifying systems can be found.

The declination error due to the combined effect of the two systems will be $\delta = \delta_1 + \delta_2$, since the angles are small.

THE ANISEIKONIC ELLIPSE

The concept of the magnification ellipse and the combination of such ellipses is useful in the problem of the measurement and correction of aniseikonia, especially if the meridional image magnification difference is at an oblique axis.

Clearly a magnification of the image in one eye would give the same relative difference between the images of the two eyes as would an equal per cent minification (diminution) of the image in the other eye. Thus, the relative magnifications of the images of the two eyes can always be described in terms of an increase or a decrease of the magnification of the image in one particular eye, say, the right eye.

Suppose that a different meridional and overall magnification of the images occurs in each of the two eyes; then the answer to the question, "What are the relative magnifications of the images in the two eyes in any specified meridian?" can be found in the theory of the combination of two meridional magnifying ellipses given in the previous section. The difference in the magnification of the images would be the difference in the per cent magnifications of these two ellipses for any given meridian. For all meridians the differences as deviations from a unit circle would themselves approximately describe an ellipse.* This approximate ellipse can be designated appropriately the *aniseikonic ellipse.*

Suppose the per cent magnification in the meridian σ for the image in the right eye is from equation (5),

$$m_R = b_R + f_R \cos^2 (\sigma - \theta_R)$$

and similarly for the left eye,

$$m_L = b_L + f_L \cos^2 (\sigma - \theta_L)$$

These two magnification ellipses might be illustrated schematically as shown

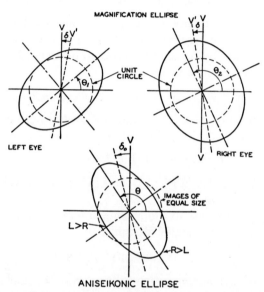

Fig. 177. Schematic illustration of magnification ellipses for each of the two eyes, and the resultant aniseikonic ellipse which represents the difference between those magnifications of the images in the two eyes for all meridians.

in Fig. 177. The per cent difference s in the magnifications of the images in the two eyes for the meridian σ would be

$$s = m_R - m_L = (b_R - b_L) + f_R \cos^2 (\sigma - \theta_R) - f_L \cos^2 (\sigma - \theta_L) \quad (18)$$

This, according to theory, must correspond for all meridians to the "ellipse" described by

$$s = u + w \cos^2 (\sigma - \theta) \quad (19)$$

where, now, u is the per cent *overall* difference in image magnification and w is the per cent meridional difference for the meridian θ. The three quantities u, w and θ describe the aniseikonic ellipse; u will specify the minor diameter, and $(u + w)$ will specify the major diameter at meridian θ. Both

* Rigorously, magnifications should be used, in which case the relative magnifications of the images in the two eyes would be described by the ratio of the magnifications of the images.

quantities describe deviations from the unit circle, where the per cent difference between the images would be zero for all meridians.

Figure 177 illustrates the aniseikonic ellipse derived from the two ellipses. The quantities u, w and θ can be found from the discussion of the preceding section wherein it is only necessary to change the sign of f_2.

The total vertical declination error between the two eyes δ_b will be the difference in the two declination errors of the two eyes; namely,

$$100 \tan \delta_b = -\tfrac{1}{2}(f_R \sin 2\theta_R - f_L \sin 2\theta_L) \tag{20}$$

which in turn will be equal to $-\tfrac{1}{2}w \sin 2\theta$ of the aniseikonic ellipse.

For a given patient, of course, the aniseikonic ellipse is unknown and it cannot easily be measured directly. However, the ellipse can be determined from measurements of the component differences in relative image magnifications in several meridians, together with a measure of the vertical declination error between the images in the two eyes.

THE DETERMINATION OF THE ANISEIKONIC ELLIPSE

The objective in measuring the aniseikonic condition in a given subject is to determine the aniseikonic ellipse. Three independent measurements are necessary in order to find the three parameters, u, w and θ, which determine this ellipse.

The measurements of the difference in magnification in the horizontal and vertical meridians have been the simplest to obtain and these may be considered the basic aniseikonic measurements. The third measurement may be the vertical declination error between the eyes as determined on the space eikonometer.*

The aniseikonic correction necessary to equalize the magnifications of the images in the two eyes is usually written in terms of per cent magnification. Thus, the aniseikonic ellipse would be described in terms of the *aniseikonic correction ellipse*. A meridional correction might read: R.E. 3 per cent axis 65 degrees, which indicates that a 3 per cent meridional magnification at axis 65 degrees is needed for the right eye. As those for cylindrical power lenses, the axes of meridional magnifying corrections are specified in the same way. It is necessary then to rewrite some of the formulas developed previously so that the meridian angle θ will be replaced by the standard axis designations. If ϕ denotes the axis, then $\phi = 90$ degrees $- \theta$.

The per cent vertical and horizontal components of the corrections, v and h, respectively, would be from formula (6),

$$\begin{aligned} v &= o + f \cos^2\phi \\ h &= o + f \sin^2\phi \end{aligned} \tag{21}$$

where o now is the per cent overall correction (the minor diameter of the

* Other "third" measurements would be the axis and meridian of the aniseikonic ellipse, which may be obtained with suitable test elements in a binocular test, and the image size difference in one or more of the oblique meridians measured by the vernier or alignment method of the standard eikonometer.[188]

ellipse) and f is the per cent meridional correction [where $(o + f)$ determines the major diameter of the ellipse] at axis ϕ. The quantities o, f, v and h will be considered *positive* if the magnifying correction is to be placed before the *right* eye, negative if placed before the left eye. The declination error between the eyes δ_b described from the aniseikonic correction ellipse will be [from equation (13)] given by

$$100 \tan \delta_b = \tfrac{1}{2} f \sin 2\phi \tag{22}$$

The angle δ_b will now be positive in the same direction as ϕ is measured positive.

THE ANISEIKONIC CORRECTION

The problem is: Given the three independent measurements of the correction which equalize the sizes of the images in the two eyes, v, h and δ_b, what are the quantities o, f and ϕ which describe the resultant aniseikonic correction ellipse? Subtracting the equations given by (21), one has

$$v - h = f(\cos^2\phi - \sin^2\phi) = f \cos 2\phi \tag{23}$$

Likewise dividing (22) by this relation, the axis of the ellipse can be found from

$$\tan 2\phi = 200 \tan \delta_b/(v - h) \tag{24}$$

or, more simply,

$$\tan 2\phi = 3.5 \, \delta_b/(v - h)$$

When δ_b is positive, 2ϕ is less than 180 degrees, if negative, 2ϕ lies between 180 degrees and 360 degrees. The angle, ϕ, can be found by calculation or by graphic means. Having this angle, the per cent meridional correction f, at axis ϕ, can be found from either

$$f = (v - h)/\cos 2\phi^*$$

or

$$f = 200 \tan \delta_b/\sin 2\phi = 3.5 \, \delta_b/\sin 2\phi \tag{25}$$

Graphically, f is given by the length of the hypotenuse of the triangle; it is always positive. The overall per cent image magnification correction o will be [from equation (21)]

$$o = \tfrac{1}{2}(v + h - f) \tag{26}$$

The aniseikonic correction ellipse can also be described in terms of two meridional magnifications. The meridional correction at axis ϕ will be

$$m_\phi = \tfrac{1}{2}(v + h + f) = o + f \tag{27}$$

and at the axis ($\phi + 90$ degrees)

$$m_{\phi + 90} = \tfrac{1}{2}(v + h - f) = o \tag{28}$$

* The first of these formulas becomes indeterminate when $\phi = 45$ degrees or 135 degrees, for then $v - h = 0$ also. The second formula is applicable except when $\phi = 0$ or 90 degrees, but in these two instances δ_b would likewise be zero and the first formula could be used. Of course, the formula eliminating ϕ, namely, $f^2 = (v - h)^2 + (200 \tan \delta)^2$, is always applicable.

Equations (24), (25) and (26) provide the solution to the problem of determining the constants of the aniseikonic correction ellipse, if the vertical and horizontal corrections and the total vertical declination error between the two eyes are known. These are the quantities measured on the space eikonometer. Using these formulas, reference tables can be prepared from which, for given measurements of v, h and δ_b, the values of o, f and ϕ (or m_ϕ, $m_{\phi\,+\,90}$ and ϕ) can be found directly. The quantities which specify the aniseikonic correction ellipse give directly the correction to be prescribed according to the conditions under which the original measurements were made.[75]

There are, of course, a number of different combinations of a meridional magnification before each of the two eyes, together with overall magnification, which will result in the same aniseikonic ellipse. This follows from the fact that only three parameters, o, f and ϕ, are necessary to describe that

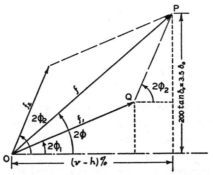

Fig. 178. Graphic representation of quantities involved in finding equivalent aniseikonic correction so that the meridional corrections will be at specified axes in each of the two eyes.

ellipse, while in the combination of two meridional magnifications and an overall magnification (see previous text) there are five parameters; namely, o ($= b_1 + b_2$), f_1, f_2, ϕ_1 and ϕ_2. Thus, two of these parameters are free to fulfill other conditions.

It is frequently desired to find the equivalent combination of the overall correction o, and for the right eye and the left the two meridional corrections, f_1 and f_2, the axes of which coincide with those of the astigmatism of the two eyes.* This limitation automatically specifies ϕ_1 and ϕ_2, and then o, f_1 and f_2 are determined from the data available.

The equivalent prescription which places the two meridional corrections at specified axes for the two eyes, such as for the axes of astigmatism, can be found by applying the procedure outlined previously for the combinations of two magnification ellipses. Theoretically, this is possible in every case except, as will be shown, when the axes of astigmatism of the two eyes

* Corrections determined in this manner sometimes simplify the lens-grinding problems and in many cases reduce cost.

are parallel or at right angles. Practically, it may not be possible in many cases because of the physical limitations of the magnification that can be obtained with ophthalmic lenses.

In Fig. 178, the meridional part of the aniseikonic correction ellipse, namely, f, at axis ϕ, is represented by the line OP. This line (vector) according to the foregoing text is determined by the difference between the vertical and horizontal components $(v - h)$ of the image size correction, and by the correction of the vertical declination error δ_b between the eyes. The problem now is to find f_1 and f_2, the meridional parts of the corrections at the specified axes ϕ_1 and ϕ_2, respectively, for the right eye and the left, whose resultant will be f at axis ϕ. The points O and P in the figure, therefore, are fixed, and graphically it is only necessary to lay out the triangle OQP with proper orientation of the angles.* The quantities f_1 and f_2 can be found by measurement of the sides of the triangle, for $f_1 = OQ$ and $f_2 = QP$. They can be computed from the formulas [see equation (16)].

$$f_1 = f \frac{\sin 2(\phi_2 - \phi)}{\sin 2(\phi_2 - \phi_1)} \tag{29}$$

$$f_2 = f \frac{\sin 2(\phi_1 - \phi)}{\sin 2(\phi_2 - \phi_1)} \tag{30}$$

Inspection of these relations shows that this solution to the problem becomes impossible, for the denominators become zero, when the axes are parallel, $\phi_1 = \phi_2$, or when the axes are at right angles, $\phi_1 - \phi_2 = \pm 90$ degrees.

The final overall correction o_F can be computed from

$$o_F = \tfrac{1}{2}[v + h - (f_1 + f_2)] \tag{31}$$

or

$$o_F = o + \tfrac{1}{2}[f - (f_1 + f_2)] \tag{32}$$

If the signs of o_F, f_1 or f_2 are *positive*, the correction is for the *right* eye; if negative, for the left.

THE CORRECTION OF ANISEIKONIA WITH OPHTHALMIC LENSES

After the aniseikonia has been measured on the eikonometer with suitable correction lenses, the problem is to provide the subject with the equivalent spectacle lenses which will correct not only the refractive errors, but also the aniseikonic ellipse. The task of designing such lenses may be quite complicated. Not only must the powers and magnification requirements be fulfilled, but the lenses should have good field properties, should not be too heavy, and the appearance of the spectacles should be acceptable.

From the point of view of simplicity, the easiest method is to measure the aniseikonia of the patient on the eikonometer while he wears his customary

---

* In the graphic solution, in order to complete the parallelogram, if f_1 or f_2 must be taken opposite to their positive directions, then they should be considered negative.

spectacle correction. The aniseikonia measured is then corrected by attaching suitable afocal magnification lenses over the spectacle lenses as fitovers (Fig. 179). This type of correction usually has the best field properties, since the fitover lenses introduce few or no aberrations. The fitover lenses are mounted in separate eye-wires and are held before one or both spectacle lenses by spring clips. This method is especially practical for those cases of complicated meridional corrections at oblique axes. The method is also practical as a trial correction. The fitover type of correction is not usually desirable as a permanent correction, however, because of weight, difficulty of keeping clean, fogging and for cosmetic reasons.

Lenses can be designed which will incorporate the refractive and aniseikonic corrections, and these usually have to be ground from special design.

For each meridian we can write from the theory outlined on p. 305.

$$\frac{M_R}{M_L} \frac{S_R P_R}{S_L P_L}\Bigg]_e = \frac{S_R P_R}{S_L P_L}\Bigg]_s = 1$$

in which the subscripts e and s pertain to the eikonometer test and to the

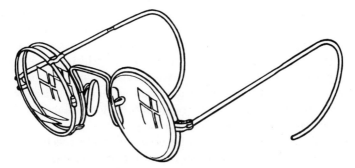

Fig. 179. Spectacles with a fitover lens for the correction of aniseikonia.

spectacle lenses, respectively. The factor k is the same on both sides of the equation and hence divides out.

Since the vertex powers of the spectacle lenses must be the same as those of the lenses in the eikonometer, the foregoing equation can be written, after dividing through by $P_R/P_L]_e$

$$\frac{M_R}{M_L} \frac{S_R}{S_L}\Bigg]_e = \frac{S_R}{S_L} \frac{P_R'}{P_L'}\Bigg]_s$$

where $P' = 1 + V_0 (\triangle h)$, with sufficient accuracy, and $(\triangle h)$ is the displacement of the spectacle lens from the position of the test lens in the eikonometer. With standard trial case lenses in the eikonometer, carefully adjusted to the correct distance from the eyes, the factor $S_R/S_L]_e$ will be unity, except for a correction necessary for astigmatic lenses which are usually placed in front of the spherical lenses in the eikonometer. Astigmatic lenses so used may actually introduce an artificial aniseikonic error.

Apart from this correction, it is clear that one need only select the dimensions of the spectacle lenses so that for each meridian the S and P' satisfy the foregoing relationship. This means selecting different base curves (D_1) and thicknesses (t), but keeping in mind the effect of the ($\triangle h$) factor in the position of the lenses before the eyes.

Aniseikonic spectacle lenses must be prescribed to be worn at specified distances from the eyes, distances selected by the optician to make the best-appearing spectacles. Usually it is customary to specify the "eye-wire" distance—the distance of the center of the eye-wires of the spectacles from the corneas. This distance together with the shapes and thicknesses of the lenses will determine ($\triangle h$). In general we would increase the base curve and the thickness to increase the magnification, and if the vertex power of the lens is positive (a hyperopic correction), an increase in ($\triangle h$) will also increase the magnification. With a fixed eye-wire distance, it must be remembered that an increase in D_1 causes the vertex of the lens to move away from the eye, which causes an increase in ($\triangle h$). Thus for myopic corrections (V_0 negative) an increase in the power of the front surface (D_1) may so cause a forward displacement of the lens that the decrease in magnification due to the [V_0 ($\triangle h$)] factor may more than offset the gain in magnification due to the [$D_1 t/n$] factor. Thus, for myopic corrections of about -1.50 diopters, no change in magnification is made when the base curves alone are increased. It is possible, in general, however, to select the curves, thicknesses and positions for the two corrective lenses to duplicate any measured aniseikonia, provided that this is not too large. Where the aniseikonia is different in the two meridians, at least one bitoric lens, that is, a lens both surfaces of which are toric, may be necessary.

Some simplification of design can be obtained if the spectacle lenses are mounted before the patient's eyes so that the ocular surfaces are the same distances from the eyes as were the corresponding trial case lenses in the eikonometer. Then $\triangle h = 0$, and the power factor (P') in the magnification formula disappears. In general, this method is not feasible, because of the mechanical problems that arise in the fitting of special type frames, or in designing of excessively thick lenses.

In many cases when the aniseikonia is large or quite different in the principal meridians, doublet correcting lenses may be necessary. These doublets act as air-spaced telescopic units but include the refractive correction, and may be designed to fit into ordinary eye-wires. They provide a means for obtaining higher overall and meridional magnifications than can be obtained practically with single lenses.

The procedure of modifying the base curves and thicknesses of the ophthalmic lenses to obtain differences in the magnifications obviously disregards the aberrations of these lenses for oblique rays. Generally this problem is taken into account in the design of the lenses, but it has been considered of secondary importance, unless those aberrations become large.

The Apparent Orientation of the Cross
of the Space Eikonometer

INTRODUCTION

THE OBLIQUE CROSS is the key to the space eikonometer, for it will appear as though turned about a vertical axis in one direction if the image of one eye is magnified in the horizontal meridian only, and in the opposite direction if the image is magnified in the vertical meridian only. An apparent inclination of the plane of the cross relative to the vertical cords of the space eikonometer will occur if the image of one eye is magnified in an

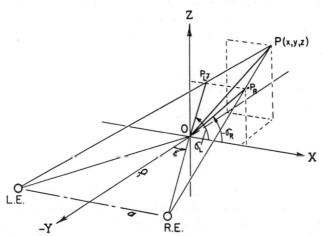

Fig. 180. Perspective of coordinate system used to investigate analytically the apparent orientation of the cross of the space eikonometer.

oblique direction. A cyclotorsion between the images of the two eyes can cause the plane of the cross to appear inclined with respect to the vertical lines.

The theory for the apparent orientation of the cross is a simple problem in three-dimensional analytic geometry.[189]

In Fig. 180, let the center of the cross coincide with the origin of a coordinate system: the visual plane corresponding to the XY plane, the median plane to the YZ plane, and the plane of the cross corresponding to the XZ plane. The right and left eyes are located symmetrically with respect to the

Y axis at points $(a, -b, 0)$ and $(-a, -b, 0)$, respectively. Assume that the eyes converge to the center of the cross, an assumption which, however, will not make the following discussion less general.

Consider, first, only a single oblique line corresponding to one of the lines of the cross. Suppose this line appears out of the original plane of the cross, as though it were an actual objective line in a position $<OP>$.

The projections of the images of this line for each of the two eyes upon the frontoparallel plane (plane of the cross) will be the two lines $<OP_L>$ and $<OP_R>$, for the left eye and the right, respectively. Let the "elevation" angles to these lines in the plane of the cross be represented by the angles σ_L and σ_R, respectively, measured positively counterclockwise from the horizontal plane.

The line $<OP>$ can, then, be described by the two planes $<E_LOP>$ and $<E_ROP>$ given by

$$x - y(a/b) - z \cot \rho_L = 0$$

and

$$x + y(a/b) - z \cot \rho_R = 0$$

respectively. The elevation angles σ_R and σ_L in the plane of the cross are related to the elevation angles ρ_R and ρ_L, of the retinal images themselves, by $\tan \sigma = \tan \rho \cos \epsilon$, where ϵ is the angle of convergence of each eye, and whence $\tan \epsilon = a/b$. Substituting the equivalent expressions of ρ and σ one obtains

$$x \cos \epsilon - y \sin \epsilon - z \cot \rho_L = 0$$
$$x \cos \epsilon + y \sin \epsilon - z \cot \rho_R = 0$$

or when written in symmetric form

$$x/p \sin \epsilon = y/q \cos \epsilon = z/\sin 2\epsilon \qquad (1)$$

where

$$p = \cot \rho_R + \cot \rho_L \text{ and } q = \cot \rho_R - \cot \rho_L$$

Consider, now, two intersecting lines through 0, namely, OP_1 and OP_2, these again being described by the angles ρ_{R1}, ρ_{R2}, and ρ_{L1}, ρ_{L2} for the right and the left eye, respectively. For the present consider these angles quite generally. According to equation (1) these two lines would be described by the direction cosines, which are proportional to $p_1 \sin \epsilon$, $q_1 \cos \epsilon$ and $\sin 2\epsilon$, and to $p_2 \sin \epsilon$, $q_2 \sin \epsilon$ and $\sin 2\epsilon$, respectively. These two lines would determine a plane (the apparent plane of the cross) described by

$$Ax + By + Cz = 0 \qquad (2)$$

where

$$A = (q_1 - q_2) \cos \epsilon$$
$$B = (p_2 - p_1) \sin \epsilon$$
$$C = \tfrac{1}{2}(p_1 q_2 - p_2 q_1)$$

The apparent position of this plane is easily described, first by its apparent transverse rotation about a vertical axis (measured from the frontoparallel plane), and second by its apparent inclination about a horizontal axis (measured from the vertical). If ψ and ι represent these angles, respectively, then,

$$\tan \psi = -A/B = (q_1 - q_2) \cot \epsilon/(p_1 - p_2)$$

and

$$\tan \iota = -C/B = \tfrac{1}{2}(p_1 q_2 - p_2 q_1) \csc \epsilon/(p_1 - p_2)$$

(3)

ψ being positive if the right side of the plane appears rotated away from the observer, and ι being positive if the top of the inclined plane appears inclined away from the observer.

The first problem is to find how ψ and ι vary when a meridional magnification of the image in one eye is introduced at an oblique axis.

A MAGNIFICATION OF THE RETINAL IMAGE AT AN OBLIQUE AXIS

If one magnifies the image of an extended object with a meridional magnifier, all meridians, except those parallel with or perpendicular to the meridian of the magnification, are deviated a small amount in a rotary sense toward the meridian of maximal magnification. In Fig. 181, the meridian OP, defined by angle ρ, is deviated to OP' specified by angle ρ', when the image of the field is magnified M times at the oblique meridian θ. One can easily show (from equation 3, p. 306) that ρ' and ρ are related by

$$\tan \rho' = \left[\frac{F}{G} \right] \left[\frac{G + \tan \rho}{1 + F \tan \rho} \right]$$

(4)

where

$$F = K \sin 2\theta/(1 + K \cos 2\theta)$$

and

$$G = K \sin 2\theta/(1 - K \cos 2\theta)$$
$$K = (M - 1)/(M + 1)$$

While both eyes are fixating the center of the cross, suppose a meridional magnification lens is placed at the meridian θ before the right eye.[*] Then, in general, for the right eye the images of the intersecting lines of the cross will be rotated slightly. Writing $r = \cot \rho = \cot \sigma \cos \epsilon$, one has for the elevation angles in the retinal images of the two lines of the cross for the two eyes

$$\cot \rho_{R1} = \frac{G}{F} \frac{F + r_1}{1 + G r_1} \qquad \cot \rho_{R2} = \frac{G}{F} \frac{F + r_2}{1 + G r_2}$$

$$\cot \rho_{L1} = r_1 \quad \text{and} \quad \cot \rho_{L2} = r_2$$

(5)

If these are substituted into the expressions for the coefficients A, B and C of equation (2), one has the general equation of the apparent position of the plane of the cross caused by the meridional magnification of the image of the right eye. The apparent angle of transverse rotation, ψ, about a vertical axis, and that of the inclination, ι, about a horizontal axis can also be readily found from equations (3).

[*] For the effect of magnifying the image of the left eye, it is only necessary to substitute $1/M$ for M in subsequent formulas.

Since the intersecting lines of the cross of the space eikonometer are approximately $\sigma_1 = 45$ degrees and $\sigma_2 = -45$ degrees or 135 degrees* the apparent transverse rotation (about a vertical axis) will be given by

$$\tan \psi = K \cos 2\theta \cot \epsilon/(1 - k) \qquad (6)$$

and the apparent inclination by

$$\tan \iota = \frac{K^2 \sin 4\theta}{2(1 - K \cos 2\theta)(1 - k)} \csc \epsilon \qquad (7)$$

where $k = K^2 \sin^2 2\theta/(1 - K \cos 2\theta)$. Since magnification of the lens used or difference in magnification between the images of the two eyes rarely differs from unity by more than 5 per cent and $K = (M - 1)/(M + 1)$, the term k can, in most cases, be neglected.

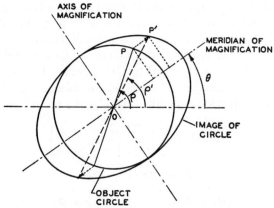

Fig. 181. Rotary deviation of meridians when a meridional magnification is introduced.

It will be seen from the first of the foregoing relations that

(1) There is a maximal positive apparent transverse rotation (the right side of the cross appears farthest back) when the meridional magnification is wholly in the horizontal meridian and $\theta = 0$ degrees or 180 degrees (the lens at axis 90 degrees);

(2) There is a maximal negative apparent transverse rotation of the cross (the left side of the cross appears farthest back) when the meridional magnification is wholly in the vertical meridian and $\theta = 90$ degrees (the lens at axis 180 degrees); and

(3) There is no apparent transverse rotation of the cross when the meridional magnification is in the oblique position $\theta = 45$ degrees or 135 degrees, $\psi = 0$. Obviously, when the axis and meridian of the magnification coincide with the meridians of the two lines of the cross, there can be no effect. Nor will an overall magnification (where the magnification is the same in all

---

* In order for the formulas to be strictly correct the elevation angles of the lines should be such that $\tan \sigma = \cos \epsilon$. For the visual distances ordinarily used, the error in taking $\sigma = \pm 45$ degrees is negligible.

meridians) of the image of one eye as compared with that of the other eye affect the apparent orientation of the cross.

Inspection of equation (7) shows that the *apparent inclination* of the plane of the cross is essentially *negligible*, for under any circumstance tan ι substantially never exceeds K^2, and hence ι will generally be less than 2 minutes of arc. The inclination is precisely zero when the meridian of the magnification, θ, is 0 degrees, 45 degrees, 90 degrees, and so forth. One can state, therefore, that the meridional magnification, regardless of its meridian, does not *itself* affect the apparent inclination of the cross.

That the plane of the cross usually appears inclined in the space eikonometer when an oblique meridional magnification lens is placed before one eye is due to the presence of vertical plumb lines in the field of view. It is these lines that are affected by the magnification of the lens. Experimentally, this can be shown by withdrawing all the vertical lines, for then the cross appears vertical, unless, as will be shown, a cyclotorsion exists between the two eyes. Theoretically, these vertical lines should have the false stereoscopic appearance of being inclined in space with tops toward or away from the observer, when either a meridional magnification at an oblique meridian is introduced between the two eyes, or a cyclotorsion exists between the eyes.

The magnitude of the apparent inclination ι_v, of the central vertical cord in the plane of the cross, can be determined directly from equation (1); namely,

$$\tan \iota_v = y/z = g/h$$

This would give the well-known relation,[107]

$$\tan \iota_v = \tfrac{1}{2}(\tan \delta_R - \tan \delta_L) \csc \epsilon = \tfrac{1}{2} \tan \delta \csc \epsilon \qquad (8)$$

where $\delta_R = 90$ degrees $- \rho_R$ and $\delta_L = -(90$ degrees $-\rho_L)$. The quantity $(\delta_R - \delta_L) = \delta$ is the total angular difference (declination) in the two eyes between the images of the vertical lines. In the case of a meridional magnification, M, of the image of the right eye, at an oblique meridian θ, the declination error would be $\delta = \rho' - \rho$ and

$$\tan \delta = K \sin 2\theta/(1 - K \cos 2\theta) \qquad (9)$$

where, as before, $K = (M - 1)/(M + 1)$ [equation (10), p. 308]. Thus, one obtains for the apparent inclination of the vertical cord

$$\tan \iota_v = \tfrac{1}{2}K \sin 2\theta \csc \epsilon/(1 - K \cos 2\theta) \qquad (10)$$

The apparent angle of inclination, ι_v, will be taken, as before, positive when the line appears inclined with the top away from the observer.

According to these results, a meridional magnification lens at an oblique meridian before one eye will not cause an apparent inclination of the cross of the space eikonometer itself, while it should cause the vertical plumb lines to appear inclined. The experimental fact is, however, that usually the reverse occurs in part or in full; namely, the plumb lines appear vertical and the plane of the cross appears inclined, though in the direction opposite to that expected of the vertical lines. This phenomenon will be discussed later when the effect of the cyclotorsions of the images of the eyes is considered.

More generally, if one considers the configuration of the cross of the space eikonometer in which the elevation angles of the intersecting lines are other than ±45 degrees, very different results are obtained.[189] In fact, it then appears that the ±45 degree configuration is in many respects unique. The results of this more general analysis have been experimentally verified in the laboratory with an apparatus in which the orientation of the frame supporting the configuration of the cross could be adjusted by the observer.

CYCLOTORSIONS OF THE EYES (CYCLOTROPIA)[*]

A small rotation of the image in one eye about the visual axis should, if the eyes do not make a compensating cyclofusional movement, cause a false apparent orientation of the cross. This is an important factor that enters into the use of the space eikonometer and it must be considered in a theory of that instrument.

Suppose each of the eyes undergoes equal cyclotorsions of $\frac{1}{2}\tau$ degrees, in opposite directions in the "incyclo" sense (the upper parts of the vertical meridians of the retinas are deviated toward the forehead).[†] This torsion results in a relative torsion of the retinal images in the opposite direction, the image of the right eye being apparently rotated in a clockwise direction, a direction which will be taken as positive (Fig. 182). One can write then for the cross of the space eikonometer, quite generally corresponding to expressions (5) on p. 321,

$$\cot \rho_{R1} = \cot (\rho_1 - \tau/2) \qquad \cot \rho_{R2} = \cot (\rho_2 - \tau/2)$$
$$\cot \rho_{L1} = \cot (\rho_1 + \tau/2) \qquad \cot \rho_{L2} = \cot (\rho_2 + \tau/2)$$

in which ρ_1 and ρ_2 are the retinal elevation angles of the two arms of the cross. Putting $\rho_1 = 45$ degrees and $\rho_2 = 135$ degrees (-45 degrees), one finds on substituting in the coefficients for A, B and C in equation (3), for the apparent transverse rotation of the cross, $\tan \psi = 0$, and for the apparent inclination of the cross, ι_c,

$$\tan \iota_c = (2 \tan \tau/2 \csc \epsilon)/(1 - \tan^2 \tau)$$

or

$$\tan \iota_c = \tan \tau \csc \epsilon \tag{11}$$

since τ (the total rotary deviation between the two images) is small—usually less than 2 degrees.

[*] A cyclotorsion pertains to any rotary movement of the eyes about their axes of fixation, and is designated as parallel if in the same direction in the two eyes and contra (or disjunctive) if in opposite directions. A cyclotropia defines an anomalous contracyclotorsional position of the eyes with binocular vision. A cyclophoria defines the tendency for contracyclotorsions, which, when the eyes are dissociated, results in an actual cyclotropia.
[†] Under normal circumstances the cyclotorsional movements occur equally in the two eyes.[119]

This result must be compared with that given in equation (8) which describes the apparent inclination of a vertical line in space due to a deviation between its images in the two eyes. Replacing δ by τ, one sees that, for a cyclotorsion between the two eyes, the cross and the vertical line should both appear to be inclined in space, but the cross is inclined nearly *twice* the amount. This fact is also to be kept in mind: that a declination error introduced by a meridional magnification lens at an oblique axis will not affect the apparent inclination of the cross. Again, if one considers the elevation angles of the intersecting lines of the cross more generally than the ±45 degrees, the apparent orientation of the cross will be influenced differently by a cyclotorsion of the images in the two eyes.[188]

If one observes the test elements of the space eikonometer through Dove-erecting prisms, which have been rotated slightly so as to introduce a cyclotorsion of the images, one sees that the vertical lines of the elements tend

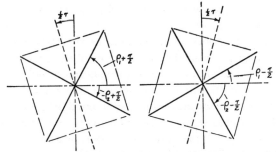

Fig. 182. An equal incyclotorsion of the two eyes and the orientation of the retinal images of the cross of the space eikonometer.

to remain vertical but the plane of the cross definitely appears inclined fore and aft in space. If one compares the apparent orientation of the cross (a) when a cyclotorsion (τ) is introduced, and (b) when an equal declination error (δ) due to meridional magnification lenses at an oblique axis is introduced before both eyes, the vertical lines tend to remain vertical but the plane of the cross will appear inclined in space although in directions opposite in the two cases.

THE SPACE EIKONOMETER

The apparent tendency for the vertical lines to remain vertical even though a deviation has been introduced optically between their images in the two eyes can be explained by cyclofusional movements which reduce that deviation in the interest of binocular single vision (Chapter 10). With this explanation for the appearance of the verticals in mind, the apparent behavior of the cross in the two cases follows immediately from the theory outlined previously. In the case of the meridional magnification lens at an oblique axis, it was shown that a declination δ was introduced between the retinal images of the vertical lines, but that the apparent inclination of the cross itself was unaffected. Clearly, if cyclofusional movements of the eyes occur to reduce the declination between the images of the verticals, then a cyclotorsion (τ) of the images of the lines of the cross has been introduced and as a result the cross would appear inclined in the direction opposite to that expected for the inclination of the vertical lines. In the case of the introduction of a cyclotorsion, both the vertical lines and the cross should appear inclined in the same direction, but with the cross inclined at nearly twice the angle of inclination of the verticals. A cyclofusional movement which reduces the deviation between the images of the verticals also reduces the deviation between the images of the cross lines, but the apparent inclination of the cross will always be greater than that of the vertical lines. If the counter cyclofusional movement completely compensates for the torsion introduced, no apparent inclination of either cross or vertical lines will occur.

Thus, it is clear that a cyclotropia can increase or decrease the effect of a declination error due to an oblique meridional aniseikonia.

Since it has been shown that a cyclotropia between the images of the two eyes can influence the apparent inclination of the cross of the space eikonometer, it is proper to raise the question whether, in any test on the instrument, the entire declination error δ is being measured. In the first place, because of the ease with which cyclofusional movements can occur under normal circumstances according to the spatial configurations in the binocular field of view, it is probable that these movements occur in the space eikonometer test.[193] The particular amount of the cyclotorsions so introduced would not represent a functional anomaly of the eyes, but its effect must nevertheless be eliminated from the test in order that a true measurement of the declination error may be obtained.[188] There will be subjects, however, in whom a definite anomaly, a small cyclotropia with dissociated eyes, will exist, and this would probably affect the test to an even greater extent.

References

1. Adler, F. H. and Fliegelman, Maurice: Influence of Fixation on the Visual Acuity. Arch. Ophth., n. s., **12**:475–483 (Oct.) 1934.
2. Allen, D. G.: A Test for Aniseikonia by the Use of Central Fixation and Fusion. Arch. Ophth., n. s., **17**:320–327 (Feb.) 1937.
3. Ames, Adelbert, Jr.: Cyclophoria. Am. J. Physiol. Optics, **7**:3–38 (Jan.) 1926.
4. Ames, Adelbert, Jr.: Aniseikonia—a Factor in the Functioning of Vision. Am. J. Ophth., **18**:1014–1019 (Nov.) 1935.
5. Ames, Adelbert, Jr.: The Space Eikonometer Test for Aniseikonia. Am. J. Ophth., **28**:248–262 (March) 1945.
6. Ames, Adelbert, Jr.: Binocular Vision as Affected by Relations Between Uniocular Stimulus-Patterns in Commonplace Environments. Am. J. Psychol., **59**:333–357 (July) 1946.
7. Ames, Adelbert, Jr.: Unpublished data.
8. Ames, A., Jr. and Gliddon, G. H.: Ocular Measurements. Tr. Sect. Ophth., A. M. A., 1928, pp. 102–175.
9. Ames, A., Jr. and Ogle, K. N.: Size and Shape of Ocular Images. III. Visual Sensitivity to Differences in the Relative Size of the Ocular Images of the Two Eyes. Arch. Ophth., n. s., **7**:904–924 (June) 1932.
10. Ames, A., Jr., Gliddon, G. H. and Ogle, K. N.: Size and Shape of Ocular Images. I. Methods of Determination and Physiologic Significance. Arch. Ophth., n. s., **7**:576–597 (April) 1932.
11. Ames, A., Jr., Ogle, K. N. and Gliddon, G. H.: Corresponding Retinal Points, the Horopter and Size and Shape of Ocular Images. J. Optic. Soc. America, **22**:538 (Oct.); **22**:575 (Nov.) 1932.
12. Ames, A., Jr., Ogle, K. N. and Gliddon, G. H.: Lenses for Changing the Size and Shape of Dioptric Images. Ann. Distinguished Serv. Found. Optom., **1**:61–70, 1932.
13. Bair, H. L.: Some New Conceptions Regarding Egocentric Visual Localizations. Arch. Ophth., n. s., **18**:415–427 (Sept.) 1937.
14. Barany, E.: A Theory of Binocular Visual Acuity and an Analysis of the Variability of Visual Acuity. Acta ophth., **24**:63–92, 1946.
15. Barker, W. B.: The Barker Eikonometer. The Optician, **91**:224 (May 1) 1936.
16. Berger, A. and Monjé, M.: Über den Einfluss der Aniseikonie auf das Tiefensehen. Arch. f. Ophth., **148**:515–528, 1948.
17. Biedermann, Heinz: Untersuchungen über die Sehschärfe beim Nahsehen. Ztschr. f. ophth. Optik., **15**:1–10; **16**:34–45, 1927.
18. Bielschowsky, A.: Lectures on Motor Anomalies. Hanover, N. H., Dartmouth College Publications, 1943, 128 pp.
19. Bielschowsky, A. and Ludwig, A.: Das Wesen und die Bedeutung latenter Gleichgewichtsstörungen der Augen insbesondere der Vertikalablenkungen. Arch. f. Ophth., **62**:400–463, 1906.
20. Boeder, Paul: An Introduction to the Mathematics of Ophthalmic Optics. Fall River, Mass., The Distinguished Service Foundation of Optometry, 1937, pp. 98–110.
21. Boeder, Paul: Power and Magnification Properties of Contact Lenses. Arch. Ophth., **19**:54–67 (Jan.) 1938.
22. von Bonin, Gerhardt, Garol, H. W. and McCulloch, W. S.: The Functional Organization of the Occipital Lobe. In Klüver, Heinrich: Biological Symposia, Vol. 7, Visual Mechanisms. Lancaster, Pa., Jaques Cattell Press, 1942, pp. 165–192.

23. Bordier, H.: Modifications de la grandeur des images rétiniennes par les verres correcteurs dans les différentes amétropies. Arch d'opht. 14:279–297, 1894.
24. Boring, E. G.: Size Constancy and Emmert's Law. Am. J. Psychol. 53:293, 1940.
25. Boring, E. G.: Sensation and Perception in the History of Experimental Psychology. New York, D. Appleton-Century Co., Inc., 1942, Chaps. 3, 7 and 8.
26. Boring, E. G.: The Moon Illusion. Am. J. Physics, 11:55–60, 1943.
27. Brecher, G. A.: Die optokinetische Auslösung von Augenrollung und rotatorischem Nystagmus. Arch. f. d. ges. Physiol., 234:13–28, 1934.
28. Brecher, G. A.: Form und Ausdehnung der Panumschen Areale bei fovealem Sehen. Arch. f. d. ges. Physiol., 246:315–328, 1942.
29. Brecher, G. A.: Aniseikonie und Fusion. Arch. f. Ophth., 147:17–53 (June) 1944.
30. Brewster, David: On the Knowledge of Distance Given by Binocular Vision. Philosoph. Mag., s. 3, 30:305–318, 1847.
31. Bridgman, C. S. and Smith, K. U.: Bilateral Neural Integration in Visual Perception After Section of the Corpus Callosum. J. Comp. Neurol., 83:57–68 (Aug.) 1945.
32. Burian, H.: Studien über zweiäugiges Tiefensehen bei örtlicher Abblendung. Arch. f. Ophth., 136:172–214, 1936.
33. Burian, H. M.: Fusional Movements; Role of Peripheral Retinal Stimuli. Arch. Ophth., n. s., 21:486–491 (March) 1939.
34. Burian, H. M.: Clinical Significance of Aniseikonia. Arch. Ophth., n. s., 29:116–133 (Jan.) 1943.
35. Burian, H. M.: Influence of Prolonged Wearing of Meridional Size Lenses on Spatial Localization. Arch. Ophth., n. s., 30:645–666 (Nov.) 1943.
36. Burian, H. M.: Sensorial Retinal Relationship in Concomitant Strabismus. Tr. Am. Ophth. Soc., 43:373–494, 1945; Arch. Ophth., n. s., 37:336 (March); 504 (April); 618 (May) 1947.
37. Burian, H. M.: The History of the Dartmouth Eye Institute. Arch. Ophth., n. s., 40:163–175 (Aug.) 1948.
38. Burian, H. M. and Ogle, K. N.: A Study of the Aniseikonia in a Case of Increasing Unilateral Index Myopia. Am. J. Ophth., 26:480–490 (May) 1943.
39. Burian, H. M. and Ogle, K. N.: Relation of Anisometropia to Aniseikonia. Am. J. Ophth., 28:215–216 (Feb.) 1945.
40. Burian, H. M. and Ogle, K. N.: Meridional Aniseikonia at Oblique Axes. Arch. Ophth., n. s., 33:293–309 (April) 1945.
41. Chidester, Leona: A Preliminary Study of Bisection of Lines. J. Exper. Psychol., 18:470–481 (Aug.) 1935.
42. Chodin, A.: Ist das Weber-Fechner'sche Gesetz auf das Augenmaass anwendbar? Arch. f. Ophthal., 23 (pt. 1): 92–108, 1877.
43. Le Gros Clark, W. E.: The Visual Centres of the Brain and Their Connexions. Physiol. Rev., 22:205–232 (July) 1942.
44. Cogan, D. G.: Neurology of the Ocular Muscles. Springfield, Ill., Charles C Thomas, 1948, 214 pp.
45. Culbertson, H.: Binocular Astigmatism. Am. J. Ophth., 5:117–123 (May) 1888.
46. Cusick, P. L. and Hawn, H. W.: Prism Compensation in Cases of Anisometropia. Arch. Ophth., n. s., 25:651–654 (April) 1941.
47. Czellitzer: Totalrefraktion und Hornhautrefraktion mit besonderer Berücksichtigung des physiologischen Linsen-Astigmatismus. Klin. Monatsbl. f. Augenh., 79:301–312, 1927.
48. Dahlmann, R.: Über Querdisparation und Gestaltauffassung mit besonderer Berücksichtigung des Panumschen Phänomens. Arch. f. d. ges. Psychol., 90:504–560, 1934.
49. Dartmouth Eye Institute: Incidence and Effect of Aniseikonia on Aircraft Pilotage. Technical Development Report No. 30. Washington, D. C., U. S. Department of Commerce, Civil Aeronautics Administration (March) 1943, 22 pp.
50. Dearborn, W. F. and Anderson, I. H.: Aniseikonia as Related to Disability in Reading. J. Exper. Psychol., 23:559–577 (Dec.) 1938.
51. Deller, J. F. P., O'Connor, A. D. and Sorsby, A.: X-ray Measurement of the Diameter of the Living Eye. Proc. Roy. Soc., London, s. B., 134:456–467 (Sept.) 1947.

52. Desaguliers, J. T.: Quoted by M. v. Rohr: Zur Kenntnis älterer Ansichten über das beidäugige Sehen. Ztschr. f. Instrumentenk., 36:226, 1916.
53. ten Doesschate, J.: Visual Acuity and Distribution of Percipient Elements on the Retina. Ophthalmologica, 112:1–18 (July) 1946.
54. Donders, F. C.: On the Anomalies and Accommodation and Refraction of the Eye. London, The New Sydenham Society, 1864.
55. Dove, H. W.: Ueber Stereoskopie. Annalen d. Physik., 110:494–499, 1860.
56. Duke-Elder, W. S.: Text-Book of Ophthalmology. Vol. 1, The Development, Form and Function of the Visual Apparatus. St. Louis, Mo., C. V. Mosby Co., 1933, 1124 pp.
57. Dupuy-Dutemps, L.: Les modifications de la sensation de relief produites par les verres de lunettes décentrés et par les prismes dans la vision binoculaire. Ann. d'ocul., 163:673–683, 1926.
58. Eggers, Harry: Effect of Position of a Correcting Lens on the Size of the Retinal Image. Arch. Ophth., n. s., 17:328–339 (Feb.) 1937.
59. Ellerbrock, V. and Fry, G. A.: Effects Induced by Anisometropic Corrections. Am. J. Optom., 19:444–459 (Nov.) 1942.
60. Elliot, A. J.: Significance of Aniseikonia in Aviation. Arch. Ophth., n. s., 35:354–360 (April) 1946.
61. Elvin, F. T.: Aniseikonia—a Simplified Method of Measurement and a Case Report. Am. J. Optom., 26:78–82 (Feb.) 1949.
62. Emsley, H. H.: Some Notes on Space Perception. Proc. Physical Soc. London, 56:293–304 (Sept.) 1944.
63. Emsley, H. H.: Visual Optics. Ed. 4, London, Hatton Press, Ltd., 1946.
64. Erggelet, H.: Zur Korrektion der einseitigen Aphakie. Ztschr. f. ophth. Optik., 1:33–42; 65–73, 1913–14.
65. Erggelet, H.: Über Brillenwirkungen. Ztschr. f. ophth. Optik., 3:170–183, 1916.
66. Erggelet, H.: Versuche zur beidäugigen Tiefenwahrnehmung bei hoher Ungleichsichtigkeit. Klin. Monatsbl. f. Augenh., 66:685–694, 1921.
67. Erggelet, H.: Brillenlehre. In Schieck, F. and Brückner, A.: Kurzes Handbuch d. Ophthalmologie. Berlin, Julius Springer, Vol. 2, 1932, pp. 790–791.
68. Fechner, G. T.: Elemente der Psychophysik. I. Aufl., Leipzig, Breitkopf and Härtel, 1860.
69. Fick, A. E.: Ueber Stäbschensehschärfe und Zapfensehschärfe. Arch. f. Ophth., 45:336–356, 1898.
70. Field, H. B.: A Comparison of Ocular Imagery. Arch. Ophth., n. s., 29:981–988 (June) 1943.
71. Fischer, F. P.: Fortgesetzte Studien über Binokularsehen (Tschermak)· II. Über Asymmetrien des Gesichtssinnes speziell des Raumsinnes beider Augen. Arch. f. d. ges. Physiol., 204:203–233, 1924.
72. Fischer, F. P.: Fortgesetzte Studien über Binokularsehen (Tschermak): III. Experimentelle Beiträge zum Begriff der Sehrichtungsgemeinschaft der Netzhäute auf Grund der binokularen Noniusmethode. Arch. f. d. ges. Physiol., 204:234–246, 1924.
73. Fischer, F. P.: Fortegesetzte Studien über Binokularsehen. IV. Über Stereoscopie im indirekten Sehen. Arch. f. d. ges. Physiol., 204:247–260, 1924.
74. Fischer, R.: Grössenschätzungen im Gesichtsfeld. Arch f. Ophth., 37 (pt. 1): 97–136, 1891.
75. Fisher, H. M.: A Modification of Space-eikonometer Technique. Am. J. Optom., 26:137–143 (April) 1949.
76. Fleischer, E.: Die Granzlinienerregungen beim Sehen mit beiden Augen. Ztschr. f. Psychol. u. Physiol. d. Sinnesorg., Abt. I, 141:283–342, 1937.
77. Fleischer, E.: Die Querdisparation als physiologische Grundlage des binokularen Tiefensehens. Ztschr. f. Psychol., 147:65–132, 1939.
78. Frank, M.: Beobachtungen betreffs der Übereinstimmung der Hering-Hillebrand'-schen Horopterabweichung und des Kundt'schen Teilungsversuches. Arch. f. d. ges. Physiol., 109:63–72, 1905.
79. Freeman, E.: Anomalies of Visual Acuity in Relation to Stimulus-distance. J. Optic. Soc. America, 22:285–292 (May) 1932.

80. Friedenwald, Harry: Binocular Metamorphopsia Produced by Correcting Glasses. Arch. Ophth., o. s., 21:204–212, 1892.
81. Friedenwald, J. S.: Diagnosis and Treatment of Anisophoria. Arch. Ophth., n. s., 15:283–304 (Feb.) 1936.
82. Fruböse, A. and Jaensch, P. A.: Der Einfluss verschiedener Faktoren auf die Tiefensehschärfe. Ztschr. f. Biol., 78:119–132, 1923.
83. Fry, G. A. and Kent, P. R.: The Effects of Base-in and Base-out Prisms on Stereoacuity. Am. J. Optom., 21:492–507 (Dec.) 1944.
84. Fuog, H. L.: Results of Experimental Work to Develop a Rapid Screening Test for Aniseikonia. Am. J. Optom., 20:383–397 (Nov.) 1943.
85. Gassovsky, L. N. and Nikolskaya, N. A.: Magnitude of the Threshold of Stereoscopic Vision as Affected by the Period of Observation. Compt. Rend. Acad. Sc. U. S. S. R., 38:15–19, 1943.
86. Gaus, J.: Die Tiefenwahrnehmung im indirekten Sehen. Ophthalmologica, 112:267–287 (Oct.–Nov.) 1946.
87. Gertz, H.: Über die Blickaberration und ihre Beziehung zur Netzhautkorrespondenz. Acta ophth., 13:192–224, 1935.
88. Gibson, J. J.: Adaptátion, After-effect and Contrast in the Perception of Curved Lines. J. Exper. Psychol., 16:1–31 (Feb.) 1933.
89. Gibson, J. J.: Adaptation, After-effect, and Contrast in the Perception of Tilted Lines. II. Simultaneous Contrast and the Areal Restriction of the After-effect. J. Exper. Psychol., 20:553–569 (June) 1937.
90. Gibson, J. J.: Motion Picture Testing and Research. A. A. F. Aviation Psychology Program Research Report No. 7, Washington, D. C., U. S. Government Printing Office. Vol. 11, 1947, 267 pp.
91. Giraud-Teulon: De l'influence des lentilles positives et négatives et de celle de leur distance a l'oeil sur les dimensions des images ophthalmoscopiques de la papille ou disque optique, dans les anomalies de la refraction oculaire, et particulièrement dans l'astigmatisme. Ann. d'ocul., 62:93–156, 1869.
92. Goldmann, H. and Hagen, R.: Zur direkten Messung der Totalbrechkraft des lebenden menschlichen Auges. Ophthalmologica, 104:15–22, 1942.
93. Graham, C. H.: Visual Space Perception. Federation Proc., 2:115–122 (June) 1943.
94. Graham, C. H., Baker, K. E., Hecht, M. and Lloyd, V. V.: Factors Influencing Thresholds for Monocular Movement Parallax. J. Exper. Psychol., 38:205–223 (June) 1948.
95. de Gramont, A.: Anamorphoseur à prismes d'apres Brewster. Rev. d'optique, 9:164–167, 1930.
96. de Gramont, A.: La grandeur relative des deux images retiniennes. Rev. d'optique, 21:1–14, 1942.
97. Green, J.: On Certain Stereoscopical Illusions Evoked by Prismatic and Cylindrical Spectacle-glasses. Tr. Am. Ophth. Soc., 1889, pp. 449–456.
98. Grimm, R.: Erscheinungen und Messungen bei Konvergenz und Fusion. Arch. f. Ophth., 133:121–130, 1934.
99. Guggenbühl, August: Das stereoskopische Sehen des hell- und dunkeladaptierten Auges. Ophthalmologica, 115:193–218, 1948.
100. Guilford, J. P.: Psychometric Methods. New York, McGraw-Hill Book Co., Inc., 1936, p. 166.
101. Hartinger, H.: Ueber Veränderungen der Raumwahrnehmung durch Brillengläser. Klin. Monatsbl. f. Augenh., 70:763, 1923.
102. Hartinger, H.: Die Verzeichnungsfehler einfacher Prismen. Ztschr. f. ophth. Optik., 15–17:129–146, 1928–29.
103. Hartinger, H.: Zur Haftglasberichtigung linsenloser Augen. Klin. Monatsbl. f. Augenh., 85:584, 1930.
104. Hartinger, H.: Brillen für Anisometropie und Aniseikonie. Klin. Monatsbl. f. Augenh., 100:278, 1938.
105. Heine, L.: Sehschärfe und Tiefenwahrnehmung. Arch. f. Ophth., 51:146–173, 1900.
106. von Helmholtz, H.: Über die Augenbewegungen. Heidelberg, Germany, Jahrb. d. Literatur, 1865, p. 258.

107. von Helmholtz, H.: Helmholtz's Treatise on Physiological Optics. Southall, J. P. C.: Translated and edited from the 3rd German edition. Vol. 3, The Perceptions of Vision. The Optical Society of America, 1925.
108. Hering, Ewald: Der Raumsinn und die Bewegungen der Auges. In Hermann, Ludimar: Handbuch der Physiologie 3 (pt. 1), 1879. See English translation by C. A. Radde, Am. Acad. Optom., Baltimore, 1942.
109. Hermans, T. G.: Torsion in Persons With No Known Eye Defect. J. Exper. Psychol., 32:307–324 (April) 1943; Am. J. Ophth., 27:153–158 (Feb.) 1944.
110. Herzau, Werner: Über den Horopter bei schiefer Betrachtung. Arch. f. Ophth., 121:756–780, 1929.
111. Herzau, Werner: Über das Verhältnis von erzwungener Vertikal-divergenz und Rollung bei der Fusion. Arch. f. Ophth., 122:59–74, 1929.
112. Herzau, Werner: Demonstration des Amesschen Kippfeldes. Zentrabl. f. d. ges. Ophth., 41:396, 1938.
113. Herzau, Werner and Ogle, K. N.: Über den Grössenunterschied der Bilder beider Augen bei asymmetrischer Konvergenz und seine Bedeutung für das zweiäugige Sehen. Arch. f. Ophth., 137:327–363, 1937.
114. Hillebrand, Franz: Die Stabilität der Raumwerte auf der Netzhaut. Ztschr. f. Psychol. u. Physiol. d. Sinnesorg., 5:1–60, 1893.
115. Hillebrand, Franz: Lehre von den Gesichtsempfindungen. Wien, Julius Springer, 1929, 205 pp.
116. Hoefer, P.: Beitrage zur Lehre vom Augenmaass bei zweiäugigem und bei einaugigem Sehen. Arch. f. d. ges. Physiol., 115:483–513, 1906.
117. vom Hofe, Karl: Beitrag zur Frage der eidetischen Anlage. Arch. f. Ophth., 117:40–57, 1926.
118. Hofmann, F. B.: Physiologische Optik (Raumsinn). In Graefe, A. and Saemisch, T.: Handbuch der gesamten Augenheilkunde. Ed. 2, Berlin, Julius Springer, 1925, Vol. 3, Chap. 13, 667 pp.
119. Hofmann, F. B. and Bielschowsky, A.: Ueber die der Willkür entzogenen Fusionsbewegungen der Augen. Arch. f. d. ges. Physiol., 80:1–40, 1900.
120. Hofmann, F. B. and Bielschowsky, A.: Über die Einstellung der scheinbaren Horizontalen und Vertikalen bei Betrachtung eines von schrägen Konturen erfüllten Gesichtsfeldes. Arch. f. d. ges. Physiol., 126:453–475, 1909.
121. Householder, A. S.: A Note on the Horopter. Bull. Math. Biophysics, 2:135–140, 1940.
122. Householder, A. S.: A Theory of the Induced Size Effect. Bull. Math. Biophysics, 5:155–160, 1943.
123. Hughes, W. L.: Aniseikonia in Emmetropia. Am. J. Ophth., 20:887–890 (Sept.) 1937.
124. Irvine, S. R. and Ludvigh, E. J.: Is Ocular Proprioceptive Sense Concerned in Vision? Arch. Ophth., n. s., 15:1037–1049, 1936.
125. Jackson, Edward: Importance of Aniseikonia. Am. J. Ophth., 20:16–21 (Jan.) 1937.
126. Jackson, Edward: Practical Importance of Aniseikonia. Am. J. Ophth., 26:18–20 (Jan.) 1943.
127. Jaensch, E. R.: Quoted by Fleischer, E.[77]
128. Jaensch, E. R. and Reich, F.: Über den Aufbau der Wahrnehmungswelt und ihre Struktur im Jugendalter. Ztschr. f. Psychol. u. Physiol. d. Sinnesorg., 86 (pt. 1): 278–367, 1921.
129. Jones, L. A. and Higgins, G. C.: Photographic Granularity and Graininess. IV. Visual Acuity Thresholds; Dynamic Versus Static Assumptions. J. Optic Soc. America, 38:398–405 (April) 1948.
130. Junker, H.: Über die Häufigkeit von Heterophorien und ihren Einfluss auf das stereoskopische Sehvermögen. Arch. f. Ophth., 142:367–388, 1940.
131. Knapp, H.: The Influence of Spectacles on the Optical Constants and Visual Acuteness of the Eye. Arch. Ophth. & Otol., 1:377–410, 1869.
132. Köhler, Wolfgang and Emery, D. A.: Figural After-effects in the Third Dimension of Visual Space. Am. J. Psychol., 60:159–201 (April) 1947.
133. Koller, Carl: Ueber eine eigenthümliche Sorte dioptrischer Bilder: Ein Beitrag zur Theorie der Cylinderlinsen. Arch. f. Ophth., 32 (pt. 2):169–204, 1886.

134. Koller, Carl: The Form of Retinal Images in the Astigmatic Eye. Tr. Am. Ophth. Soc., **6**:425–437, 1892.
135. Kröncke, Karl: Zur Phänomenologie der Kernfläche des Sehraums. Ztschr. f. Psychol. u. Physiol. d. Sinnesorg., **52** (pt. 2):217–228, 1921.
136. Kundt, August: Untersuchungen über Augenmass und optische Täuschungen. Ann. de Phys. u. Chem., **120**:118–158, 1863.
137. Lancaster, W. B.: Aniseikonia. Arch. Ophth., **20**:907–912 (Dec.) 1938.
138. Lancaster, W. B.: A Reply to Criticisms of Aniseikonia. Tr. Am. Ophth. Soc., **40**: 82–109, 1942.
139. Lancaster, W. B.: Eikonometer and Comparator. Arch. Ophth., **30**:278–279 (Aug.) 1943.
140. Land, E. H.: Vectographs: Images in Terms of Vectorial Inequality and Their Application in Three-dimensional Representation. J. Optic. Soc. America, **30**: 230–238 (June) 1940.
141. Langlands, N. M. S.: Experiments on Binocular Vision. Optic. Soc. London Tr., **28**:45–82, 1926–27.
142. Larrabee, M. G. and Bronk, D. W.: Prolonged Facilitation of Synaptic Excitation in Sympathetic Ganglia. J. Neurophysiol., **10**:139–154 (March) 1947.
143. Lau, Ernst: Versuche über das stereoskopische Sehen. Psychol. Forsch., **2**:1–4, 1922.
144. Lau, Ernst: Neue Untersuchungen über das Tiefen- und Ebenensehen. Ztschr. f. Psychol. u. Physiol. d. Sinnesorg., Abt. II, **53**:1–35, 1921.
145. Lesser, Otto: Über Linien- und Flächenvergleichung. Ztschr. f. Psychol. u. Physiol. d. Sinnesorg., Abt. I, **74**:1–127, 1916.
146. Lehnert, K.: Über Wahre und Scheinhoroptern. Arch. f. d. ges. Physiol., **245**:112–120, 1941.
147. Lewin, Kurt and Sakuma, Kanae: Die Sehrichtung monokularer und binokularer Objekte bei Bewegung und das Zustandekommen des Tiefeneffektes. Psychol. Forsch., **6**:298–357, 1924–25.
148. von Liebermann, K.: Beiträge zur Lehre von der binokularen Tiefenlokalisation. Ztschr. f. Psychol. u. Physiol. d. Sinnesorg., **44**:428–443, 1910.
149. Life Magazine: Aniseikonia. **13**:82–85 (Aug. 3) 1942.
150. Linksz, A.: On the Perception of Size (Remarks to the Induced Size Effect and the Relative Sizes of Perceptual Images in Asymmetric Convergences). Personal Communication to the Author.
151. Lippincott, J. A.: On the Binocular Metamorphopsia Produced by Correcting Glasses. Arch. Ophth., **18**:18–30, 1889.
152. Lippincott, J. A.: New Tests for Binocular Vision. Tr. Am. Ophth. Soc., **5**:560–564, 1890.
153. Lippincott, J. A.: On the Binocular Metamorphopsia Produced by Optical Means. Arch. Ophth., **46**:397–426, 1917.
154. Lorente de Nó, R.: Studies on the Structure of the Cerebral Cortex. II. Continuation of the Study of the Ammonic System. J. f. Psychol. u. Neurol., **46**:113–177, 1934.
155. Lowry, J. B.: The Retinal Images in Oblique Astigmatism. Ophthalmic Record, **5**:41–48 (Aug.) 1895.
156. Luckiesh, M. and Moss, F. K.: Dependency of Visual Acuity Upon Stimulus-distance. J. Optic. Soc. America, **23**:25–29 (Jan.) 1933.
157. Luckiesh, M. and Moss, F. K.: The Variation in Visual Acuity With Fixation-distance. J. Optic. Soc. America, **31**:594–595 (Sept.) 1941.
158. Ludvigh, Elek: Extrafoveal Visual Acuity as Measured With Snellen Test-letters. Am. J. Ophth., **24**:303–310 (March) 1941.
159. Luneburg, R. K.: Mathematical Analysis of Binocular Vision. Princeton, N. J., Published for the Hanover Institute by Princeton Univ. Press, 1947, 104 pp.
160. Lyding: Über die Netzhautdeckstellen. Klin. Monatsbl. f. Augenh., **102**:874, 1939.
161. Maddox, E. E.: The Clinical Use of Ophthalmic Prisms, and Decentering of Lenses. Ed. 5, Bristol, England, John Wright & Sons, Ltd., 1907.
162. Marshall, W. H. and Talbot, S. A.: Recent Evidence for Neural Mechanisms in Vision Leading to a General Theory of Sensory Acuity. In: Klüver, Heinrich: Vol. VII, Visual Mechanisms. From: Biological Symposia; a Series of Volumes

Devoted to Current Symposia in the Field of Biology. (Edited by Jaques Cattell.) Lancaster, Pa., The Jaques Cattell Press, 1942, pp. 117–164.

163. McKee, T. L.: Restoration of Binocular Vision After Unilateral Cataract Extraction. Arch. Ophth., **29**:996–999 (June) 1943.

164. Merkel, J.: Die Methode der mittleren Fehler, experimentell begründet durch Versuch aus dem Gebeite des Raumasses. In: Wundt Philos. Studien, **9**:400–428, 1894.

165. Meservey, A. B.: Depth Effects in Roentgenograms. Am. J. Roentgenol., **39**:439–449 (March) 1938.

166. van der Meulen, S. G.: Stereoskopie bei unvollkommenen Sehvermögen. Arch. f. Ophth., **19** (pt. 1):100–136, 1873.

167. Miles, P .W.: Factors in the Diagnosis of Aniseikonia and Paired Maddox-rod Tests. Am. J. Ophth., **30**:885–897 (July) 1947.

168. Miles, P. W.: A Comparison of Aniseikonic Test Instruments and Prolonged Induction of Artificial Aniseikonia. Am. J. Ophth., **31**:687–696 (June) 1948.

169. Morgan, M. W., Jr. and Olmsted, J. M. D.: Quantitative Measurements of Relative Accommodation and Relative Convergence. Proc. Soc. Exper. Biol. & Med., **41**:303–307 (June) 1939.

170. Mueller, C. G. and Lloyd, V. V.: Stereoscopic Acuity for Various Levels of Illumination. Proc. Nat. Acad. Sc., **34**:223–227 (May) 1948.

171. Müller, J.: Zur vergleichenden Physiologie des Gesichtssinnes des Menschen und der Thiere. Leipzig, C. Cnobloch, 1826, 462 pp.

172. Münsterberg, Hugo: Augenmass. Beitr. z. exper. Psychol., **2**:125–181, 1889.

173. Nagel, Albrecht: Das Sehen mit zwei Augen und die Lehre von den identischen Netzhautstellen. Leipzig, C. F. Winter, 1861, p. 32; 51.

174. Nagel, Albrecht: Ueber das Vorkommen von wahren Rollungen des Auges um die Gesichtslinie. Arch. f. Ophth., **14** (pt. 2):228–246, 1868.

175. Neuhaus, Wilhelm: Experimentelle Untersuchung über das Sehen mit beiden Augen. Ztschr. f. Psychol. u. Physiol. d. Sinnesorg., Abt. 1, **137**:87–108, 1936.

176. Noji, R.: Über optisch erzwungene Rollungen der Augen. Arch. f. Ophth., **122**:562–571, 1929.

177. Ogle, K. N.: Analytical Treatment of the Longitudinal Horopter; Its Measurement and Application to Related Phenomena, Especially to Relative Size and Shape of Ocular Images. J. Optic. Soc. America, **22**:665–728 (Dec.) 1932.

178. Ogle, K. N.: Correction of Aniseikonia With Ophthalmic Lenses. J. Optic. Soc. America, **26**:323–337 (Aug.) 1936.

179. Ogle, K. N.: Die mathematische Analyse des Langshoropters. Arch. f. d. ges. Physiol., **239**:748–766, 1938.

180. Ogle, K. N.: Induced Size Effect. I. A New Phenomenon in Binocular Space Perception Associated With the Relative Sizes of the Images of the Two Eyes. Arch. Ophth., **20**:604–623 (Oct.) 1938.

181. Ogle, K. N.: Induced Size Effect. II. An Experimental Study of the Phenomenon With Restricted Fusion Stimuli. Arch. Ophth., **21**:604–625 (April) 1939.

182. Ogle, K. N.: Induced Size Effect. III. A Study of the Phenomenon as Influenced by Horizontal Disparity of the Fusion Contours. Arch. Ophth., **22**:613–635 (Oct.) 1939.

183. Ogle, K. N.: Relative Sizes of Ocular Images of the Two Eyes in Asymmetric Convergence. Arch. Ophth., **22**:1046–1067 (Dec.) 1939.

184. Ogle, K. N.: Induced Size Effect With the Eyes in Asymmetric Convergence. Arch. Ophth., **23**:1023–1038 (May) 1940.

185. Ogle, K. N.: An Optical Unit for Obtaining Variable Magnification in Ophthalmic Use. J. Optic. Soc. America, **32**:143–146 (March) 1942.

186. Ogle, K. N.: Association Between Aniseikonia and Anomalous Binocular Space Perception. Arch. Ophth., **30**:54–64 (July) 1943.

187. Ogle, K. N.: Some Aspects of the Eye as an Image-forming Mechanism. J. Optic. Soc. America, **33**:506–512 (Sept.) 1943.

188. Ogle, K. N.: Meridional Magnifying Lens Systems in the Measurement and Correction of Aniseikonia. J. Optic. Soc. America, **34**:302–312 (June) 1944.

189. Ogle, K. N.: Theory of the Space-eikonometer. J. Optic. Soc. America, 36:20–32 (Jan.) 1946.
190. Ogle, K. N.: Binocular Depth Contrast Phenomenon. Am. J. Psychol., 59:111–126 (Jan.) 1946.
191. Ogle, K. N. and Ames, A., Jr.: Ophthalmic Lens Testing Instrument. J. Optic. Soc. America, 33:137–142 (March) 1943.
192. Ogle, K. N. and Boeder, P.: Distortion of Stereoscopic Spatial Localization. J. Optic. Soc. America, 38:723–733 (Aug.) 1948.
193. Ogle, K. N. and Ellerbrock, V. J.: Stereoscopic Sensitivity in the Space Eikonometer. Arch. Ophth., 34:303–310 (Oct.) 1945.
194. Ogle, K. N. and Ellerbrock, V. J.: Cyclofusional Movements. Arch. Ophth., 36:700–735 (Dec.) 1946.
195. Ogle, K. N. and Ellerbrock, V. J.: Unpublished data.
196. Ogle, K. N. and Madigan, L. F.: Astigmatism at Oblique Axes and Binocular Stereoscopic Spatial Localization. Arch. Ophth., 33:116–127 (Feb.) 1945.
197. Ogle, K. N. and Triller, Wendell: Aniseikonia for Distant and Near Vision. Am. J. Ophth., 32:1719–1724 (Dec.) 1949.
198. Ogle, K. N., Mussey, Frances and Prangen, A. de H.: Fixation Disparity and the Fusional Processes in Binocular Single Vision. Am. J. Ophth., 32:1069–1087 (Aug.) 1949.
199. Ogle, K. N., Imus, H. A., Madigan, L. F., Bannon, R. E. and Wilson, E. G.: Repeatability of Ophthalmo-eikonometer Measurements. Arch. Ophth., 24:1179–1189 (Dec.) 1940.
200. Panum, P. L.: Untersuchungen über das Sehen mit zwei Augen. Kiel, 1858.
201. Panum, P. L.: Ueber die einheitliche Verschmelzung verschiedenartiger Netzhauteindrücke beim Sehen mit zwei Augen. Arch. f. Anat. u. Physiol., 1861, pp. 63–111; 178–227.
202. Paul Ludwig: Beiträge zur Lokalisationsophthalmoskopie. III. Die Berechnung der Achsenlänge des Auges, ein Anwendungsgebiet des relativen Berechnungsverfahrens. Arch. f. Ophth., 133:254–297, 1935.
203. Peckham, R. H.: Foveal Projection During Ductions. Arch. Ophth., 12:562–566 (Oct.) 1934.
204. Peirce, B. O.: The Perception of Horizontal and Vertical Lines. Science, n. s., 10:425–430 (Sept.) 1899.
205. Perry, C. H.: Rotation in Oblique Astigmatism. Ophth. Rec., 5:175–178 (Nov.) 1895.
206. Phillips, R. J.: Some Ocular Perceptions, and How They Are Influenced by Lenses. Ann. Ophth. & Otol., 2:31–43 (Jan.) 1893.
207. Pirenne, M. H.: Binocular and Uniocular Threshold of Vision. Nature, London, 152:698–699 (Dec. 11) 1943.
208. Porsaa, K.: The Central Visual Field After Occipital Lobectomy. Acta ophth., 22:243–260, 1944.
209. Roelofs, C. O.: Die optische Lokalisation. Arch. f. Augenh., 109:395–415, 1935.
210. v. Rohr, Louis Otto M.: Die Brille als optisches Instrument. Leipzig, Wilhelm Engelmann, 1911, 172 pp.
211. v. Rohr, M.: Die Brille als optisches Instrument. IV. Die Änderungen der Raumfüllung durch die Brille. Ed. 3, Berlin, Julius Springer, 1921, pp. 195–223.
212. v. Rohr, M. and Stock, W.: Über eine Methode zur subjektiven Prüfung von Brillenwirkungen. Arch. f. Ophth., 83:189–205, 1912.
213. v. Rohr, M. and Stock, W.: Über eine Methode zur subjektiven Prüfung von Brillenwirkungen. Arch. f. Ophth., 84:152–163, 1913.
214. Rushton, R. H.: The Clinical Measurement of the Axial Length of the Living Eye. Tr. Ophth. Soc. U. Kingdom, 58 (pt. 1):136–142, 1938.
215. Sachs, M. and Meller, J.: Über einige eigentümliche Lokalisationsphänomene in einem Falle von hochgradiger Netzhautinkongruenz. Arch. f. Ophth., 57:1–23, 1904.
216. Savage, G. C.: Ophthalmic Myology. Ed. 2, Nashville, Tenn., McQuiddy Ptg. Co., 1911, p. 418.
217. Schubert, G.: Zur "Aniseikonie"-Frage. Arch. f. Ophth., 140:55–60, 1939.

218. Schwarz, O.: Quoted by Wundt, Wilhelm.[258]
219. Sherrington, C.: The Integrative Action of the Nervous System. New Haven, Yale University Press, 1947, p. 375.
220. Stenström, Sölve: Untersuchungen über die Variation und Kovariation der optischen Elemente des menschlichen Auges. (Suppl.) Acta ophth., 26:1–103, 1946. English translation by Daniel Woolf, Arch. Optom., 25:218–503 (May–Oct.) 1948.
221. Stevens, G. T.: The Directions of the Apparent Vertical and Horizontal Meridians of the Retina and Their Modification From Physiological and Pathological Causes, With a Description of the Clinoscope. Arch. Ophth., 26:181–203, 1897.
222. Stevens, G. T.: A Treatise on the Motor Apparatus of the Eye. Philadelphia, F. A. Davis Co., 1906, 496 pp.
223. Suter, W. N.: Handbook of Optics for Students of Ophthalmology. New York, The Macmillan Co., 1899, p. 140.
224. Talbot, S. A. and Marshall, W. H.: Physiological Studies on Neural Mechanisms of Visual Localization and Discrimination. Am. J. Ophth., 24:1255–1263 (Nov.) 1941.
225. Troland, L. T.: The Principles of Psychophysiology. New York, D. Van Nostrand Co., Inc., 1930, Vol. 2, p. 55.
226. Tron, Eugen: Über die optischen Grundlagen der Ametropie. Arch. f. Ophth., 132:182–223, 1934.
227. Tron, Eugen: Ein Beitrage zur Frage der optischen Grundlagen der Aniso- und Isometropie. Arch. f. Ophth., 133:211–230, 1935.
228. Trump, R. J.: Binocular Vision and the Stereoscopic Sense. Tr. Optic. Soc. London, 25:261–270, 1924.
229. Tschermak, A.: Beitrage zur Lehre vom Langshoropter. (Ueber die Tiefenlokalisation bei Dauer- und bei Momentreizen nach Beobachtungen von Dr. Kiribuchi, Tokio.) Pflüger, Arch. Physiol., 81:328–348, 1900.
230. Tschermak, A.: Fortgesetzte Studien über Binokularsehen. I. Ueber Farbenstereoskopie. Arch. f. d. ges. Physiol., 204:177–202, 1924.
231. Tschermak, A.: Beiträge zur physiologischen Optik III; Raumsinn. In: Bethe, A., Bergmann, G. V., Embden, G. and Ellinger, A.: Handbuch der normalen und pathologischen Physiologie. Berlin, Julius Springer, 1930, Vol. 12, pt. 2, pp. 833–1000.
232. Tschermak, A.: Beiträge zur physiologischen Optik IV; Augenbewegungen. In: Bethe, A., Bergmann, G. V., Embden, G. and Ellinger, A.: Handbuch der normalen und pathologischen Physiologie. Berlin, Julius Springer, 1930, Vol. 12, pt. 2, pp. 1001–1094.
233. Tschermak, A.: Demonstration eines Horopterapparates nach dem Facherprinzip. Ber. ü. d. ges. Physiol., 61:379–380, 1931.
234. Tschermak-Seysenegg, A.: Über Parallaktoskopie. Arch. f. d. ges. Physiol., 241:455–469, 1939.
235. Tschermak-Seysenegg, Armin: Methodik des optischen Raumsinnes und der Augenbewegungen. In: Abderhalden, Emil: Handbuch der biologischen Arbeitsmethoden. Berlin and Wien, Urban & Schwarzenberg, 1937, Abt. V, Vol. 6, pt. 2, pp. 1427–1754.
236. Veniar, Florence A.: Difference Thresholds for Shape Distortion of Geometrical Squares. J. Psychol., 26:461–476, 1948.
237. Verhoeff, F. H.: A Description of the Reflecting Phorometer and a Discussion of the Possibilities Concerning Torsions of the Eyes. Tr. Am. Ophth. Soc., 8:490–503, 1899.
238. Verhoeff, F. H.: Cycloduction. Tr. Am. Ophth. Soc., 32:208–228, 1934.
239. Verhoeff, F. H.: A New Theory of Binocular Vision. Arch. Ophth., n. s., 13:151–175, 1935.
240. Vernon, M. D.: The Perception of Inclined Lines. Brit. J. Psychol., 25:186–196, 1934.
241. Vieth: Über die Richtung der Augen. Annalen d. Physik., 58:233–253, 1818.
242. Volkmann, A. W.: Die stereoskopischen Erscheinungen in ihrer Beziehung zu der

Lehre von den identischen Netzhautpunkten. Arch. f. Ophth., **5** (pt. 2):1–100, 1859.

243. Wadsworth, O. F.: On the Effect of a Cylindrical Lens, With Vertical Axis Placed Before One Eye. Tr. Am. Ophth. Soc., 1876, pp. 342–344.

244. Walls, G. L.: Factors in Human Visual Resolution. J. Optic. Soc. America, **33**:487–505 (Sept.) 1943.

245. Walls, G. L.: Is Vision Ever Binocular? Optic. J. & Rev. Optom., **85**:33–43 (Aug.) 1948.

246. Wallwork, P. M.: Magnification by the Use of Thickness Lenses. Brit. J. Physiol. Optics, **12**:77–80, 1938.

247. Walsh, F. B.: Clinical Neuro-Ophthalmology. Baltimore, Md., Williams & Wilkins Company, 1947, 1532 pp.

248. Weiss, E.: Die prismatischen Fehler der Brillengläser. Ber. ü. d. Versamml. d. deutsch. ophth. Gesellsch., **43**:101–106, 1922.

249. Werner, Heinz: Dynamics of Binocular Depth Perception. Psychol. Monog. Gen'l & App'l, **49** (No. 218):1–127, 1937.

250. Werner, Heinz: Binocular Depth Contrast and the Conditions of the Binocular Field. Am. J. Psychol., **51**:489–497, 1938.

251. Werner, Heinz: Binocular Vision—Normal and Abnormal. Arch. Ophth., n. s., **28**:834–844, 1942.

252. Wertheim, T.: Über die indirekte Sehschärfe. Ztschr. f. Psychol. u. Physiol. d. Sinnesorg., **7**:172–187, 1894.

253. Wheatstone, C.: Contributions to the Physiology of Vision. I. On Some Remarkable and Hitherto Unobserved Phenomena of Binocular Vision. Phil. Tr., 1838, pp. 371–394.

254. Whitwell, A.: On the Best Form of Spectacle Lenses for the Correction of Small Amounts of Anisometropia. Tr. Optic. Soc., London, **24**:96–101, 1922–1923.

255. Wibaut, F.: Über die Emmetropisation und den Ursprung der sphärischen Refraktionsanomalien. Arch. f. Ophth., **116**:596–612, 1926.

256. Wolffberg: Störung der perspektivischen Sehens durch binokular korrigierende Zylinderglässer. Zentralbl. f. d. ges. Ophth., **1**:430–431, 1914.

257. Woodworth, R. S.: Experimental Psychology. New York, Henry Holt & Co., Inc., 1938, p. 408.

258. Wundt, Wilhelm: Zur Theorie der räumlichen Gesichtswahrnehmungen. Phil. Stud., **14**:1–118, 1898.

259. Zimmerman, W. and Schubert, G.: Aniseikoniephänomene und ihre physiologisch-optischen Grundlagen. Arch. f. d. ges. Physiol., **244**:59–67, 1940.

Pertinent References Since 1949

Ames, A., Jr.: Visual perception and the rotating trapezoidal window. Psychol. Monogr. No. 7, **65**:1–32, 1951. (American Psychological Association, Washington, D. C.)

Amigo, G.: Variation of stereoscopic acuity and observation distance. J. O. S. A., **53**:630–635, 1963.

Bagolini, B. and Tittarelli, R.: Osservazioni sul fenomeno cosiddetto della "disparita di fissazione." Bollettino d'oculistica, **38**:853–866, 1959.

Bender, M. B.: The oculomotor system. Hoeber Medical Division, Harper & Row, Publishers, Inc., New York, 1964.

Berens, C. and Bannon, R. E.: Aniseikonia. A present appraisal and some practical considerations. Arch. Ophth., **70**:181–188, 1963.

Berte, A. P. and Harwood, K. A.: The clinical correction of aniseikonia. Brit. J. Physiol. Optics, **18**:108–116, 1961.

Blank, A. A.: Analysis of experiments in binocular space perception. J. O. S. A., **48**:911–925, 1958.

Bourdy, C.: L'Aniséiconie. Annales d'oculistique, **194**:1048–1079, 1961.

Brown, K. T.: Factors affecting differences in apparent size between opposite halves of a visual meridian. J. O. S. A., **43**:464–472, 1953.

Carter, D. B.: Studies in fixation disparity. III. The apparent uniocular components of fixation disparity. Amer. J. Optometry, **37**:408–419, 1960.

Charnwood, J. R. B.: Essay on binocular vision. 6th edition. Hatton Press, London, 1951.

Cibis, P. A.: Faulty depth perception caused by cyclotorsion. Arch. Ophth., **47**:31–42, 1952.

ten Doesschate, G.: Results of an investigation of depth perception at a distance of 50 metres. Ophthalmologica, **129**:56–57, 1955.

––– and Kummer, R.: Heterophoria and depth discrimination. Ophthalmologica, **134**:113–120, 1957.

Dyer, J. A. and Ogle, K. N.: Correction of unilateral aphakia with contact lenses. Amer. J. Ophth., **50**:11–17, 1960.

Ellerbrock, V. J.: The effect of aniseikonia on the amplitude of vertical divergence. Amer. J. Optometry, **29**:403–415, 1952.

Engel, E.: Stereoscopic distortion and structurally imposed retinal-image-size-differences. Perceptual and Motor Skills, **18**:31–38, 1964.

Fisher, H. M. and Ludlam, W. M.: An approach to measuring aniseikonia in nonfusing strabismus. A preliminary report. Amer. J. Optometry, **40**:653–655, 1963.

Frey, R. G.: Die Beziehung zwischen Sehschärfe und Tiefensehschärfe. Wien. med. Wschr., **103**:436–438, 1953.

Gillott, H. F.: The effect on binocular vision of variations in the relative sizes and levels of illumination of the ocular images. Brit. J. Physiol. Optics.
       13:122–146 (July) 1956.
       13:218–234 (Oct.) 1956.
       14:43–58 (Jan.) 1957.
       14:95–119 (Apr.) 1957.

Gogel, W. C.: Perception of the relative distance position of objects as a function of other objects in the field. J. Exp. Psychol., **47**:335–342, 1954.

Halldèn, U.: An optical explanation of Hering-Hillebrand's horopter deviation. Arch. Ophth., **55**:830–835, 1956.

Hebbard, F. W.: Comparison of subjective and objective measurements on fixation disparity, J. O. S. A., **52**:706–712, 1962.

———: Foveal fixation disparity measurements and their use in determining the relationship between accommodative convergence and accommodation. Amer. J. Optometry, **37**:3–26, 1960.

Ittelson, W. H.: Visual space perception. Springer, New York, 1960.

Jonkers, G. H.: A comparison of methods of determining stereoscopic vision. **137**:15–21, 1959.

Junker, G. H.: Bestimmung des wahren (Sehrechtungskonstanz–) Horopters mittels der Oscillationsmethode. Graefes Arch. Ophthal., **153**:471–476, 1953.

Keystone, M.: How to screen patients for aniseikonia on the Keystone Professional Orthoscope. Keystone View Co., Meadville, Pa., 1958.

Kogan, A. I.: Phenomena of aniseikonia in the act of single binocular vision. Uch. Zap. I Inform.-Metod. Mat. Insti. Glazn. Bolez., Im. Gelmgoltsa (Moscow), **5**:239–244, 1957.

Linksz, A.: Aniseikonia—with notes on the Jackson-Lancaster controversy. Trans. Amer. Acad. Ophth. and Otolaryn., **63**:117–140, 1959.

———: Physiology of the Eye, Vol. 2, Vision, pp. 346 ff. Grune & Stratton, New York, 1952.

Linschoten, J.: Strukturanalyse der binokularen Tiefenwahrnehmung. J. B. Wolters, Groningen, Djakarta, 573 pp., 1956.

Lit, A.: Depth-discrimination thresholds as a function of binocular differences of retinal illuminance at scotopic and photopic levels. J. O. S. A., **49**:746–752, 1959.

Ludvigh, Elek: Direction sense of the eye. Amer. J. Ophth., **36**(1):139–143, 1953.

McEwen, P.: Figural after-effects. Brit. J. Psychol. Monograph Supplement No. 31, 106 pp., Cambridge University Press, Cambridge, 1958.

Mitchell, A. M. and Ellerbrock, V. J.: Fixation disparity and the maintenance of fusion in the horizontal meridian. Amer. J. Optometry, **32**:520–534, 1955.

Ogle, K. N.: Basis of stereoscopic vision. Arch. Ophth., **52**:197–211, 1954.

———: Disparity limits of stereopsis. Arch. Ophth., **48**:50–60, 1952.

———: Distortion of the image by prisms. J. O. S. A., **41**:1023–1028, 1951.

———: Fixation disparity. Amer. Orthoptic J., **4**:35–39, 1954.

———: Note on stereoscopic acuity and observation distance. J. O. S. A., **48**:794–798, 1958.

———: The optical space sense. Vol. 4, Part II, of: The eye. (H. Davson, ed.) Academic Press, New York, 1962.

———: Precision and validity of stereoscopic depth perception from double images. J. O. S. A., **43**:906–913, 1953.

———: Present status of our knowledge of stereoscopic vision. Arch. Ophth., **60**:755–774, 1958.

———: Stereopsis and vertical disparity. Arch. Ophth., **53**:495–504, 1955.

———: Stereoscopic acuity and the role of convergence. J. O. S. A., **46**:269–273, 1956.

———: Theory of stereoscopic vision. In: Psychology: A study of a science. Study I, Conceptual and systematic; Vol. 1, Sensory, perceptual, and physiological formulations, pp. 362–394. (S. Koch, ed.) McGraw-Hill, New York, 1959.

———, Burian, H. M. and Bannon, R. E.: On the correction of unilateral aphakia with contact lenses. A.M.A. Arch. Ophth., **59**:639–652, 1958.

—— and Groch, Judith: Stereopsis and unequal luminosities of the images in the two eyes. Arch Ophth., **56**:878–895, 1956.

—— and Pragen, A. de H.: Observations on vertical divergences and hypophorias. Arch. Ophth., **49**:313–334, 1953.

—— and Weil, Marianne P.: Stereoscopic vision and the duration of the stimulus. Arch. Ophth., **59**:4–17, 1958.

Palmer, D. A.: Binocular eye movements and stereoscopic depth discrimination. Optica Acta (Internat.), **9**:311–334, 1962.

——: Measurement of the horizontal extent of Panum's area by a method of constant stimuli. Optica Acta (Internat.), **8**:151–159, 1961.

Pastore, N.: Some remarks on the Ames oscillatory effect. Psychol. Rev., **59**:319–323, 1962.

Pratt, C. C.: The role of past experience in visual perception. J. Psychol., **30**:85–107, 1950.

Roelofs, C. O.: Is double localization of monocular stimuli possible on binocular vision with normal eyes? Ophthalmologica, **133**:424–430, 1957.

Ronne, G.: The physiological basis of sensory fusion. Acta Ophthal., Kbh., **34**:1–26, 1956.

Shipley, T.: The horopter in eidetic subjects. Psychol. Bull., **55**:171–175, 1958.

Sloan, Louise L. and Altman, Adelaide: Aniseikonia and the Howard-Dolman test. J. O. S. A., **43**:473–478, 1953.

Sloan, Louise L. and Altman, Adelaide: Factors involved in several tests of binocular depth perception. Arch. Ophth., **52**:524–544, 1954.

Teichner, W. H., Kobrick, J. L. and Dusek, E. R.: Commonplace viewing and depth discrimination. J. O. S. A., **45**:913–920, 1955.

Toselli, C. and Venturi, G.: Experimental studies of the interference between aniseikonia and fusion. Ann. Ottal., **84**:111–117, 1958.

Troutman, R. C.: Artiphakia and aniseikonia. Amer. J. Ophth., **56**:602–639, 1963.

Vos, J. J.: Some new aspects of color stereoscopy. J. O. S. A., **50**:785–790, 1960.

Walls, G. L.: The problem of visual direction. Amer. J. Optometry, **28**:55–83, 115–146, 173–212, 1951.

——: A theory of ocular dominance. Arch. Ophth., **45**:387–412, 1951.

Zoubec, Ratmir: Eine neue Methode der Aniseikoniekorrektion. Augenoptik, **80**:274–280, 1963.

Index